DIRECT ENERGY CONVERSION

INTER-UNIVERSITY ELECTRONICS SERIES

Consulting Editor

Charles Susskind, *University of California, Berkeley*

Advisory Committee

Frederick E. Terman, *Vice President Emeritus, Stanford University*
Ernst Weber, *President, Polytechnic Institute of Brooklyn*
John R. Whinnery, *Professor of Electrical Engineering, University of California, Berkeley*

Steering Committee

Edward E. David, Jr., *Bell Telephone Laboratories*
Hubert Heffner, *Stanford University*
John G. Linvill, *Stanford University*
William R. Rambo, *Stanford University*
Mischa Schwartz, *Polytechnic Institute of Brooklyn*
John G. Truxal, *Polytechnic Institute of Brooklyn*
Lotfi A. Zadeh, *University of California, Berkeley*

Vol. 1: *Jamieson et al.* Infrared Physics and Engineering, 1964
Vol. 2: *Bennett and Davey.* Data Transmission, 1965
Vol. 3: *Sutton.* Direct Energy Conversion, 1966
Vol. 4: *Schwartz, Bennett, and Stein.* Communication Systems and Techniques, 1966

Inter-University Electronics Series, Vol. 3

DIRECT
ENERGY CONVERSION

Edited by *GEORGE W. SUTTON*

AVCO-Everett Research Laboratory

McGRAW-HILL BOOK COMPANY

New York St. Louis San Francisco Toronto London Sydney

Direct Energy Conversion

Copyright© 1966 by McGraw-Hill, Inc.   All Rights
Reserved.   Printed in the United States of America.
This book, or parts thereof, may not be reproduced
in any form without permission of the publishers.

Library of Congress Catalog Card Number 65-28135

62381

1234567890 MP 7321069876

INTER-UNIVERSITY ELECTRONICS SERIES

Series Purpose

The explosive rate at which knowledge in electronics has expanded in recent years has produced the need for unified state-of-the-art presentations that give authoritative pictures of individual fields of electronics.

The Inter-University Electronics Series is designed to meet this need by providing volumes that deal with particular areas of electronics where up-to-date reference material is either inadequate or is not conveniently organized. Each volume covers an individual area, or a series of related areas. Emphasis is upon providing timely and comprehensive coverage that stresses general principles, and integrates the newer developments into the over-all picture. Each volume is edited by an authority in the field and is written by several coauthors, who are active participants in research or in educational programs dealing with the subject matter involved.

The volumes are written with a viewpoint and at a level that makes them suitable for reference use by research and development engineers and scientists in industry and by workers in governmental and university laboratories. They are also suitable for use as textbooks in specialized courses at graduate levels. The complete series of volumes will provide a reference library that should serve a wide spectrum of electronic engineers and scientists.

The organization and planning of the Series is being carried out with the aid of a Steering Committee, which operates with the counsel of an Advisory Committee. The Steering Committee concerns itself with the scope of the individual volumes and aids in the selection of editors for the different volumes. Each editor is in turn responsible for selecting his coauthors and deciding upon the detailed scope and content of his particular volume. Over-all management of the Series is in the hands of the Consulting Editor.

Frederick Emmons Terman

PREFACE

The purpose of this volume is to present in some detail the principles of direct energy conversion, the present state of knowledge of devices employing these principles, and the future prospects and applications. In this rather abbreviated preface, I would like to point out some of the salient features, limitations, and comparisons between the various devices which are described in detail in subsequent chapters. It is interesting to note that, although the principles of direct energy conversion have been known for a long time, only very recently has there been research and development on a scale large enough to permit practical application of the various concepts.

At the present time, the simplest device for direct electrical-energy production is the photovoltaic cell since it is only a converter, the source of energy usually being the sun. Because of its simplicity for space applications, it is presently the most utilized of all the existing direct-conversion techniques. Although batteries can be used for short satellite flights, long satellite flights (except in one or two cases) have been made possible by the successful development of semiconductor photovoltaic cells, even though the production costs of such units have been relatively high, and relatively large surface areas are required. At present, the largest such satellite power supply is about 500 watts, but somewhat larger power supplies are planned for the near future. In addition to the high cost, the major disadvantage of larger powers is the large surface area, which requires either extensive cell coverage over the surface area of the satellite or, for larger sizes, the use of extended and oriented paddles with their attendant mechanical problems. In addition, rechargeable batteries are used whenever the satellite is in the earth's shadow. This causes a weight limitation so that presently the photovoltaic power supply is of the order of a pound or two per watt. However, recent experiments on very thin cells and extremely light-weight structures have led to an optimism that eventually 25 watts can be generated for each pound of cell plus supporting structure! Such developments can lead to an early realization of such applications as space electric propulsion or high-power communications satellites so that simple ground terminals can be used. In addition, the photovoltaic cell possesses extremely high intrinsic reliability. This property, which has been so valuable for satellites, also may make such cells attractive for the generation of modest power levels at remote and unattended locations, for example, ground communications or meteorological stations.

The fuel cell is at the opposite end of the scale because it derives its energy from chemical fuels rather than directly from solar energy. One may regard the fuel cell as a type of battery into which the chemicals to be reacted are fed continuously and the chemical product is withdrawn continuously. At present, operational fuel cells use primarily hydrogen and oxygen, although experimental units have been operated with other fuels and with air. The main advantage of fuel cells is their high efficiency of conversion of chemical energy into electrical energy of about 60 percent, although for most fuels higher efficiencies are theoretically possible. Thus, the fuel cell plus its fuel supply has a weight advantage over batteries, and, in fact, the first practical application of fuel cells has been for satellites where weight is at a premium.

The major interest in fuel cells is the possibility of using fuels which are less expensive and troublesome than hydrogen or, it is hoped, even fossil fuels such as petroleum products, natural gas, or coal. For example, in many locations the cost of delivered natural gas is only a fraction of the cost of delivered electricity which has been produced from central power stations. If practical fuel cells could be developed which could convert the chemical energy of the gas into electricity at high efficiency, a major revolution in energy distribution could occur. On the other hand, one must keep in mind the relatively high investment cost in the fuel cell and that its present long-term reliability does not equal that of electricity generated centrally by steam turbomachinery. Until cost and long-term reliability improve, it is unlikely that each home will have its own fuel-cell power generator. One can, however, visualize their future use in perhaps smaller central stations. Fuel cells will be feasible sooner for power in remote areas or in transportable units. Increased understanding in this area may make such units a reality in the near future.

The other three devices covered in this volume convert thermal energy into electrical energy and therefore require an intermediate step of converting solar, chemical, or nuclear energy into thermal energy. Conceptually simplest, and the device which is furthest developed, is the thermoelectric unit which utilizes the Seebeck effect, namely, that in a circuit of two dissimilar conductors, if one junction is held at a temperature different from the other, a voltage will develop. The resulting current can be connected through a suitable electrical load and thereby convert thermal energy at the hot junction into electrical energy at the load. The Seebeck effect depends on the distribution function of electrons in the conductor when a temperature gradient exists, more exactly, on the fact that the time between electron scattering by the lattice is dependent on the electron speed, and the greater this dependence, the greater the thermoelectric effect. Unfortunately, in general this is a second-order effect, so that it is not surprising that the voltages which can be generated by this technique are small. In addition, the thermoelectric unit also conducts heat from the hot junction to the cold junction not only by electron motion but also by lattice motion, and it is therefore not surprising that generally the electrical-conversion efficiency is of the order of a few percent. This situation improves at lower temperatures, and one finds that thermoelectric units are also in commercial application for the *reverse* effect, namely, thermoelectric refrigeration. However, in spite of their low efficiency, thermoelectric electric generators have been manufactured for specialized applications such as generators for remote areas, including one type which fits over kerosene lamps and presumably generates enough power for a small radio; cathodic protection of pipelines; remote weather stations; and satellites and buoys. For the latter applications, thermoelectric units possess the advantage of simplicity and reliability when used with either radioisotope or nuclear fuels, and, for satellites, the weights are comparable to present photovoltaic-cell arrays. However, the growth potential for higher powers slightly favors thermoelectric power generators, since the thermoelectric radiator (needed to reject the heat) will usually be much smaller than the solar photovoltaic-cell array because of the relatively high temperature of the thermoelectric cold junction. The smaller radiator simplifies considerably the satellite boost and launch operations and subsequent erection and deployment of the radiator surfaces, makes the satellite less cumbersome and requires less gas for attitude control, eliminates the need for special orientation with respect to the sun, and interferes less with the satellite sensors, as compared with large solar photovoltaic arrays. For these reasons, it is possible that increased use will be made of thermoelectric generators in satellites which require large power supplies, such as the 580-watt SNAP 10A, which was recently tested for 43 days in orbit.

The thermionic converter, in contrast to the thermoelectric generator, depends upon the equilibrium electron properties of metals and, in particular, the difference in the Fermi levels between different metals which are physically separated, except for electrons which can cross from the metal with the higher Fermi level to the metal of the lower level, thereby creating a potential difference between them which can then be used to cause the electron current to flow through a load.   For the electrons to cross the gap between the metals, the emitter must be heated. This heat, of course, supplies the thermal energy which is converted into electrical energy. While this technique is in an earlier state of development than thermoelectric devices, higher efficiencies have already been produced in laboratory units.   On the other hand, since the emitter must operate by thermionic emission, the thermionic converter must operate at higher temperature than the thermoelectric element.   Again, for satellites, the higher temperature is an advantage, since the thermal energy which is not converted into electrical energy must be thermally radiated into space and the higher the rejection temperature, the smaller the radiator.   Other specialized applications which take advantage of the higher conversion efficiency are also visualized.

For all the devices discussed above, the unit-operating voltage is about 1 volt, while the current, and hence power, is proportional to the cross-sectional area of the device.   In other words, these devices are *area* devices and are probably not suitable for the production of *bulk* electrical power.   For example, modern central steam turbomachinery can generate 10^9 watts.   But thermionic converters which can produce about the highest power per unit area of the devices discussed previously, say 20 watts/cm², would require an area of about two football fields!   While this is not impossible, at the present time it does appear impractical.

On the other hand, the magnetohydrodynamic electrical-power generator is a *volume* device and bypasses the area restriction mentioned above. Power densities of the order of 3×10^7 watts/m³ have already been demonstrated with ordinary magnets; thus 10^9 watts can be generated in a volume of tens of cubic meters and possibly less with high-field superconducting magnets.   In addition, the magnetohydrodynamic generator is capable of high voltages, typically 10^3 to 10^4 volts.   Such high voltages are convenient for several reasons: Conversion to alternating current is relatively simple; the electrode current can be low and yet high powers per unit area of electrode are possible; and finally electrode voltage losses are trivial in comparison with the available voltages.

Since the magnetohydrodynamic generator operates on the Faraday principle, certain other factors must be considered.   First, the Faraday generator converts *kinetic* energy (of a moving conductor) into electrical energy; thus an additional step is needed, namely the conversion of thermal energy (from the thermal source) into kinetic motion.   Since this process is most easily accomplished in a gas (or vapor) by the successive processes of pressurization, heating, and expansion (and possibly repressurization), most present interest is in gases. However, since gases are not easily ionized, the use of very high temperatures and seeding is almost mandatory. Even so, the resulting electrical conductivity is smaller than that of metals by several orders of magnitude. Fortunately, this is compensated for by the very high velocities attainable by modest expansion of the gas. However, as electrical energy is extracted from the gas, the combination of gas temperature and velocity must decrease, leaving the gas essentially incapable of further MHD power conversion while still at very high temperature. Fortunately, there are numerous concepts for recovery of this energy. Finally, the generator length must be considered since this varies inversely with the square of the magnetic field. While MHD generators have been successfully operated with low magnetic fields, the potential impact of high-field superconducting magnets is so large that this may become the overriding consideration.

The prospects of eventual utilization of large MHD generators presently appear good; for example, a 40-Mw unit is presently under construction for operation of a special wind tunnel, but the practicality of smaller units is still questionable. In addition, much work is in progress on techniques to remove the thermal limitations mentioned above. While the prospects for this last achievement appear promising, it is premature to prognosticate its practicality.

It therefore appears that each of the methods of direct energy conversion covered in this volume will achieve increasing use in practical applications, the specific application being peculiar to the particular characteristics of the converter. One or more techniques may achieve bulk power generation, while the others are generally more suitable for remote or transportable generation of smaller power levels. It is important to realize that the progress to date has been made possible by diligent, sophisticated, and often difficult research. One hopes that additional research and engineering development will be encouraged and increased in the future in order to develop these devices to their fullest potential.

George W. Sutton

CONTENTS

1

PHOTOVOLTAIC ENERGY CONVERSION

J. F. Elliott

1. INTRODUCTION

> The solar cell, to my mind, is one device that has had a tremendous impact upon the space explorer agencies of this country. It would be quite difficult to envision the kind of a program that we would have over the past four years if the solar cell had not been available to us. As a matter of fact, I suspect it would be hard to find a single device that so many space missions have critically depended upon. We all, I know, realize that the solar cell has been in almost a position of monopoly in terms of space power systems, and I am sure we all realize that these systems are the ones that provide the lifehood to the space vehicles.†

A high-efficiency silicon solar cell was first demonstrated in 1954 by the Bell Telephone Laboratories. It was then apparent that the direct conversion of solar radiation into electrical energy by means of the photovoltaic effect would someday prove to be a useful source of electrical power. The successful flight of Vanguard I, and the other numerous space probes that have followed, have confirmed this speculation. While the success of the solar cell in the space field has probably justified the rather large amount of effort that has been expended on its development, it is quite possible that even this success will someday be overshadowed by the terrestrial uses of the device.

The potential applications for the solar cell now extend from the 100-microwatt region (a power supply for electronic devices implanted in the human body) to the kilowatt region (a power supply for the electrical requirement of a home) up into the megawatt region (as a power source for ion-propelled space vehicles).

Electronics Laboratory, General Electric Company, Syracuse, New York.

† From the opening remarks of Walter Scott, Chief of the Space Power Technology Program, NASA, delivered at the Photovoltaic Specialist Conference, Washington, D.C., Apr. 10, 1963.

The major advantages of the solar cell are:

1. By far the highest overall conversion efficiency of solar radiation to electricity, at present about 14 percent.   (A thermoelectric solar-energy converter, for example, can approach efficiencies of only 1 percent.)
2. Unlimited life.
3. Simplicity and ease of fabrication.   The device requires no auxiliary optical equipment, nor is there a need for a source of heat to obtain high efficiencies.
4. High power-output/weight ratio.

Its main disadvantages are:

1. High cost.
2. The need for a storage device in most applications.
3. Degradation in certain high-energy radiation fields.

The purpose of this chapter is to provide an understanding of the physics of the photovoltaic effect and the application of the phenomenon to the conversion of solar radiation to electrical energy.   This is done first by presenting a "pictorial" explanation of the device, followed by a more exact discussion based upon the semiconductor junction diode equation. With this basic understanding, the reader should then be able to appreciate the fundamental limitations of the device, as well as the reasons for the directions of the present-day development activities in the field.   The latter portion of the chapter is concerned with several of these development programs and a brief discussion of the present state of the art.

2.   *Conceptual Description of Photovoltaic Effect*

The photovoltaic effect is used by the solar cell to convert the radiation from the sun directly into electrical energy.   This effect has been known for many years and has been demonstrated in a number of different device configurations.   While physicists have a general understanding of the phenomenon, some of the details of the process are still not fully appreciated in several specific cases (e.g., in selenium and cadmium sulfide photovoltaic cells).   Only when the cell consists of a *p-n* junction in one of the simple semiconductor materials such as germanium or silicon can it be said that anything like a complete theoretical understanding of the effect exists.   In the following section this theoretical exposition is given. It is of such a nature, however, that one is apt to be left with little insight into the physical nature of the effect. In this section, an attempt is made to achieve this insight by providing a nonmathematical description of the various processes that are involved in the photovoltaic effect. This is done by first constructing a *p-n* junction in a semiconductor material and pointing out how the electric field in the junction is established. Next, the mechanism by which incident photons create free electrical charges which are then separated by the junction is discussed. Finally, it is noted that electrical energy is made available by the return of these charges through an external circuit to reestablish the equilibrium situation that existed before the photons were absorbed by the device.

The construction of a *p-n* junction is done in a very deliberate manner so that it will be possible to visualize what is happening at every step. We start with a piece of intrinsic or chemically pure silicon† (Fig. 1-1*a*). The block has been left blank to imply that each of the four valence electrons associated with each silicon atom is tied up in a chemical bond; that is, there are no free electrons. Now suppose this block is cut in half and in one half some of the silicon atoms are replaced by phosphorus atoms. Phosphorus has five valence electrons (one more than silicon). Four of the electrons are used for chemical bonds with adjacent silicon atoms; the fifth can be separated from the phosphorus atoms by thermal energy and becomes free to wander about in the lattice. Similarly, if in the other half of the block some of the silicon atoms are replaced by boron, which has only three valence electrons, there will be one electron missing to complete the chemical bonds with the adjacent silicon atoms. This missing electron acts in many ways as though it were a free *positive* electron and is called a hole.

The situation is now as pictured in Fig. 1-1*b* and *c*. The charges with circles represent the positive phosphorus and negative boron ions which are fixed in the lattice as they are bonded chemically to the silicon atoms. The uncircled charges are free to wander throughout the lattice. The free charge carriers on the right are negative and the material is called *n*-type silicon. Those on the left are positive and the material is called *p*-type silicon. One more point should be made before we pass on to the next sketch. It is important to note that there is complete charge compensation in both regions; there are just as many positive charges as there are negative. This, of course, means that there are no macroscopic electric fields present in either material.

The next step is to join the two regions back into a single block and to follow the effects upon the free carriers (Fig. 1-1*d*). The free electrons

---

† Silicon has been chosen as a representative semiconductor material for this example because it is the most successful solar-cell material, and as noted above, the physics of the material is rather well understood.

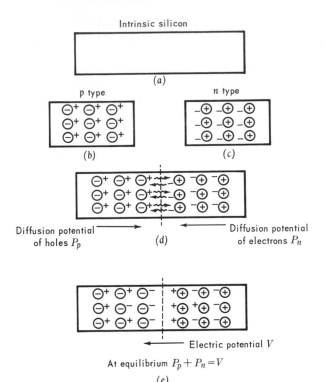

Fig. 1-1. *Conceptual representation of the construction of a p-n junction.*

in the n material will see a region to the left where there are no free electrons, and hence, there will be a flow of these carriers to the left in an attempt to rectify the situation. The free holes will see a region in which there are no holes, and there will be a flow of positive charge carriers to the right. This diffusion phenomenon is very similar to the process which takes place in the mixing of gases and is familiar to everyone. These diffusions of charges can be represented by diffusion potentials P_n and P_p. As time goes on, the situation can be visualized as shown in Fig. 1-1e. Notice that on the left side there is now an excess of negative charges and on the right side an excess of positive charges. Thus, an electric field has been established in the region of the interface of the two materials. As the holes and electrons continue to diffuse to the opposite sides, the electric field becomes larger and larger. The process continues until the electrical potential becomes of such a magnitude that further diffusion of holes and electrons is prohibited. When this equilibrium is established, the construction of the *p-n* junction has been completed.   A permanent macroscopic electric field has been established in a material without the aid of an external electric field.   This is the important point to be remembered.

The drawings will now be somewhat simplified so that it will be possible to see how a photovoltaic cell works.   In Fig. 1-2*a*, the symbols representing electrical charges have been removed, and only the internal electric field is indicated.   In Fig. 1-2*b*, the electrical potential is shown in detail.   On the top is the potential as seen by an electron, and below, the potential as seen by a hole.   Inasmuch as all physical systems like to be in a state of lowest energy, in general, electrons would move to the right and holes to the left.   In Fig. 1-2*b* and *c*, note that the potential energy

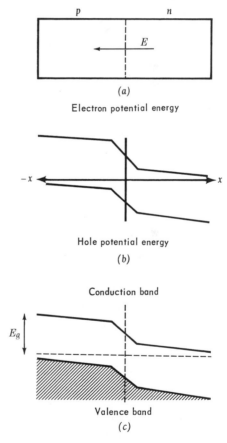

Fig. 1-2.   *Energy representation of a p-n junction.*

of an electron increases in the upward direction while that of a hole increases in the downward direction.

Figure 1-2c represents the usual manner of picturing a p-n junction. There are several further points that should be mentioned. It is noted that the magnitude of the electrical potential in the transition region increases as the number of p-type impurities is increased in the left side and as the number of n-type impurities is increased in the right side. One can continue to increase the potential in this way, at least until the potential for the holes on the left becomes equal to the potential of the electrons on the right. At this point, other phenomena such as tunneling become important. This situation exists when the potential difference between the left and right side is approximately equal to the forbidden band gap E_g of the semiconductor material.

The forbidden band gap (or, more briefly, the band gap) is an important materials parameter in a semiconductor device. It is, among other things, a direct measure of the energy required to break a bond in the silicon lattice, or, said in another way, the energy required to produce a free hole-electron pair.

With this same schematic drawing of the p-n junction, it is now possible to inquire what will be the effect of the absorption of a photon in the neighborhood of the junction. Let a quantum of light $h\nu$ enter the p-type material (Fig. 1-3a). If the photon has an energy greater than the band gap of the material, it will be absorbed and create a hole-electron pair. The electron sees a lower energy state to the right and will move in that direction. If a photon of sufficient energy had entered the n material, the created hole would move to the left. This is the charge-separation mechanism of the junction that is of great importance to the photovoltaic phenomenon. At this point one other important fact is noted. During the time interval between the creation of the hole-electron pair and their separation by the junction, they must not be given an opportunity to recombine or annihilate each other. That is, the electron in the p-type material and the hole in the n-type material must have sufficient time to reach the junction. This important materials parameter is called the minority carrier lifetime. The greater the lifetime, the greater the probability of the carriers being separated by the junction.

Now suppose that the junction region is flooded with many photons (Fig. 1-3b). The process just described will be repeated many times, and there will be an accumulation of positive charges at the left and negative charges at the right. This, of course, establishes an electric field that is opposite to the one established by the diffusion mechanism. As more and more photons are added, the fields tend to cancel each other. At this point, there is no longer an internal field that will separate any further

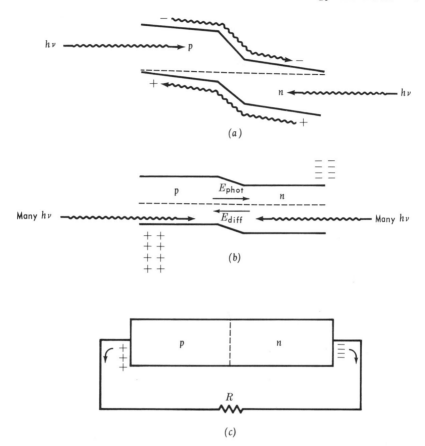

Fig. 1-3. *Pictorial description of the generation of electrical energy using the photovoltaic effect.*

created hole and electron pairs. We have thus arrived at the condition that determines the open-circuit voltage of the device. This open-circuit voltage will be directly proportional to the junction potential, which was noted previously to be directly proportional to the band gap of the semiconductor material. Thus, for a large open-circuit voltage, it is necessary to use a material having a large band gap.

The construction of the photovoltaic cell is now about complete except for one perhaps trivial step, putting electrodes on the surfaces and completing the electrical circuit so that use can be made of the electrical potential that has been established (Fig. 1-3c).

Many uses have been found for the basic device just described in the

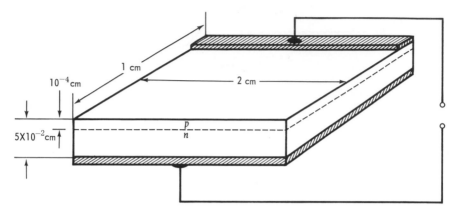

Fig. 1-4. *Typical geometry and physical configuration of a p-on-n silicon solar cell. Characteristics:* $V_{oc} \approx 0.58$ volt; $I_{sc} \approx 45$ ma; $V_m \approx 0.44$ volt; $P_{out} \approx 12$ Mw/cm²; $\eta \approx 12$ percent.

years since its first experimental demonstration, but probably the most significant application is the use of the sun to provide the energy to the cell. When the device is used in this manner, it is termed a solar cell and is the particular device of interest here.

Before proceeding further, it is perhaps appropriate to describe briefly the configuration and method of manufacture of a conventional silicon solar cell. Such a cell is shown in Fig. 1-4. The cell is constructed from a wafer of *n*-type silicon with a resistivity between 1 and 10 ohm-cm. The wafer is placed in a high-temperature oven and a *p-n* junction constructed by diffusing a *p*-type impurity into the surface to a depth of a few tenths of a micron to a few microns. The diffused layer is then removed from all the surfaces except the top. The final step is to place an electrode over the complete bottom surface and along one of the top edges. The solar energy is incident on the top surface. The dimensions in the drawing are typical of those associated with commercially available cells.†

The basic function of a solar cell is the conversion of electromagnetic energy into electrical energy. The more efficiently this conversion is carried out, the more useful the transducer. Now that a basic understanding of photovoltaic phenomenon has been developed, it is instructive to point out the important materials parameters that determine this efficiency.

---

† A more complete description of the solar-cell manufacturing process is given in Ref. 1.

The maximum conversion efficiency for any process under matched-load conditions can be written as

$$\eta_{max} = \frac{\text{output power}}{\text{input power}} = \frac{kV_{oc}I_{sc}}{\text{input power}}$$

The last expression applies particularly to cases where the output is in the form of electrical energy, where V_{oc} and I_{sc} are the open-circuit voltage and short-circuit current of the converter. The factor k is usually between one-quarter and unity and depends upon the mechanism by which the power is generated.

It is clear that for a given input power and a given k, it is desirable to have the largest possible open-circuit voltage and short-circuit current. In the case of the solar cell, it has just been pointed out that the maximum open-circuit voltage is proportional to the band gap of the material E_g; that is, the greater the band gap of the material used to construct the cell, the larger the V_{oc}. The short-circuit current is proportional to the number of hole-electron pairs created by the incident radiation. As noted, only those photons having energy greater than the band-gap energy will create pairs. When the sun is used as the excitation source, the smaller the band gap, the greater the short-circuit current. This can be made more obvious by Fig. 1-5, where the number of photons in the sun's spectra having energy greater than the band gap is plotted as a function of the band-gap energy. As the band gap increases, the short-circuit current decreases rapidly.

Therefore the power output can be written in functional form as

$$P = k'V_{oc}(E_g)I_{sc}\left(\frac{1}{E_g}\right)$$

and for some particular value of E_g, P will be maximized.

Several further basic considerations can be noted at this point. As mentioned, the minority carrier created by the absorbed photon must not recombine before it is collected by the junction. The probability of recombination is many times greater for a carrier in the neighborhood of a surface than it is for a carrier in the bulk material. This implies that carriers created behind the junction (i.e., in the n region in Fig. 1-4) will have a greater chance of diffusing to the junction than will carriers created in front of the junction where there is a nearby surface. The region in which the photons are absorbed and the hole-electron pairs created is determined by the absorption spectrum of the material used to construct the cell. The spectrum of several possible solar-cell materials is shown in Fig. 1-6. From these curves, it is seen that most photons will either be absorbed

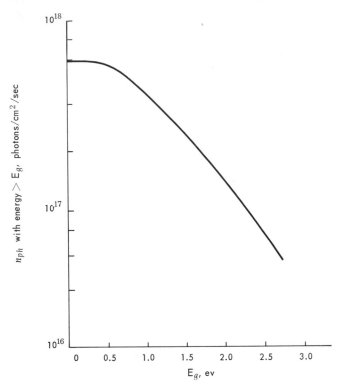

Fig. 1-5. *The number of photons in the sun's spectrum with energy greater than E_g. (The data are for solar radiation outside the earth's atmosphere.[2])*

in a very short distance (i.e., 10^{-4} to 10^{-6} cm) after they enter the material, or will not be absorbed at all. Thus, in order to ensure that absorption takes place behind the junction, it is desirable to place the junction as close to the incident surface as possible. However, as the junction is moved closer to the surface, another effect becomes important. The direction of current travel in the cell is normal to the bottom surface in the n region, but parallel to the surface in the p region (Fig. 1-4). As the junction is brought near the incident surface, the cross-sectional area of the conducting path in the p region is reduced; hence, its electrical resistance increases. Thus, although the collection efficiency of the junction is increased by moving the junction closer to the surface, the increase may well be dissipated by I^2R losses due to the high sheet resistance of the p region. This is one of the important design considerations in the construction of solar cells.

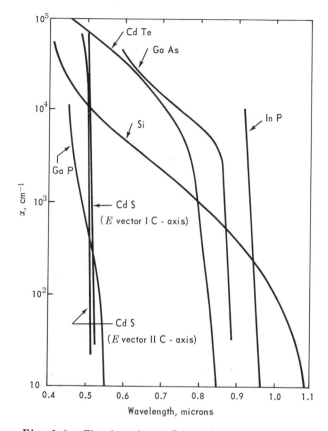

Fig. 1-6. *The absorption coefficient of several semiconductor materials of interest for solar cells. (Note how the curve for silicon differs from the others. This absorption characteristic is to a great extent responsible for the ease with which silicon solar cells can be constructed in comparison with cells made from other materials.[3])*

The current generated in the cell depends directly upon the number of hole-electron pairs that are created. It is therefore desirable that provisions be made to ensure that a large portion of the incident photons are not reflected at the surface. Because of the high index of refraction n of solar-cell materials ($n \approx 3$ to 4), this is not a trivial problem. For example, if the solar radiation is incident on the cell from a medium whose index of refraction is unity (that is, from air or vacuum), then the reflectivity R is

$$R = \frac{(n-1)^2}{(n+1)^2} \approx \frac{3^2}{5^2} = 36\%$$

Efforts have been made to reduce this large loss of available energy by the development of suitable nonreflecting coatings.

In this section, an attempt has been made to provide a lucid explanation of the photovoltaic effect and its application to a solar-cell device. This has been done by showing how an internal electric field is established in the cell by the construction of a *p-n* junction in a semiconducting material. The junction separates the hole-electron pairs that are created by absorbed photons. The movement of the separated carriers through an external circuit, making useful electrical energy available, reestablishes the equilibrium situation that existed before the photon absorption took place. The importance of the magnitude of the forbidden band gap when the photovoltaic cell is used to convert solar radiation into electrical energy was pointed out. Two pertinent solar-cell design considerations, junction depth and low reflectivity of the incident surface, were briefly discussed. In the following section, the theory of the photovoltaic cell and its application to the conversion of solar energy will be placed upon a more rigorous foundation.

3. Theory of the Photovoltaic Effect in p-n Junctions and Its Application to the Solar Cell

The purpose of this section is to derive the current-voltage relationship for the *p-n* junction when it is illuminated, in terms of measurable parameters. The derivation, in general, follows that presented by Cummerow.[4] This relationship having been obtained, the next objective is to determine the particular combination of materials parameters that optimizes the conversion efficiency of the device when excited by solar radiation.

The junction model used in the discussion is defined by the following assumptions:

1. The thickness of the junction region is small compared with the extent of the *p* or *n* regions and the diffusion length of the minority carriers.

2. The electrostatic field is confined to the junction region.

3. The carrier densities are small enough that Boltzmann statistics can be used.

The junction is represented as a region of width 2δ at $x = 0$ (see Fig. 1-7). The carrier concentrations on opposite sides of the barrier are related as follows:

$$p_n = p_p \exp \frac{-eV_e}{kT} \tag{1-1}$$

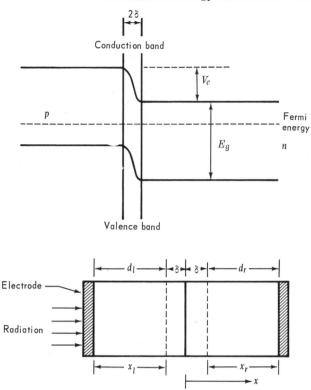

Fig. 1-7. *The model and notation used by Cummerow.*

where p_n and p_p are the equilibrium concentration of holes in the n material, and in the p material, respectively, V_e is the electrostatic potential difference across the transition region, and e, k, and T have their usual meanings. If a voltage V is placed across the junction by either the use of a battery or the generation of nonequilibrium charge concentrations near the barrier by means of radiation, the quasi equilibrium equation may be written

$$p_n(0) = p_p \exp \frac{-e(V_e - V)}{kT} \qquad (1\text{-}2)$$

where $p_n(0)$ is the value of p_n at $x = \delta$ or $x_r = 0$.

Equations (1-1) and (1-2) are combined to give

$$p_n(0) = p_n \exp \frac{eV}{kT} \qquad (1\text{-}3)$$

and a similar relation can be given for the electrons in the p material.

The rate of thermal generation of holes in the n material is given by $g_p = p_n/\tau_p$, and the recombination rate under nonequilibrium conditions is $r_p = p/\tau_p$ where τ_p is the hole lifetime and p is the nonequilibrium hole concentration. If holes are also generated because of the absorption of light quanta, the net generation is

$$g_p + g(x) - \frac{p}{\tau_p}$$

which must equal the net rate at which holes are leaving the volume under consideration:

$$g_p + g(x) - \frac{p}{\tau_p} = e^{-1}\frac{\partial I_p}{\partial x} \tag{1-4}$$

The current of interest I_p is a diffusion current; that is, it is caused by a concentration gradient of holes

$$I_p = -eD_p\frac{\partial p}{\partial x} \tag{1-5}$$

where D_p is the appropriate diffusion constant. Combining Eqs. (1-4) and (1-5),

$$g_p + g(x) - \frac{p}{\tau_p} + D_p\frac{\partial^2 p}{\partial x^2} = 0 \tag{1-6}$$

Equation (1-6), together with a similar one describing the electrons in the p material, is the general differential equation that is solved using the following boundary conditions:

At

$$x_r = 0: \qquad p = p_n \exp\frac{eV}{kT}$$

$$x_r = d_r: \qquad \frac{\partial p}{\partial x} = 0 \tag{1-7}$$

$$d_r \rightarrow \infty: \qquad p \rightarrow p_n \qquad \text{for all large } x_r$$

The solution presented by Cummerow is

$$I = eg_oL - egL'\left[\exp\left(\frac{eV}{kT}\right) - 1\right] \tag{1-8}$$

The first term, which acts as a current source, expresses the current generated by the photons in terms of the number of photons absorbed, where they are absorbed, and the probability that the minority carrier created by the absorption will diffuse to the junction.

The second term is the description for the current in an ideal *p-n* junction diode when a potential difference V is applied across the junction. The factor egL' expresses the magnitude of the reverse saturation current I_o due to thermally generated carriers, in terms of the temperature and the probability that they will reach the junction.

If $V = 0$, the short-circuit current from Eq. (1-8) is given by

$$I_{sc} = eg_oL \tag{1-9}$$

Solving Eq. (1-8) for V,

$$V = \frac{kT}{e} \ln \left(1 + \frac{eg_oL - I}{egL'} \right) \tag{1-10}$$

Then, if $I = 0$, the open-circuit voltage is

$$V_{oc} = \frac{kT}{e} \ln \left(1 + \frac{eg_oL}{egL'} \right) \tag{1-11}$$

If the power is delivered to an external resistor R,

$$P = IV = I \frac{kT}{e} \ln \left(1 + \frac{eg_oL - I}{egL'} \right) \tag{1-12}$$

Setting $dP/dI = 0$, the current for maximum power output is

$$I_m = \frac{egL'(1 + g_oL/gL')eV_m/kT}{1 + eV_m/kT} \tag{1-13}$$

and the voltage V_m for maximum power is

$$\exp \frac{eV_m}{kT} = \frac{1 + g_oL/gL'}{1 + eV_m/kT} \tag{1-14}$$

Hence, the maximum power output P_m is

$$P_m = \frac{egL'(1 + g_oL/gL')eV_m/kT}{1 + eV_m/kT} V_m \tag{1-15}$$

Equations (1-9) and (1-11) are useful for determining the quantities gL' and g_oL experimentally for a given cell and thus allow the calculation for the maximum power output from Eq. (1-15).

The equivalent circuit which represents Eq. (1-8) is shown in Fig. 1-8*a*. It consists of a constant current source shunted by an ideal diode. A more detailed equivalent circuit is shown in Fig. 1-8*b*, where R_s and R_{sh} are internal-loss mechanisms due to the inability to construct an ideal diode in practice. An experimental method for the determination of the magnitude of these loss terms has been described.[1]

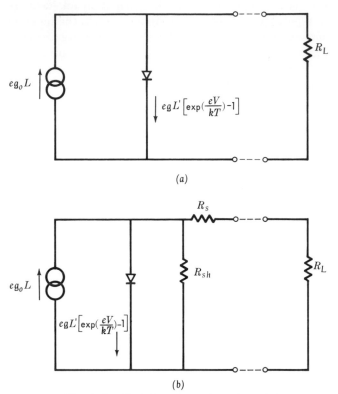

Fig. 1-8.   *Equivalent circuits for a photovoltaic cell.*

Loferski,[2] using Eq. (1-15) together with a change in notation, writes the maximum conversion efficiency of the photovoltaic p-n-junction cell when excited by N_{ph} photons of average energy E_{av} as

$$\eta_{max} = Q(1-r)(1-e^{\alpha l}) \frac{\lambda V_m}{1+\lambda V_m} \frac{en_{ph}(E_g)V_m}{N_{ph}E_{av}} \qquad (1\text{-}16)$$

where

$$Q(1-r)(1-e^{-\alpha l})en_{ph}E_g = I_{sc} = eg_o L$$

$$\exp \lambda V_m = \left(\frac{I_{sc}}{I_o} + 1\right)$$

$$\lambda = \frac{e}{kT}$$

and Q is the collection efficiency of the junction, r the optical reflection coefficiency of the cell, $e^{-\alpha l}$ the fraction of radiation transmitted, α the absorption constant, l the thickness of the cell, and $n_{ph}(E_g)$ the number of photons per second per unit area of junction, whose energies are large enough to create hole-electron pairs in the semiconductor.

Equation (1-16) is now written in a form in which, with the exception of Q and I_o, all the terms are expressed as intrinsic properties of the cell material and the nature of the radiation source. All the extrinsic parameters, that is, those that depend upon the details of how the junction is constructed, have been lumped in Q and I_o.

Equation (1-16), or one cast in a similar form, has been examined by a number of workers when the excitation source is the sun. The most lucid summary of the conclusions of these studies as they pertain to the selection of the best material for the highest-efficiency solar cell has been given by Kleinman.[5]

1. Unless precautions are taken, the coefficient r can be expected to be large for the semiconductor materials of interest. For example, about 30 percent of the incident light on a clean silicon surface is reflected. Other materials of interest also have high reflectivities. In the actual manufacture of silicon cells the processing leaves a thin glossy layer on the surface which has a low reflectivity (and, fortunately, low absorptivity). It is reasonable to expect that this loss could be minimized for other materials in a similar manner.

2. Light which enters the cell is either absorbed or is eventually transmitted out of the cell. Only light which is absorbed by the intrinsic absorption process, in which a photon is annihilated and a hole-electron pair created, can be converted to electrical energy by the photovoltaic process. Thus only those photons having a wavelength shorter than the intrinsic absorption edge are useful. Of these photons only those whose wavelengths are the same as the absorption edge create a hole-electron pair without further loss of useful energy. Any pair which is created by the absorption of a photon having energy greater than the minimum required amount will quickly dissipate the excess to the lattice in the form of heat. In a solar cell these losses are due to the spectrum of the solar radiation and would not be present if the cell were radiated with monochromatic light at the wavelength of the absorption edge. For silicon these losses amount to over 50 percent of the solar energy which actually enters the cell. By the choice of a material of somewhat larger band gap these spectrum losses can be somewhat reduced.

3. The factor Q, termed the *collection efficiency*, is a measure of the number of minority carriers produced by the absorbed photons that actually reach the junction. Some of the minority carriers diffuse toward the junction; others diffuse away and recombine in the bulk of the cell or

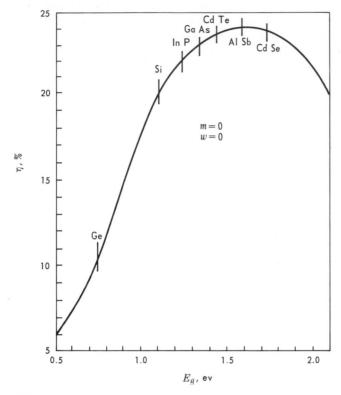

Fig. 1-9. *The theoretical efficiency of solar cells constructed from semi-conductor materials having different band gaps.*[2]

at the surface. In a silicon cell the collection efficiency is about 60 to 70 percent; thus, carrier recombination is one of the major reasons these cells do not approach their expected theoretical efficiency. This loss is due to the degradation of the silicon bulk and surface minority carrier lifetimes during the manufacturing process. In other semiconductor materials of interest the recombination losses are apt to be considerably more serious, as the bulk lifetimes are down some four orders of magnitude from that of silicon.

4. The voltage developed by the solar cell is, as noted above, due to the excess of minority carriers on both sides of the junction. This voltage, however, is considerably less than the energy of the hole-electron pair. For example, in silicon the energy of a hole-electron pair is about 1.2 ev, that is, the energy of the band gap; while the voltage of the silicon solar

cell under full sunlight at maximum power conditions is about 0.4 volt. Thus, the cell is able to convert only a portion of the energy stored as hole-electron pairs into useful energy. This loss is referred to as the junction loss. This loss should vanish and the voltage should approach the energy gap when the minority carrier density approaches the majority carrier density, a condition corresponding to infinite light intensity. From the equivalent-circuit point of view the short-circuit current flows partly through the load and partly through the junction in the forward direction. The voltage and the junction loss therefore depend upon the forward current-voltage characteristics of the junction. The theory of p-n junctions predicts that the forward current should decrease exponentially with increasing band gap. Therefore, the junction loss can be reduced by increasing the band gap. A number of authors have considered the spectrum and junction loss as a function of energy gap. Neglecting all other energy losses, the maximum efficiency is obtained for a band gap of about

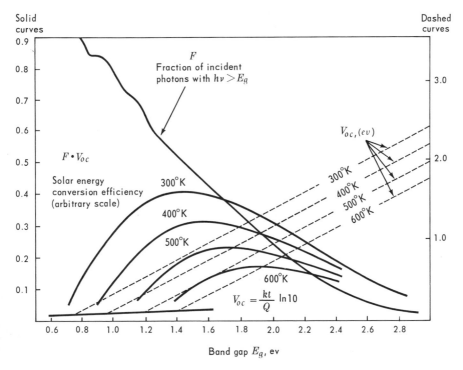

Fig. 1-10. *Theoretical temperature dependence of the efficiency of solar cells made from different band-gap semiconductor materials.*[6]

1.6 ev for the solar radiation spectrum that exists above the earth's atmosphere (Fig. 1-9).   The greatest difference in efficiency between silicon and the optimum material (about 5 percent in efficiency) is for the spectrum above the atmosphere.   For terrestrial use the difference is only a few percent.

5.   The final loss is due to the resistance of the very thin side of the junction next to the surface, through which the current must flow to reach the contact electrode.   In practice this internal resistance in a silicon cell is a few ohms.   If this loss were completely eliminated, the efficiency of the cell could be increased several percent.   Unlike the other losses considered, the resistance loss is not characteristic of the material used for the cell, but rather is a result of the geometry used in the construction of the cell.

The final theoretical conclusion that will be noted is the effect of the cell temperature upon the conversion efficiency.   The short-circuit current has been assumed to be, and is found experimentally to be, insensitive to temperature.   The major effect is due to the fact that V_m is a function of I_o, which is quite dependent on temperature.   The required calculations have been carried out by several authors, and results typical of the work are shown in Fig. 1-10.

4.   Solar-cell State of the Art

The selection of a power supply for a particular application is based upon a comparison of various figures of merit for the different types of supplies that are available.   Some of the common figures of merit are:

1.   Power output per unit cost
2.   Power output per unit weight
3.   Power output per unit surface area
4.   Total power output or total energy output
5.   Reliability

All the development effort expended in the field of solar cells during the past 10 years has been directed at improving one or more of the above figures.

In this final section, the major development programs that are still in progress or have recently been completed are described with the objective of presenting the current state of the art and the possible advances that may occur in the future.

4-1. Silicon Cells

The most successful cells, and still the only type that are commercially available, are those manufactured from silicon. Cells with conversion efficiencies of 12 percent are readily available, and 14 percent cells can be obtained. Further major improvements in efficiency will probably not occur, as most of the design and materials parameters have been optimized. The characteristics of engineering interest of the silicon solar cell are shown in Fig. 1-11.

Certainly one of the major unsolved problems is concerned with the manufacturing difficulty of producing a high yield of high-efficiency cells. This problem has been present since the start of the industry, and although higher-and-higher-efficiency cells have been manufactured, these cells are a small percentage of the total number of cells produced (Fig. 1-12). This low yield of the highest-efficiency cells is one of the reasons for the high cost of the silicon solar cell (i.e., about $400/watt).

In the late 1950s, it was realized that the degradation of silicon solar cells by high-energy particle bombardment would seriously limit their usefulness in satellite applications where the orbit was in the region of the Van Allen radiation belt. At the present time, the physics of the radiation-damage mechanism in silicon is not clearly understood. This problem,

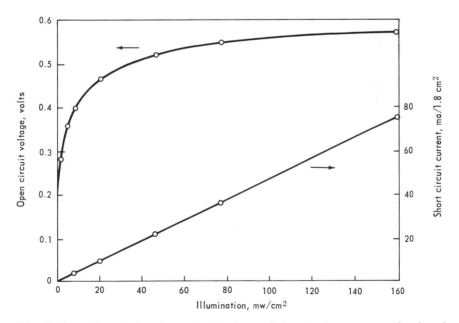

Fig. 1-11a. *The variation of open-circuit voltage and short-circuit current as a function of incident solar radiation for a commercially available silicon solar cell.*[7]

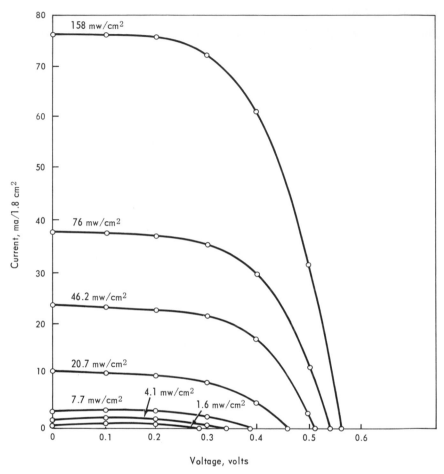

Fig. 1-11b.   *The current-voltage relationships for a silicon solar cell under different load and illumination conditions.*[7]

together with empirical attempts to construct more radiation-resistant cells, has consumed a large part of the research effort in silicon cells during the past five years.

The conventional *p*-on-*n* cell (that is, the cell is constructed from an *n* wafer with a diffused *p* layer, as in Fig. 1-4) is damaged by electrons of energy greater than 170 kv.   Under radiation in this energy range, the cell output will decrease by 25 percent after a dosage of about 10^{18} electrons/cm^2.

One of the significant advances in this area was the demonstration by Mandelkorn[9] that *n*-on-*p* cells are less susceptible to radiation damage. Two factors contribute to this observed result.   Since the operation of the

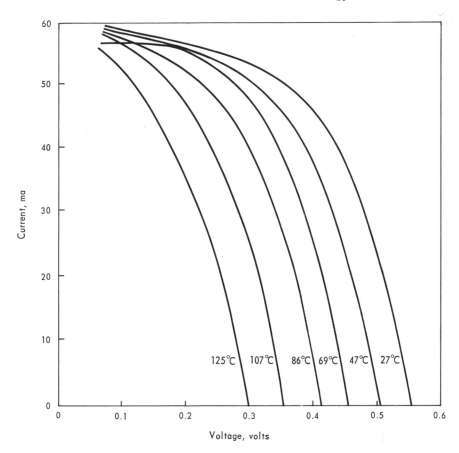

Fig. 1-11c. *The temperature dependence of the I-V curves of a silicon cell.*[7]

cell depends upon the collection of photon-generated carriers from deep within the cell, these carriers must be able to traverse large distances (up to 150 μ) in the bulk silicon. To do this, the minority carrier must have a long lifetime. The minority carrier lifetime (electrons) in p-type material is about three times greater than the minority carrier lifetime (holes) in n-type material. Hence, if the bulk material is mostly p-type, it will withstand more damage before the lifetime is lowered to an unacceptable value than would an n-type bulk material. A second factor of importance is that it takes a greater threshold energy for electrons to create a defect in p-type material (about 250 kv) than in n-type material.

A comparison of the two types of cells is shown in Fig. 1-13, and in Fig. 1-14 the performances of several types of cells in a Telstar-like orbit are compared.

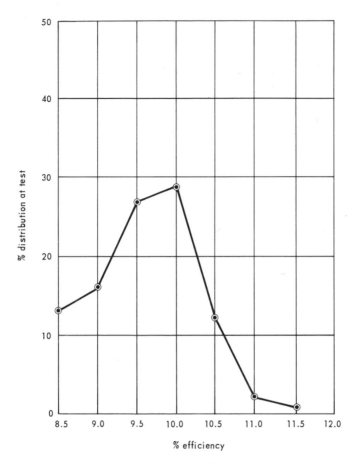

Fig. 1-12. *Typical production yield of silicon solar cells.*[8]

A second approach to increasing the useful lifetime of the silicon cell is the so-called "graded-base cell."[11] In conventional cells, the junction or space-charge region extends over an extremely small area. The process by which created carriers reach the junction is random. The graded-base approach extends the junction region deep into the bulk material so that there is a small electric field present to give a preferential direction to the drift motion of the carriers. The expected improvement in the useful lifetime of such designed cells is also indicated in Fig. 1-14.

The major detriment to the large-scale use of silicon solar cells in terrestrial application has been the high cost of the cell. A major expense in the manufacture is the large amount of expensive single-crystal silicon used. A typical cell is 45×10^{-3} cm thick. It has long been realized that most of this material does not contribute to producing useful energy; it is only required to provide mechanical strength to the cell. It has been shown, theoretically, that a silicon cell 10^{-4} to 10^{-3} cm thick should have an efficiency of 5 to 10 percent (Fig. 1-15). If such a cell could be built, then the cost per watt of output power would conceivably be reduced by two or three orders of magnitude.

Another factor has stimulated development efforts in thin-film silicon cells. The total output capacity of the solar-cell industry in the United States is about 100 kw/year.[13] Presumably, this output could be increased by several orders of magnitude; however, this still would not be sufficient to permit the consideration of megawatt solar-cell supplies, which are of some interest for ion-propelled spacecraft. Thin-film techniques would presumably increase the potential capacity by many orders of magnitude.

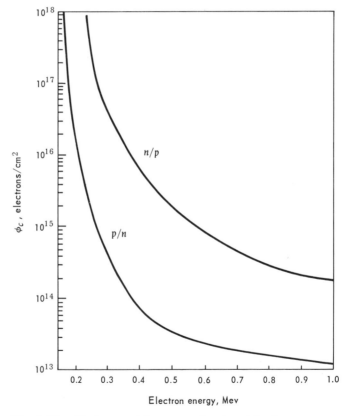

Fig. 1-13. *The integrated dosage as a function of the electron energy required to reduce the maximum power output of a silicon solar cell by 25 percent.*[7]

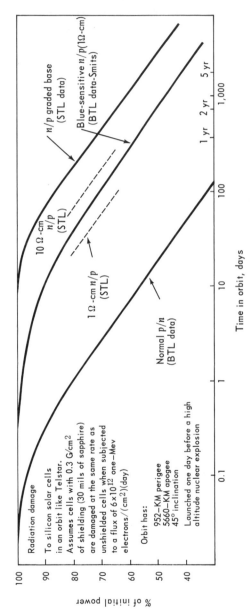

Fig. 1-14. *The degradation of several types of silicon cells for a satellite in an orbit in the Van Allen radiation belt.*[10]

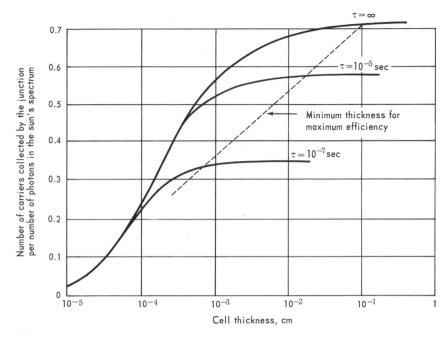

Fig. 1-15. *Relative efficiency of silicon solar cells as a function of cell thickness. (The minority carrier lifetime τ is the parameter.[12])*

Development of thin-film silicon cells began in the late 1950s. To date, although considerable progress has been made, the demonstration of a reasonably efficient and large-area thin-film cell has not been forthcoming.

The most promising approach has been the construction of thin films by the chemical deposition of silicon. The system used for the preparation of these films[14] is shown in Fig. 1-16. Pure dry hydrogen is passed through a vessel of silicon tetrachloride. The hydrogen picks up a quantity of silicon tetrachloride vapor and carries it to the reaction chamber. When the vapor comes in contact with the hot substrate, it is decomposed, with silicon being deposited upon the substrate and the hydrogen and chlorine being exhausted out of the reaction chamber. The films are doped by mixing the appropriate amount of phosphorus trichloride vapor (for n-type films) or boron tribromide (for p-type films) with the silicon tetrachloride vapor. Growth rate and the quality of the film are dependent upon such parameters as substrate temperature, flow velocity, and vapor-concentration ratios. In general, good-quality films are prepared at substrate temperatures of 1200°C and growth rates of several mils per hour. Many different substrate materials have been used, the main consideration being

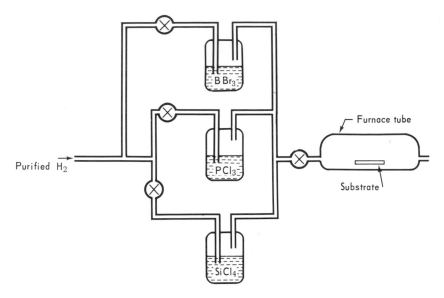

Fig. 1-16.   *Schematic representation of the apparatus for the preparation of silicon thin films.*

that the substrate material have a thermal-expansion coefficient compatible with that of silicon.   The films, when prepared on any substrate other than single-crystal silicon, are polycrystalline with a grain size of up to 3 to 5 mils.   The junction is usually constructed by a diffusion process after the film has been grown.

The highest efficiency of such cells reported to date is of the order of 3.5 percent.   Both the open-circuit voltage and short-circuit current are considerably lower than the values associated with single-crystal cells. The reason for this low efficiency is not clearly understood, as the concept of the thin-film cell is theoretically sound, and cells of 5 to 10 percent efficiency have been constructed from bulk polycrystalline material.

One additional approach is being followed to reduce the cost of silicon solar-cell power supplies.   The construction of the conventional 1- by 2-cm cell involves a considerable amount of direct labor, which is a direct result of using single-crystal ingots as a starting material.   These ingots are of circular cross section about 1 in. in diameter and perhaps 10 in. long.   The first step in the manufacturing of the cell is to saw the ingot into wafers. These circular wafers are diffused and then shaped to the final 1- by 2-cm size.   This procedure is expensive in terms of the labor involved and the amount of silicon lost.   To construct a solar power supply from these individual cells, they must be assembled in a panel—again, a process which involves considerable labor.   If the starting silicon material were in a form of a large-area sheet, the cost of a solar array would be considerably reduced. A crystal-growing technique[15] called *dendritic growth* exists which prepares single crystals of silicon in a ribbon form. The ribbon is 10 to 20 mils thick and up to 1 in. wide and is grown continuously. Cells constructed from this material have essentially the same performance as those cells available commercially. In principle, it is therefore possible to construct large-area silicon cells by a continuous manufacturing process.

4-2. Other Materials

Loferski's work pointed out that there were several materials that should be more efficient than silicon for the conversion of solar radiation. Of these GaAs and CdTe have received the most experimental attention. In addition, considerable effort has been devoted to CdS, a material which would not be predicted to be of interest from Loferski's work.

The experimental difficulties associated with GaAs and CdTe can be deduced from Fig. 1-6. If photons have the correct energy to be absorbed by these materials, they will all be absorbed in a very narrow region quite near the incident surface. While the localization of the region in which the absorption occurs greatly relieves the specification on the required minority carrier lifetime, the fact that it takes place so close to the incident surface means that the cells will have a high internal impedance due to the high sheet resistance (see page 10). This problem has been attacked by two different approaches. In both GaAs and CdTe, the resistance has been reduced by applying a grid electrode on the incident surface. While this reduces the internal impedance, at the same time, it substantially reduces the active area of the cell. A second approach that is being investigated in the case of GaAs is to make the incident surface from GaP.[16] Since GaP has a higher band gap than GaAs (2.2 ev as opposed to 1.35 ev), many of the incident photons are not absorbed until they travel through the GaP region and reach the GaAs material. Thus, since the absorption region is some distance beyond the incident surface, the sheet resistance is reduced by increasing the junction depth.

Several factors in addition to possible increases in efficiency have encouraged work in GaAs and CdTe. Cells made from these materials maintain a high efficiency at high temperatures; for example, the efficiency of a GaAs cell as a function of temperature is compared with a silicon cell in Fig. 1-17. This characteristic is of interest when focusing systems are used or for space probes directed toward the sun. The second point of interest is that these cells are expected to demonstrate a higher resistance to radiation than silicon (Fig. 1-18).

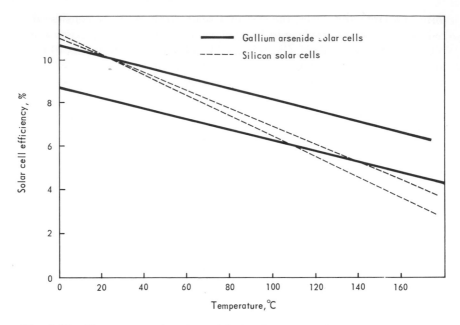

Fig. 1-17. *The temperature dependence of GaAs cells as compared with silicon cells. (The two curves for each type tend to indicate the spread in this characteristic that can be expected.[3])*

Most of the work in GaAs has been with single-crystal material.   The steps in the construction of the GaAs cells are practically identical with those used in preparing silicon cells.   One additional step is required, however.   Because the position of the junction in relation to the incident surface is so critical, it has been found that it can best be fixed by first diffusing a relatively deep junction and then removing material from the surface by a chemical etch.   Optimization of the junction depth is the final step in the cell's construction and is carried out by alternately etching and measuring the cell's performance.   Efficiencies of 11 percent have been reported.   Because the yield of the high-efficiency cells is poor, a considerable portion of the development effort is being directed toward this problem at the present time.   The *I-V* characteristic of a GaAs cell is compared with that of silicon in Fig. 1-19.

The effort in CdTe has been concerned with both single-crystal and thin-film cells.   The understanding of the physics of the single-crystal cell has aided considerably the progress in the thin-film area.

CdTe films are prepared by a vapor-reaction technique.   Appropriate amounts of Cd and Te powder are placed in the reaction chamber, which is maintained at 400 to 500°C and at a reduced pressure.   The constituents are vaporized and the chemical reaction takes place on the surface of the substrate (e.g., molybdenum or titanium) to form the film 5 to 15 μ thick. The film is removed from the chamber and the surface treated with a solution containing cuprous ions for about a minute at 50 to 85°C. This step forms the junction. The junction is between the p-type cuprous telluride and the n-type cadmium telluride. Such a junction is more closely approximated by a metal-semiconductor junction than by a p-n junction such as used to describe silicon and gallium arsenide cells. The final step is to press a gold or nickel meshed foil onto the incident surface to serve as the second electrode. The same method of forming the junction and applying the top electrode is used in the construction of the single-crystal CdTe cells.

Conversion efficiencies of 5 to 6 percent for film cells and 6 to 8 percent for single-crystal cells have been demonstrated. Typical I-V characteristics of both types of cells are shown in Fig. 1-20. Thin-film cells of 9 in.^{2} have been demonstrated with efficiencies of greater than 4 percent.

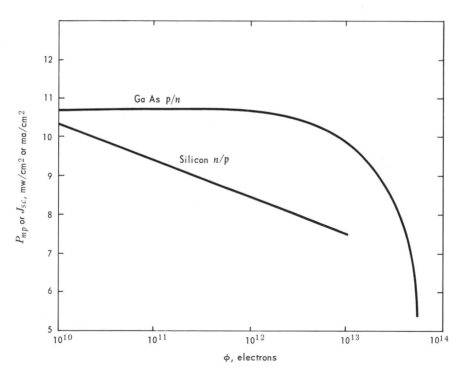

Fig. 1-18. *A comparison of the effect of radiation on GaAs and silicon solar cells. (ϕ is the total integrated dosage, P_{mp} and J_{sc} are the maximum power and short-circuit current. The energy of the beta radiation is not identified by the author.[3])*

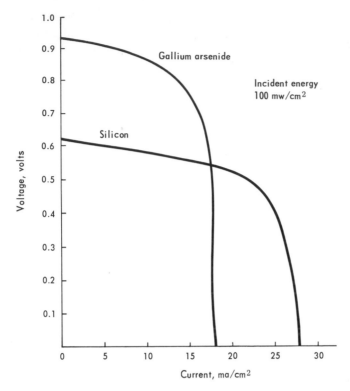

Fig. 1-19.   *The current-voltage curve for a GaAs solar cell.*[3]

In 1954, the potentiality of CdS as a solar-cell material was recognized. Since that time, considerable effort has been devoted to developing both single-crystal and thin-film cells. CdS has a band gap of 2.4 ev. Loferski's work, based upon the simple *p-n* junction theory, would predict a maximum efficiency of about 6 percent for such material. Single-crystal cells from CdS have been constructed with efficiencies greater than this. While it is obvious that the CdS cell cannot be understood in terms of a simple *p-n* junction, no satisfactory explanation has been offered.

During the past several years, most of the experimental attention has been directed to the so-called "front-wall" and "back-wall" thin-film cells. A description of a front-wall cell indicates the status of the CdS work.

A schematic representation of the front-wall cell is given in Fig. 1-21. A 1- to 2-mil layer of CdS is evaporated on a 1-mil molybdenum substrate. This is followed by the electrodeposition of copper, which is subsequently oxidized. Finally, a metal screen of silver or gold is pressed on the surface

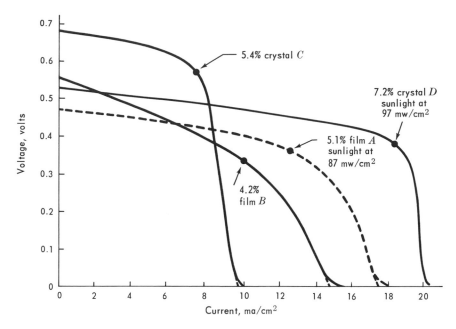

Fig. 1-20.   *The I-V curves for several different experimental CdTe cells.*[17]

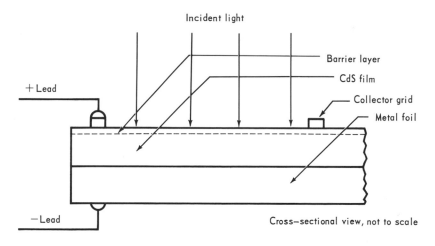

Fig. 1-21.   *Schematic representation of a front-wall CdS solar cell.*[18]

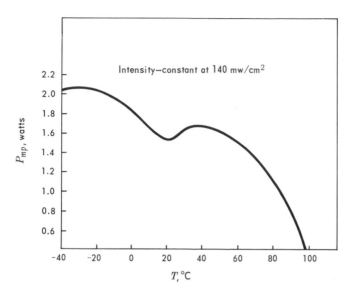

Fig. 1-22a. *The power output of a CdS panel under matched load conditions as a function of temperature.*[18]

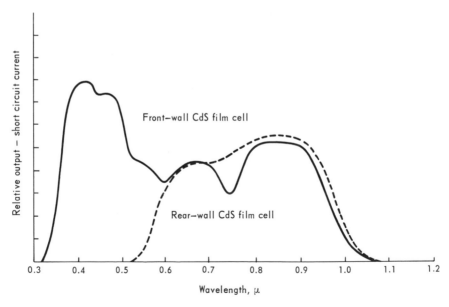

Fig. 1-22b. *The wavelength dependence of the sensitivity of front- and rear-wall CdS cells.*[18]

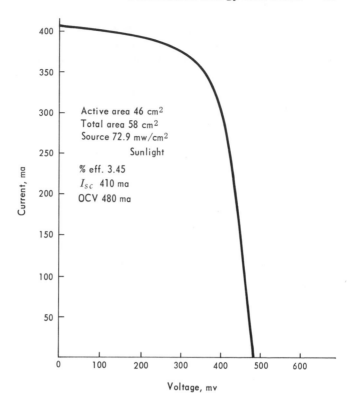

Active area 46 cm^2
Total area 58 cm^2
Source 72.9 mw/cm^2
Sunlight

% eff. 3.45
I_{sc} 410 ma
OCV 480 ma

Fig. 1-22c. *The current-voltage relationship of a CdS solar panel.*[18]

to serve as the top electrode. The barrier is probably formed between the copper oxide and the CdS. Since this barrier (i.e., the metal-semi-conductor junction) is formed near the surface on which the radiation is incident, it is called a front-wall cell. A back-wall cell has the barrier formed between the CdS and the substrate.

Cells of this type have been made in sizes of 6 by 6 in. with efficiencies of up to 4 percent. The power-to-weight ratio is 15 to 30 watts/lb. Of some interest is the fact that the cells are very flexible. It is predicted that the cost of this type of converter will be about $50/watt, which is about a factor of 8 lower than the present cost of silicon cells.†

Figure 1-22 conveys some of the performance characteristics that are typical of a CdS solar-cell panel. Of particular interest is the spectral-

† Although this would be a substantial cost reduction, energy generated by the photovoltaic effect would still be too expensive to be considered for large-scale terrestrial use. An additional reduction in the cost of the cell by a factor of 400 (i.e., $.15/watt) would be required for a solar photovoltaic system to become competitive with conventional central-station power generators.[12]

response curve.   From Fig. 1-6, it is predicted that there is no response for photons having wavelengths longer than about 0.5 μ, as no fundamental absorption takes place for wavelengths longer than this.   The response for both the front- and back-wall cells extends out to about 1.1 μ. Once again, it is clear that the photovoltaic mechanism in the CdS cell is considerably different from that of silicon.

5.   Summary and Concluding Remarks

The solar cell at the present time has no serious competitor in its ability to convert solar radiation into electrical energy.   This statement is true regardless of the figure of merit used to rate its performance.   The high performance of the device is a direct result of the fact that the photovoltaic effect does not degrade the solar radiation to heat before transducing the energy to an electrical form; hence, the process is not limited by the Carnot efficiency associated with thermoconverters.

The use of the solar cell to provide electrical energy has been restricted almost entirely to space applications.   Economic considerations have prevented its wider utilization.   The high cost of the device is due to the low manufacturing yield of high-efficiency units and the high cost of the single-crystal material from which the device is constructed.   Higher yields should eventually be obtainable as manufacturing processes are improved and tightened.   The thin-film solar cell offers a considerable reduction in the amount of material used and would probably require a substantially smaller amount of labor per unit area of cell constructed.

In the preceding pages an attempt has been made to provide an understanding of the physics of the photovoltaic effect and the application of the phenomenon to the conversion of solar radiation.   It has not been feasible to discuss the design, construction, and testing of a complete solar-cell power system, as, in general, the problems are only specified in terms of the particular mission requirements.   The engineering problems encountered in these areas are not trivial.

References

1.   Zarem, A. M., and D. D. Erway: *Introduction to the Utilization of Solar Energy*, McGraw-Hill Book Company, New York, 1963.
2.   Loferski, J. J.: "Theoretical Considerations Governing the Choice of the Optimum Semiconductor for Photovoltaic Solar Energy Conversion," *J. Appl. Phys.*, **27**: 777 (1956).
3.   Gold, R. D.: "Current Status of GaAs Solar Cells," *Transcript of Photovoltaic*

Specialists Conf., vol. 1, Photovoltaic Materials, Devices and Radiation Damage Effects, DDC no. AD412819, Sec. A-6, July, 1963.

4. Cummerow, R. L.: "Photovoltaic Effect in *p-n* Junctions," *Phys. Rev.*, **95:** 16 (1954).
5. Kleinman, D. A.: "Considerations on the Solar Cell," *Bell System Tech. J.*, **40:** 85 (1961).
6. Halsted, R. E.: "Temperature Consideration in Solar Battery Development," *J. Appl. Phys.*, **28:** 1131 (1957).
7. Cherry, W. R.: "Solar Cells and the Applications Engineer," *Astronautics and Aerospace Eng.*, **1:** 54 (May, 1964).
8. Private communications, W. T. Eriksen, Hoffman Electronics Corp., El Monte, Calif.
9. Mandelkorn, J., et al.: "A New Radiation Resistant High Efficiency Solar Cell," *USASRDL Tech. Rept.*, 2162, October, 1960.
10. Scott, W. C.: "Space Electrical Power," *Astronautics and Aerospace Eng.*, **1:** 48 (May, 1963).
11. Kaye, S.: "Drift Field Solar Cells," *Transcript of Photovoltaic Specialists Conf., op. cit.*, Sec. B-14.
12. Elliott, J. F.: "Home Generation of Power by Photovoltaic Conversion of Solar Energy," *Elec. Eng.*, **79:** 735 (1960).
13. Elliott, J. F., V. F. Meikliham, and C. L. Kolbe: "Large Areas Solar Cells," in N. W. Snyder (ed.), *Energy Conversion for Space Power*, p. 263, Academic Press Inc., New York, 1961.
14. Heaps, J. D.: "Thin Film Silicon Solar Cells," *Transcript of Photovoltaic Specialists Conf., op. cit.*, Sec. A-4.
15. Tarneja, K. S.: "Dendritic Solar Cells and Array Investigation," AF33(615)-1049, DDC no. 451543.
16. Webb, G. N.: "Variable Energy Gap Devices," *ibid.*, Sec. A-7.
17. Cusano, D. A.: "CdTe Solar Cells," *ibid.*, Sec. A-3.
18. Schaeffer, J. C.: "Thin Film CdS Front Wall Solar Cells," *ibid.*, Secs. A-1 and A-2.

Additional Reading

Probably the most up-to-date and detailed summary of the present status of solar-cell research and development is contained in *Transcript of Photovoltaic Specialists Conf., op. cit.* Further details are available in *Proc. 4th Photovoltaic Specialists Conf.*, vols. 1 and 2, DDC no. 444113, June 3, 1964.

J. Tauc's paper "Generation of an emf in Semiconductors with Nonequilibrium Current Carrier Concentrations," *J. Appl. Phys.*, **29:** 308 (1957), is the most general and complete theoretical discussion of the photovoltaic effect and its related phenomena.

The making of solar cells and their use in high school science fairs have been popular. A description of how the device can be made in a high school laboratory is given by D. M. Chapin, "How to Make Solar Cells," *Electronics*, March, 1960, p. 89.

2

FUEL CELLS   *W. T. Grubb and L. W. Niedrach*

1. INTRODUCTION

1-1. Definition

When a fuel is burned in air, the driving force for the reaction is the chemical affinity of the fuel for the oxygen, or, in different words, the greater chemical stability of the oxidation products compared with the reactants. In ordinary combustion the energy of fuel oxidation is released in the form of heat. However, it is possible to force such an oxidation reaction to occur by an indirect, electrochemical path so that most of the energy is released directly in the form of electrical energy. The type of device by which this is accomplished is called a *fuel cell*. A fuel cell is defined as an electrochemical device which directly converts the chemical energy of a fuel oxidation reaction into electrical energy.

Physically, a fuel cell consists of two electrodes separated by an electrolyte. Fuel is fed to one electrode, and air or oxygen to the other. The electrolyte must be highly permeable to an ion which is a charged intermediate in the fuel oxidation reaction. A second charged intermediate is the electron which travels through the load circuit of the fuel cell and does electrical work en route. Depending upon the type of fuel cell, either positive or negative ions may serve as the charged intermediate passing through the electrolyte. In a most general way, the operation of a fuel cell

General Electric Research and Development Center, Schenectady, New York.

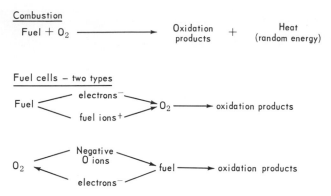

Fig. 2-1. *Schematic of the principle of fuel-cell operation.*

is illustrated by the two schemes of Fig. 2-1 for positive and negative ionic intermediates, respectively.

1-2. Modes of Operation

Conversion of chemical energy of fuels into electrical energy on a large scale with high efficiency has long defied practical realization. A basic reason for this has been that the type of process which is economic today involves the conversion of the energy of the fuel first into heat energy, second into mechanical energy, and third into electrical energy. The second process is by far the least efficient. It is accomplished by a heat engine, and Carnot showed that no closed-cycle heat engine can convert more than a certain fraction of the high-temperature heat input Q_H into macroscopic work W. The fraction converted depends upon the input absolute temperature T_H and the output absolute temperature T_L. The following equation applies:

$$W/Q_H = \frac{T_H - T_L}{T_H} \tag{2-1}$$

Q_H is derived from the combustion of the fuel, and $100 \times W/Q_H$ may be defined as the Carnot efficiency E of the heat engine.

How Eq. (2-1) influences the situation in practice is illustrated by the case of a fuel-fired steam-turbine generator system. For the most modern large units the Carnot efficiency E has a value of about 61 percent.

Thus even though the steps of converting the energy of the fuel into heat and the mechanical energy (turbine) into electric energy are highly efficient, the overall efficiency E from fuel to electricity of modern units is about 41 percent. Over the years slow, steady improvement in this efficiency has been achieved; however, a large magnitude of improvement, say by a factor of 2, seems improbable. The above considerations apply not only to steam turbines but also to internal-combustion engines, e.g., diesel and gasoline engines which operate at even lower values of E.

The efficiency limitation on closed-cycle heat engines has led to a search of alternative means for converting chemical into electrical energy. The fuel cell is today's outstanding candidate. It does not convert the fuel energy entirely into heat and is not a heat engine. It therefore is not subject to the Carnot cycle limitation [Eq. (2-1)] on its efficiency. The fuel cell, an open cycle, has a theoretical efficiency limit (to be discussed later) which arises from the thermodynamic quantities associated with the fuel oxidation reaction. The values for most fuels of interest are in the range of 80 to 99 percent.

Fuel cells have been investigated for many years as potential replacements for turbine-generator or motor-generator systems. These will be called the *energy-converter* uses for fuel cells.

In addition to their capability of converting fuel-oxidation energies into electrical energy with high efficiency, fuel cells have another basic advantage. They can oxidize electrochemically fuels of very low equivalent weight. The equivalent weight is that weight of an oxidizable material which will produce a given quantity of electrical charge, usually the faraday, which is equal to 96,494 coul or 26.8 amp-hr. This is the quantity of charge produced when a gram equivalent weight of an electrochemical reactant undergoes reaction involving a one-electron transfer. For example, a fuel cell may oxidize hydrogen with an equivalent weight of 1 whereas a common flashlight cell oxidizes zinc with an equivalent weight of 32.5 (molecular weight of $Zn = 65$; it undergoes two-electron oxidation). Thus, a fuel cell integrated with a supply of hydrogen and using air as the oxidant possesses under suitable conditions a distinct weight advantage over conventional batteries. Applications of fuel cells with integral fuel supply will be called *packaged-energy* uses. It is in this category of application that fuel cells have made their greatest advances and are likely to find their earliest practical applications. A great impetus for development of fuel cells for packaged-energy applications has emerged from military and space-power requirements. It is fortunate that hydrogen is both the lightest (in terms of electrochemical equivalent weight) and the most reactive fuel for fuel cells.

A third area of application for fuel cells involves their use as rechargeable cells analogous to secondary batteries. This implies a degree of reversibility for the electrochemical couple at the fuel-cell electrodes, and only certain types of fuel cells can be used for storage of electrical energy.

1-3. Classification of Fuel Cells

A complex of technical and economic problems stand between the fuel cell as an idea and the fuel cell as a practical power producer. Some of these are beyond the scope of the present writing. However, in general this complexity has led to the existence of a large number of different types of fuel cells. The ultimate fuel cell would be a fossil fuel-air cell with low cost and high performance, this goal being extremely difficult to achieve for many reasons. A number of interim fuel-cell systems have evolved, notably ammonia, hydrazine, and methanol-air cells and cells in which a fossil fuel is preconverted into hydrogen, which is easily converted by presently available fuel cells. Hydrogen-oxygen and hydrogen-air cells are already practical for some applications, mainly in the area of packaged energy.

Two major approaches are being made toward the goal of a fossil fuel-air cell: (1) the use of forcing conditions such as high operating temperature in order to achieve sufficient reaction rates for the direct electrooxidation of fossil fuels and (2) the use of powerful catalysts (electrocatalysts) or intermediate electrochemical couples (redox cells) to achieve similar results at much lower temperatures. These types of systems will be discussed later in Sec. 4.

The next section takes up the principles underlying fuel-cell operation and will introduce as concrete examples certain fuel cells that will more clearly illustrate the general concept and some of the problems involved in achieving practical fuel cells.

2. Principles

2-1. Thermodynamics and Ideal Fuel Cells

When a fuel oxidizes isothermally and at constant pressure, the maximum heat available is given by the enthalpy change for the oxidation reaction ΔH. In a heat engine, some fraction of ΔH is converted into work, as in the case of a steam turbine, or into electrical energy, as in the case of a thermoelectric device. There is a theoretical maximum value for the amount of macroscopic work or electrical energy that can be obtained from the given oxidation reaction by *any* device operating at constant temperature and pressure. It is the value of ΔG, the Gibbs-free-energy change for the reaction. A most important relation from thermodynamics is

$$\Delta G = \Delta H - T \, \Delta S \tag{2-2}$$

where $T \, \Delta S$ is the minimum amount of heat that can be produced when the process occurs isothermally at constant pressure, the remainder appearing as work or electrical energy.   The values of ΔG, ΔH, and ΔS for a large. number of oxidation reactions have been determined.   They are extensive quantities, i.e., dependent on the amount of material oxidized, and in the present discussion ΔG, ΔH, and ΔS will refer to 1 g mole† of fuel undergoing oxidation. ΔS is related to the temperature coefficient of ΔG by the relation

$$\Delta S = -\left(\frac{\partial \, \Delta G}{\partial T}\right)_P \tag{2-3}$$

The ideal emf E_r of a fuel cell is given by the relation

$$E_r = -\frac{\Delta G}{n \mathfrak{F}} \tag{2-4}$$

(The minus sign comes from an arbitrary sign convention.)   If E_r is in volts, ΔG in kilocalories per gram mole, and n in electrons transferred per molecule of fuel oxidized (the effective change in oxidation state of the fuel), the value of $\mathfrak{F}$ is 23.06.   An example will illustrate the order of magnitude of these quantities.   Consider the hydrogen-oxygen fuel cell of Fig. 2-2 in which a positive hydrogen ion is the charged intermediate migrating through the electrolyte.

The anode reaction is

$$H_2 \rightarrow 2H^+ + 2e^- \tag{2-5}$$

The cathode reaction is

$$2e^- + \tfrac{1}{2}O_2 + 2H^+ \rightarrow H_2O(l) \tag{2-6}$$

The overall reaction is

$$H_2 + \tfrac{1}{2}O_2 \rightarrow H_2O(l) \tag{2-7}$$

For this reaction $\Delta G = -56.7$ kcal at 25°C;‡ $n = 2$; and then by Eq. (2-4), $E_r = 1.23$ volts.   The maximum amount of heat energy that could be produced by reaction (2-7) is given by the enthalpy change $\Delta H = -68.3$ kcal.§   At best, the fuel cell can convert only ΔG completely into electrical energy, and therefore the maximum electrical energy available is $100 \times \Delta G/\Delta H$ or 83 percent of the enthalpy change of the fuel oxidation reaction.

† To convert to pound moles, multiply by 453.6.
‡ For reactions that are spontaneous ΔG is negative and E_r is positive by Eq. (2-4). For all primary fuel-cell reactions ΔH is also negative.
§ Negative sign indicates heat evolved.

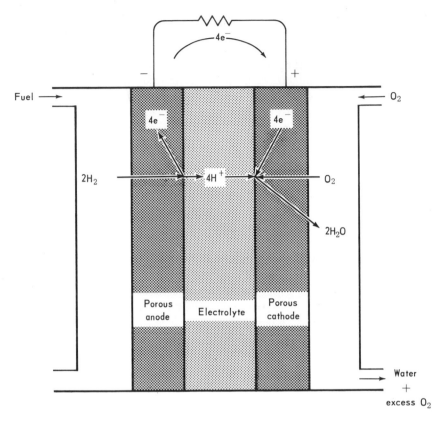

Fig. 2-2.   *Schematic diagram of a hydrogen-oxygen fuel cell.*

The maximum percentage of ΔH that can be converted into electrical energy becomes smaller as temperature increases for hydrogen-oxygen fuel cells. Because of this and the fact that hydrogen is a very reactive fuel, hydrogen-oxygen fuel cells are usually operated near ambient temperature.

Another oxidation reaction important for fuel cells is the oxidation of carbon to carbon dioxide. This may be considered to take place in the idealized fuel cell of Fig. 2-3, where an oxide ion is the charged intermediate carrying the current through the electrolyte.

The anode reaction is

$$C + 2O^{--} \rightarrow CO_2 + 4e^- \qquad (2\text{-}8)$$

The cathode reaction is

$$4e^- + O_2 \rightarrow 2O^{--} \qquad (2\text{-}9)$$

The overall reaction is

$$C + O_2 \rightarrow CO_2 \qquad (2\text{-}10)$$

For this reaction, $\Delta G = -94.26$ kcal at 25°C; $n = 4$; and by Eq. (2-4), $E_r = 1.02$ volts at 25°C.

The maximum heat energy that could be produced at 25°C is given by $\Delta H = -94.05$. Note that in this case $100 \times \Delta G/\Delta H$ is 100 percent, because the value of ΔS for the reaction is small. There is also a small temperature coefficient for ΔG. The percentage of ΔH realizable as electrical energy decreases with increasing temperature but remains near 100 percent up to 2000°K. This is fortunate since carbon is notably unreactive in the electrochemical sense and high temperatures are always required for its anodic oxidation rate to become significant. There is the further difficulty that the cell in Fig. 2-3 requires an electrolyte that is an oxide-ion conductor, and suitable electrolytes of this kind are also found to function well only at high temperatures.

The use of aqueous or fused alkali as the electrolyte for such a cell is

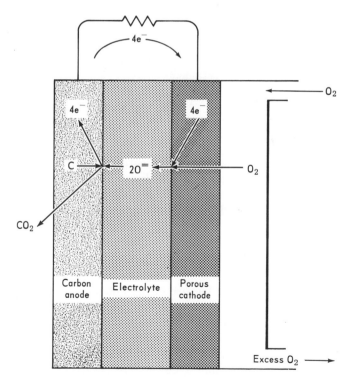

Fig. 2-3. *Schematic diagram of a carbon-oxygen fuel cell.*

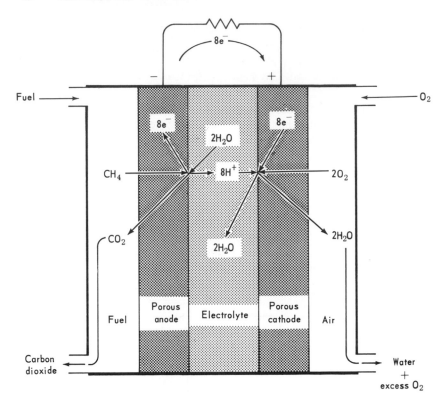

Fig. 2-4.   *Schematic diagram of a hydrocarbon-oxygen fuel cell.*

possible; in this case, OH^- is the carrier of current through the electrolyte, but such an electrolyte has the disadvantage of reacting with the product CO_2, producing carbonate and consuming the hydroxide.   It is usually not economically feasible to consume a constituent of the electrolyte in this fashion.

Potentially a most important class of fuels for fuel cells is the hydrocarbons and certain of their oxygenated derivatives such as the alcohols. A fuel cell may operate upon such fuels in the manner of the cell shown in Fig. 2-4 illustrating the case of methane.   For the complete oxidation of methane at 25°C, $\Delta H = -212.8$ kcal, $\Delta G = -195.5$ kcal, and $100 \times \Delta G/\Delta H = 92$ percent.   The maximum percentage of ΔH that can be converted into electrical energy decreases with increasing temperature at a rate slower than for hydrogen and faster than for carbon (see Table 2-1). Hydrocarbons are found to be reactive at somewhat elevated temperatures.

Certain fuels consist essentially of bound hydrogen and can be oxidized

Table 2-1

Fuel	$-\dfrac{\Delta H}{n\mathcal{F}}$	$-\dfrac{\Delta G}{n\mathcal{F}}$			$100 \times \dfrac{E_r}{E_c}$		kwhr/lb based on E_r at 127°C	D_E in whr/lb based on 1.0-volt cell potential
		25†	127°C‡	527°C‡	25°C	127°C		
$CH_4(g)$	1.15	1.06	1.04	1.04	92.2	90.5	6.30	6.05×10^3
$C_3H_8(g)$	1.15	1.09	1.08	1.10	94.8	94.0	5.96	5.56×10^3
$C_8H_{18}(l)$	1.13	1.10	1.09	1.12	97.3	96.5	5.80	5.32×10^3
iso $C_8H_{18}(l)$	1.13	1.10	1.09	1.13	97.3	96.5		
$C_{16}H_{34}(l)$	1.13	1.10	1.09	1.13	97.3	96.5	5.73	5.23×10^3
$CH_3OH(l)$	1.23	1.21	1.20	1.23	98.4	97.6	2.73	2.28×10^3
$NH_3(g)$	1.32	1.17	1.14	1.18	88.6	86.4	2.43	2.13×10^3
$H_2(g)$	1.48	1.23	1.16	1.05	83.3	78.3	14.0	12.1×10^3
$C(s)$	1.02	1.02	1.02	1.02	100.	100.	4.13	4.0×10^3

† Products: $CO_2(g)$, $H_2O(l)$.
‡ Products: $CO_2(g)$, $H_2O(g)$.
Note: Values of ΔH and ΔG were calculated from literature values[1-3] of the heats and free energies of formation of fuels and combustion products from the elements in their standard states.

to water plus an inert gaseous product; for example, the oxidation of ammonia can take place in a fuel cell by the reaction

$$2 \, NH_3 + \tfrac{3}{2} \, O_2 = N_2 + 3 \, H_2O \qquad\qquad (2\text{-}11)$$

Nitrogen is produced along with water.

A general fuel oxidation reaction may be written to include all the above examples and many others as follows:

$$F + w \, O_2 = x \, CO_2 + y \, H_2O + zI \qquad\qquad (2\text{-}12)$$

where F is a molecule of fuel, I is a molecule of inert gas, and w, x, y, and z are the numbers of molecules of oxygen, carbon dioxide, water, and inert gas involved in the reaction of one fuel molecule. (In a given case one or more of these coefficients may be zero.) For this general case the maximum theoretical emf for a fuel cell is given by

$$E_r = \frac{-\Delta G}{4w} \, 23.06 \qquad\qquad (2\text{-}13)$$

and the temperature coefficient of E_r is

$$\left(\frac{\partial E_r}{\partial T}\right)_P = \frac{\Delta S}{4w} \, 23.06 \qquad\qquad (2\text{-}14)$$

Many fuels are of potential interest in fuel cells; some of these are presented in Table 2-1 along with a number of the thermodynamic quantities associated with their complete oxidation reactions. Some of the ideal emfs and energy-density properties of these fuels are also presented.

Some of the quantities in Table 2-1 will be useful later in calculating operating parameters for a system of fuel cell plus fuel supply, where the power density for the cell alone and the efficiency of converting the fuel energy into electrical energy will react in opposite directions as the operating voltage of the cell E_a is varied (by varying current density). This leads to a particular value of E_a which minimizes total weight of system, (fuel plus fuel cell) producing a given number of watts for a given number of hours.

The emfs of Table 2-1 are for ideal fuel cells. A real fuel cell must operate so as to produce as high a number of amperes of electric current at as high an actual emf (E_a) as possible for a given size of cell. Close approach to ideal-fuel-cell performance involves speeding up to the maximum extent various kinetic and mass-transport processes involved in the overall reaction of the fuel according to Eq. (2-12). While various fuels are rather similar in their ideal emf characteristics, the extent to which real fuel cells can approach these ideal values varies markedly with the nature of the fuel.   In short, the fuel one picks for a fuel cell is influenced more by kinetic than by thermodynamic factors.   This subject is briefly considered in the next section.

2-2. Kinetics and Real Fuel Cells

A fuel cell connected across an external load is a reacting chemical system in which the overall reaction rate may be arbitrarily regulated (within limits) by control of the external load.   The rates of the individual reaction steps then adjust to attain a balance with the current passing through the load.   This is in sharp contrast to an open-ended system where a slow step in a sequence of reactions determines the overall rate.   Only in isolated cases does one of the electrode reactions represent such a limiting step.   In considering the reactions in fuel cells, one is therefore generally less interested in specific reaction rates per se than in deviations from thermodynamic reversibility—that is, losses in free energy or useful work—associated with various elements of the cell when current is flowing.   These losses when expressed in terms of voltages are called *polarizations* or *overvoltages* by the electrochemist.

To focus on this problem, a simple hydrogen-air cell similar to that in Fig. 2-2 and having the overall performance curve (current density†–voltage curve) of Fig. 2-5 may serve as an example.   Were the reaction steps in the cell all reversible in the thermodynamic sense, the potential close to 1.22‡ volts calculated from thermodynamics would be realized over the full operating range.   It is clear from the data in Fig. 2-5 that in a real cell pronounced deviations can be encountered even on open circuit.

In considering the voltage losses it will be useful to examine the individual steps involved.   Starting arbitrarily at the anode, where the oxidation of the fuel occurs, the simple half-reaction of Eq. (2-5) obscures a number of intervening steps, which include:

1.   Transport of the fuel to the electrode.   (This includes gas-phase transport as well as dissolution in and transport through a thin film of electrolyte on the surface of the electrode.)
2.   Adsorption on the electrode surface with dissociation.
3.   Transfer of an electron.   (With more complex fuels nonelectrochemical surface reactions may precede or follow the electron-transfer step.)
4.   Desorption of the product(s).
5.   Transport of the product(s) away from the electrode.

† Current density based on the geometric area of the electrode.
‡ This differs slightly from the 1.23 volts of an H_2–O_2 cell because of the reduced partial pressure of oxygen in air.

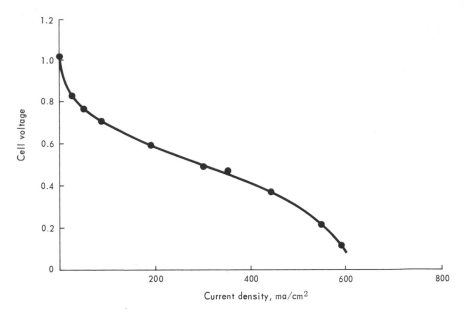

Fig. 2-5.   *Performance curve for a hydrogen-air cell with a 5 N H₂SO₄ electrolyte.*

The product formed at the hydrogen electrode is the hydrated proton which migrates through the electrolyte to the cathode.   Concurrently, the electrons pass through the electrodes to the terminal of the cell and then through the external load, where they perform useful work before continuing on to the cathode.   At the cathode the electrons are joined by the protons arriving through the electrolyte and by oxygen arriving at the electrode surface.   Here the half-reaction of Eq. (2-6) again belies the complexity of the many distinct steps that occur at the electrode.   In fact, the series of steps at an oxygen or air electrode is more involved than that at the hydrogen electrode and includes the formation of peroxide.

Any of the steps involving mass transport, adsorption, chemical reaction, or charge transfer may have associated energy barriers.   In such cases irreversibilities will be encountered to introduce polarizations which are classified according to type.   That associated with electron transfer or intervening chemical steps (including adsorption-desorption) at an electrode is generally known as *activation polarization*.   Losses resulting from concentration gradients associated with mass transport are called *concentration polarization*.   Finally, those losses associated with electron and ion transport in the electrodes and electrolyte are known as *resistive* or *ohmic polarization*.

The terminal voltage of a cell E_a may therefore be expressed as the difference between E_r, the reversible voltage derived from thermodynamics, and the sum of the individual polarizations.

$$E_a = E_r - \eta = E_r - (\eta_{act} + \eta_{conc} + \eta_{ohmic}) \tag{2-15}$$

Since activation and concentration polarization may be encountered at either or both electrodes and ohmic losses can be encountered in both the electrolyte and the electrodes, a more detailed breakdown might therefore be written as

$$E_a = E_r - (\eta_{act} + \eta_{conc} + \eta_{ohmic})_{anode} - (\eta_{act} + \eta_{conc} + \eta_{ohmic})_{cathode} \\ - (\eta_{ohmic})_{electrolyte} \tag{2-16}$$

It is to be remembered too that E_a will be exactly balanced by the voltage drop in the load circuit. On short circuit E_a will equal zero and the entire energy released by the cell reaction will be degraded to heat within the cell itself.

With the exception of ohmic polarizations, which generally vary linearly with current density, the relationship between polarization and current density is frequently complex, especially when interactions among them occur. A detailed general analysis is therefore impractical at present for the situation prevailing in a real cell. In fact, only recently have workers been addressing themselves to the general analysis of specific systems. For our immediate purposes it will be sufficiently illustrative to consider the various types of overvoltage independently to establish the major characteristics of each. Furthermore, in many practical cells, operating regions can be identified in which one or the other type of polarization predominates in defining the character of the performance curve (E versus i plot). As will be seen, activation polarization dominates at low current densities, ohmic polarization at intermediate current densities, and concentration polarization at the highest current densities.

The effect of mass transport as a limitation will be considered first since, in practice, this can be encountered even with hydrogen, which is the most reactive fuel and which frequently gives little activation polarization. The limitation on the rate of mass transport might be encountered in the gas phase as a result of interferences from inert diluents or pressure drops in a porous electrode structure. It might also be associated with dissolution in and diffusion through a thin film of electrolyte on the electrode surface.

Although an oversimplification, assumption of a constant diffusion gradient can serve to illustrate the principles. Assuming that this is a gradient in the concentration of hydrogen dissolved in a thin film of electrolyte of thickness δ, the following will define the current density in terms of the concentrations at the interfaces of the liquid film with the gas and the electrode:

$$i = n\mathfrak{F}D \frac{C_g - C_e}{\delta} \tag{2-17}$$

It will be assumed that C_g is the concentration in equilibrium with the gas at all times. Slow dissolution rates would, of course, result in changes in C_g, and hence a perturbation in the equations that will follow. From Eq. (2-17) it is seen that the current will reach a limiting value when the gradient is a maximum, i.e., when $C_e = 0$. Then

$$i_L = n\mathfrak{F}D \frac{C_g}{\delta} \tag{2-18}$$

The polarization of the electrode is determined by the difference in the concentration at the electrode surface on load and that at open circuit when $C_e = C_g$ Then

$$\eta = \frac{RT}{n\mathfrak{F}} \ln \frac{C_g}{C_e} \tag{2-19}$$

and, substituting from Eqs. (2-17) and (2-18),

$$\eta = \frac{RT}{n\mathfrak{F}} \ln \frac{i_L}{i_L - i}. \tag{2-20}$$

where it is important to note that n is the number of electrons associated with the overall electrode reaction, i.e., Eq. (2-5).

If Eq. (2-20) is plotted on rectangular coordinates, the solid curve of Fig. 2-6 is obtained. It shows that this type of polarization is negligible at low current densities but rises abruptly as the limiting current is approached. With many of the "practical" electrodes described in the literature such limiting currents are not encountered below many hundreds of milliamperes per centimeter squared.† In general, increasing the gas pressure will raise the values still higher. Increasing the temperature will usually have but a small beneficial effect, since the activation energies for the processes involved are not high and compensating effects are frequently encountered.

Activation polarization is associated with the catalyst itself and may involve the slow adsorption of step 2, the electron transfer of step 3, or the slow surface reactions alluded to in the steps enumerated above. The relationship between current density and overvoltage for the electron-

† 1 ma/cm² = 0.929 amp/ft².

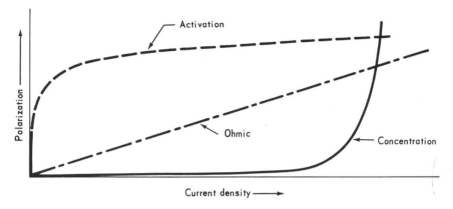

Fig. 2-6. *Types of polarization encountered in fuel cells.*

transfer step can be expressed as the sum of two terms, one for the forward and one for the back reaction. For the hydrogen example

$$i = n_t \mathfrak{F} s\{k_f \theta \exp (\alpha n_t \mathfrak{F} \eta / RT) - k_b(1 - \theta)C_{H^+} \exp -[(1 - \alpha)n_t \mathfrak{F} \eta / RT]\} \tag{2-21}$$

Here n_t is the number of electrons involved in the transfer step, s is a roughness factor for the surface of the electrode, θ is the fraction of the surface sites covered by hydrogen atoms, and α is the *transfer coefficient;* i.e., the portion of the overvoltage that accelerates the forward reaction.

On open circuit, when the overvoltage and net current flow are zero, the forward and back currents are equal and have the value of the so-called "exchange current." The exchange current is directly related to the reactivity of a system and provides a convenient basis for comparison.

For very small (and generally impractically low) values of cell current both terms of Eq. (2-21) are of importance, but when η reaches a value of ~ 0.05 volt, the term for the back reaction becomes negligible. At this point we may write

$$\eta = \frac{-RT}{\alpha n_t \mathfrak{F}} \ln n_t \mathfrak{F} s k_f \theta + \frac{RT}{\alpha n_t \mathfrak{F}} \ln i \tag{2-22}$$

where the first term and the coefficient of the second are analogous to the a and b in Tafel's well-known equation. In a plot of η versus log i, extrapolation of the linear section back to $\eta = 0$ provides a convenient method for evaluating the exchange current. When plotted on rectangular coordinates the dashed curve in Fig. 2-6 results. It is seen clearly that this overvoltage tends to plateau at relatively low current densities.

When slow sorption or surface reactions are involved, Eqs. (2-21) and

(2-22) must be modified to bring in additional kinetic factors which result in changes in θ for the species involved in the electron-transfer step. Detailed treatments of these problems will be found in the literature of electrochemistry.[5-7] Frequently the modified equations are of the same form as Eq. (2-22) except for changes in the coefficients of the logarithmic terms.   In such cases evaluation of these coefficients can often be a valuable diagnostic tool in studying reaction mechanisms.

Under some conditions, however, θ for the active species can fall to zero, and limiting currents similar to those seen with mass-transport control are encountered.   If these limits are caused by an accumulation of intermediates or by-products on the surface, current and voltage oscillations can result.   Under these conditions the electrode potential eventually reaches a value where the offending species are oxidized and removed. This releases additional sites for the primary reaction which proceeds at lower overvoltages.   As the intermediates and by-products accumulate again, the cycle repeats.   In general, a distinguishing feature of limiting currents associated with slow surface reactions is their failure to respond to steps taken to improve mass transport.

Activation overvoltage is much more sensitive to temperature than concentration polarization because of the higher activation energies associated with the reactions involved.   Hence, increasing the operating temperature of a fuel cell can have very beneficial effects in this case. Activation overvoltages often are negligible in high-temperature fuel cells (i.e., above 500°C).   Effects of pressure are less predictable, particularly if more than one surface species is involved.   In such a case, increasing the pressure of a reactant could very easily decrease the overall reaction rate if the adsorption of a second species were thereby hindered.   Such, for example, can be the case with hydrocarbons when the adsorption of water on the electrode may be suppressed by that of the fuel.   The roughness-factor term in Eqs. (2-21) and (2-22) is important.   It indicates that performance can be improved markedly by increasing the real surface area of the electrode relative to the geometric area.   In practice this is accomplished by employing catalysts of high area in making electrodes.

While not directly evident, the role of the electrolyte with regard to such properties as pH, concentration, and ionic composition can affect activation polarization.   Some of these variables may involve actual reacting species; others may affect the double-layer structure at the electrode-electrolyte interface[5-7] and thereby indirectly influence the reaction path.

The final source of overvoltage is the internal resistance of the cell. This results in a conventional "ohmic drop" that generally varies linearly— the broken line in Fig. 2-6.   It includes such drops in the electrolyte, the electrodes, and any resistant films that may form. Nonlinearity may result from concentration changes that develop at high current densities. It is evident that electrodes should be constructed of highly conducting materials. This generally is not a great problem since appropriate current collectors can be designed if necessary. With regard to the electrolyte, high concentrations are desirable. Also, strong acids and bases are better conductors than salts. Raising the operating temperature will also result in lower resistances.

When all the polarization effects are combined, the composite performance curve shown as the heavy line in Fig. 2-7 results. In form, it closely resembles that for the real hydrogen-air cell in Fig. 2-5. One major difference is evident. This is the discrepancy between the observed open-circuit voltage of 1.02 volts and the calculated value of 1.22 volts. The discrepancy is associated with the oxygen electrode. In this case the exchange current associated with the principal reaction on load is too low to maintain the theoretical open-circuit potential. Instead, the open-circuit value represents a "mixed" potential that probably also involves a peroxide couple.[8]

In evaluating cell performance, there is frequently enough separation

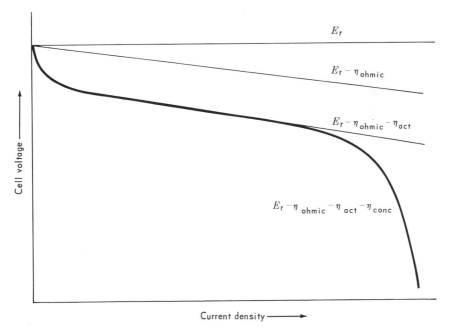

Fig. 2-7. *Effect of polarization on performance.*

between the various types of polarization that the major contributors can be identified. By incorporating a reference electrode into the cell, the polarizations can be further separated according to anodic and cathodic processes. Use of interrupter techniques also permits the elimination of the ohmic drops. For detailed study of individual electrode reactions, however, the use of half-cells is to be preferred, and in most cases the techniques of modern electrochemistry will be most rewarding. These are discussed in detail elsewhere.[9]

3. Fuel-cell Components

3-1. Electrodes

In practical fuel cells the electrode structure plays a crucial role. The electrodes provide the seat for the electrochemical reactions, serve as current collectors to carry the electronic current to the cell terminals,† and, in the cases of gaseous (and insoluble) reactants, establish the interface between them and the electrolyte. Many requirements must be met simultaneously: they must be good electrical conductors, have reasonable mechanical strength, be resistant to the corrosive electrolyte, and have satisfactory catalytic properties for the required reactions. If the structural material itself is deficient in the latter respect, it is frequently necessary to activate the electrode surface with a suitable catalyst.

Electrodes suitable for use with dissolved fuels (e.g., methanol) are fairly simple. They provide a surface exposed to the homogeneous mixture of fuel and electrolyte. Frequently their surface is coated with a thin layer of high-area catalyst, for example, platinum black. Electrodes for gaseous and immiscible fuels are complex. They must maintain an interface between the electrolyte and the fuel (or oxidant) in contact with the electrode. Were the three phases completely immiscible, the electrochemical reaction would occur at the three-phase *line* of contact. In real systems there is always some miscibility. In particular, the fuel will have some solubility in the electrolyte, and in certain systems species adsorbed on the electrode will have surface mobility. Both of these conditions will contribute to the formation of a *band*, or *diffuse zone*, at which the electrochemical reactions occur. Because of the need to maximize the area for reaction, based upon kinetic considerations, it is desirable to have the zone established within a fine porous structure, as illustrated in Fig. 2-8.

Three regions can be identified within the electrode. In Region I the

---

† In some cases additional current collectors and heat sinks are used. These consist of heavier grids or ribbed plates which are in physical contact with the electrodes.

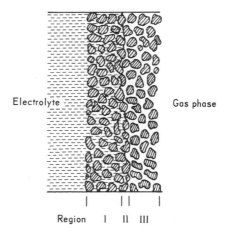

Electrolyte

Gas phase

Region   I   II   III

Fig. 2-8. Schematic diagram showing
gas-electrolyte interface in a porous electrode.

surface is submerged under electrolyte so that it is essentially inaccessible
to the slightly soluble reactants and is, therefore, inactive.   In Region II,
the region of small menisci that form within the pores, the surface is covered
with a thin film of electrolyte that permits ready transport of dissolved
reactant and offers little resistance to the transport of ionic species.   Here
the bulk of the reaction occurs.   Finally, Region III, which is again relatively inactive, is that of the gas-filled pores.   Here the surface of the electrode may be wetted with an extremely thin film of electrolyte.   It has
ready access to the reactant gas, but transport of ionic species is severely
hampered by the small cross section of the film and the long path to the
bulk electrolyte.   Clearly, a thin section of an electrode represents the
active region.   This means that thin electrodes should meet performance
requirements if they also have sufficient strength and electrical conductivity.   It is, in fact, desirable to minimize the thickness of the inactive
wetted region in order to reduce internal ohmic drops in the electrolyte
contained in the pores.   It is also desirable to minimize the thickness of
the gas-filled pores to reduce gaseous diffusion barriers.   This is especially
true with air electrodes because of the presence of the inert nitrogen and
with fuel electrodes where CO_2 is produced by the oxidation of a carbonaceous fuel.   The diffusion problems in electrodes are more fully discussed
elsewhere[10] and, to a large extent, are based upon studies by Schmid,[11]
Nobis,[12] Weber et al.,[13] and particularly Will.[14]

Because of capillary forces associated with porous media, the estab-
lishment of the desired stable interface within a porous electrode is difficult.

This problem is best considered in terms of idealized pore models.   In the case of a uniform cylindrical pore in Fig. 2-9*a*, a stable configuration as shown will exist only when the gas pressure P_g exactly balances the opposing capillary and hydraulic pressures of the electrolyte, i.e., when

$$P_g = \frac{2\gamma \cos \phi}{r} + P_E \qquad\qquad (2\text{-}23)$$

In this case the active zone would be concentrated under the meniscus near the electrode-bulk electrolyte interface.   Such a system is extremely unstable because small changes in either P_g or P_E result in either bubbling into the electrolyte or movement of the meniscus so that complete "drowning" occurs.   The form of Eq. (2-23) suggests two methods for controlling the interface within the pore structure, by control of the pore radius and by control of the contact angle ϕ (controlled wetting).

Two approaches to control of the pore radius are illustrated in Fig. 2-9*b* and *c*.   In the former, a dual-porosity structure is employed with pores of small radius contacting the electrolyte and larger pores contacting the gas.   With this approach P_g is raised sufficiently so that the small pores flood and the large pores remain filled with gas; i.e.,

$$\frac{2\gamma \cos \phi}{r_1} + P_E > P_g > \frac{2\gamma \cos \phi}{r_2} + P_E \qquad\qquad (2\text{-}24)$$

In the case of the tapered pore of Fig. 2-9*c*, the interface adjusts to a level where the system is in balance at an intermediate equilibrium value of the pore radius.   Examples of both types of pore control have been described in the literature.[15,16]   In principle the step structure has the advantage that the location of the interface is essentially fixed over a fairly wide range of pressure differentials.   It should, therefore, be possible to make better use of an expensive catalyst with such a structure, since it can be concentrated in a specific zone.   Indeed, this type of structure has received much more attention than that employing the tapered pores.

In utilizing controlled wetting to establish the interface, the electrode is partially treated with a hydrophobic substance in order to increase the contact angle in the vicinity of the active zone.   This type of control has been used only with cells employing aqueous electrolytes.   Generally, materials resulting in contact angles greater than 90° are used, and the meniscus is inverted.   Figure 2-9*d* illustrates the behavior when the material is applied to the electrode on the electrolyte side.   In this case the electrolyte does not penetrate deeply into the pores unless the hydraulic pressure is increased significantly above P_g.   The active zone is, therefore, concentrated near the electrode-bulk electrolyte interface, but the condition is more stable than that illustrated in Fig. 2-9*a* because fairly wide

Electrode   Electrolyte   Hydrophobic regions

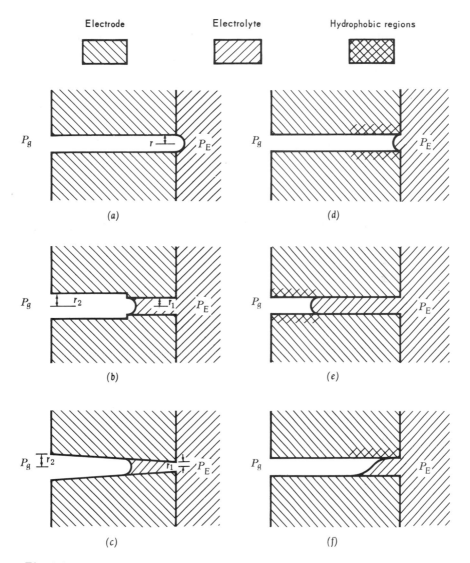

Fig. 2-9. *Types of interface control in porous electrodes.*

fluctuations in pressure can be tolerated without danger of drowning.

If the hydrophobic agent is applied to the gas side of the electrode, the condition shown in Fig. 2-9e results, with the active region established well within the pore. This system should be somewhat more stable than the previous one with regard to gas bubbling into the electrolyte, while retaining an equal resistance to drowning.

The two systems just described are probably too idealized, and real systems would be better represented by Fig. 2-9*f*, in which a heterogeneous system consisting of hydrophobic and hydrophilic phases is involved.   In such a case the active zone would be established by the balance of opposing forces involving the wetted and nonwetted phases as well as the gas and hydraulic pressures.   Examples of electrodes employing controlled wetting are described in the literature.[4,17,18]

Naturally, the simplified representations that have been discussed do not represent the entire picture for the porous sintered electrodes that are actually in use.   These structures, with cross pores and a statistical distribution of pore sizes, are much more complex, and complete mathematical treatments are not presently available.   For general discussions of the properties of porous media the reader is referred to the literature.[19,20]

Additional factors become important when cells are placed on load. Changes in electrode potentials, as well as temperatures and electrolyte concentrations, cause changes in interfacial tensions.   Furthermore, pressure drops can occur within the pore structures as reactant gases are consumed at the reaction zone, and complications are introduced by electroosmotic effects.   With proper control, however, stable interfaces can be maintained for thousands of hours of operation.

More subtle, perhaps, are aging effects that can occur, especially when controlled wetting is used.   Thus, gradual changes in the surface condition can occur, and interfaces can slowly migrate with time.   In balance, however, the use of controlled wetting results in cells that can operate at substantially atmospheric pressure.   This can be a decided advantage with regard to the engineering of practical devices.   At the present time, overriding advantages have not been demonstrated for either approach, and attractive electrodes have been developed on both principles.

One additional type of electrode has limited application with gaseous reactants.   This is the solid-diffusion electrode as exemplified by palladium or palladium-silver-alloy sheets for use with hydrogen.[21,22]   With these electrodes advantage is taken of the ability of hydrogen to dissolve in and diffuse through at reasonable operating temperatures.   To accelerate the reactions, it is frequently desirable to coat the surfaces of the sheet with finely divided platinum or palladium black.

3-2. *Electrolytes*

The electrolyte in a fuel cell should have as high an electrical conductivity as possible in order to minimize ohmic drops within the cell.   Furthermore it is desirable that the mobility be as high as possible for the ion flow, which balances the electron flow in the overall reaction (see Fig. 2-1).   Ideally, it is best if the ion which participates in the electrochemical reactions carries all the current, that is, its transference number is unity. This is strictly true of a completely leached cation-exchange membrane in the hydrogen-ion form. For practical purposes it is also sufficiently approximated for aqueous strong acids and strong bases. If the transference number is much less than unity, concentration overvoltage may develop in the cell under load.

Other properties which the fuel-cell electrolyte must possess are negligible electronic conductivity and high impermeability to the direct diffusion of both fuel and oxygen. If the electrolyte is an electronic conductor, the cell tends to be electrically loaded down by its own electrolyte. If the electrolyte permits rapid diffusion of either oxygen or fuel, some direct, nonelectrochemical oxidation of the fuel occurs, leading to development of heat and to inefficiency in terms of electrical energy produced compared with fuel oxidized. Also, the performance of either the fuel or oxygen electrode may be adversely affected. It is not often that oxygen permeates a fuel-cell electrolyte at a sufficient rate to give trouble. However, certain soluble fuels such as methanol, ammonia, and hydrazine require special handling in fuel cells because of their high solubility in and rate of permeation through aqueous electrolyte layers. Some specific examples of this are presented in the section of this chapter describing these types of fuel cells.

Most low-temperature fuel cells employ as electrolyte either a strong aqueous acid such as a sulfuric acid or phosphoric acid solution or a strong aqueous alkali such as a sodium or potassium hydroxide solution. For operation at temperatures above the boiling point of water, concentrated solutions are used; for example, concentrated phosphoric acid solutions have been used up to about 250°C, and concentrated potassium hydroxide solutions have been used up to about 300°C.[23] There has also been some work with cells containing a concentrated aqueous cesium carbonate as the electrolyte operating up to about 200°C.[24]

High-temperature fuel cells employ mainly either fused alkali carbonates or ceramics with oxide-ion conductivity. Some properties of these types of electrolytes are discussed later in the section describing high-temperature fuel cells.

In summary, today's fuel cells use as the electrolyte systems in which one or more of the following ions migrate as readily as possible: H^+, OH^-, CO_3^{--}, or O^{--}.

3-3. *Electrocatalysts*

A successful electrode structure should have a high effective area for the electrochemical reaction in which a fuel (or oxygen) molecule, one or more electrons, and one or more ions participate. It provides high electronic conductivity for electron flow either in or out, and the electrolyte provides for rapid input or removal of the appropriate participating ions.

The chemical nature of the surface of the electrode should be such that, per unit of effective area as provided by the electrode structure, the electrochemical reaction should be as high as possible. This is a problem akin to that of speeding up gaseous reactions by providing a catalyst surface to promote them. The fuel-cell electrode must provide a surface for promoting electrochemical reactions which may, therefore, be called an electrocatalyst surface.

The type of electrocatalyst used depends upon the nature of the fuel (or oxidant) and to some degree upon operating conditions; i.e., at high temperatures low inherent catalytic activity is acceptable because thermal energy adequately overcomes the activation energy barriers for the reactions involved.

Besides possessing catalytic activity, the electrocatalyst surface must be stable to its environment, i.e., not volatile at the temperatures of operation, not soluble in the electrolyte, not subject to electrochemical oxidation, and not short-lived in the sense that its activity is lost with time by processes such as sintering out of active sites or contamination with impurities.

The whole electrocatalyst problem is so complex that most of the progress to date has been made empirically. From empirical evidence, it appears that catalytic activity for a gaseous reaction is necessary but not sufficient to ensure electrocatalytic activity for a related electrochemical reaction in a fuel cell.

The type of substances that have proved to be active in fuel cells for hydrogen anodes are mainly transition metals such as nickel, iron, cobalt, platinum, palladium, rhodium, and iridium. These are all in group VIII of the periodic table. Raney forms of some of these such as Raney nickel are especially active as hydrogenation catalysts and hydrogen anodes. However, nickel must be operated at potentials which do not permit electrochemical oxidation of nickel itself; otherwise the formation of oxides or hydroxides of nickel (or possibly carbonates in carbonate electrolytes) will occur. These substances not only may be catalytically inactive but also may impede the necessary electronic conduction of the electrode. Certain other materials which are known as hydrogenation catalysts are effective hydrogen-anode materials, such as nickel boride.[25]

For direct hydrocarbon anodes in low-temperature fuel cells, only platinum[26] has so far shown high activity. Both unsupported platinum blacks and platinum supported on electronically conducting substrates have been used. The requirement of electronic conductivity excludes from consideration many catalyst supports that are widely used in gas-phase reactions and that have been extensively studied.

Oxygen-containing fuels (for example, CO, methanol) operate well with transition metals but also may be electrochemically oxidized on metals in group Ib of the periodic table such as silver and gold. For these fuels mixed oxides are effective also, and notably successful have been such materials as cobalt molybdate[27] and the spinels.

For oxygen electrodes, platinum is an effective electrocatalyst. Generally, also, the materials that are effective for oxygenated fuels are good electrocatalysts for the reduction of oxygen at a fuel-cell cathode, and, in addition, materials such as nickel oxide doped with lithium oxide to make it conducting and active have been used as electrocatalysts for oxygen. A key to the success of early Bacon-cell cathodes (see low-temperature fuel-cell section) was the use of nickel with a surface of lithium-doped nickel oxide.

It is evident from the above that platinum is an effective electrocatalyst for a wide variety of anode and cathode reactants. It has therefore been more widely used in fuel cells than any other single material. Attempts to improve platinum by alloying and by combining it with various additives have met with some success.

From the practical point of view, platinum has the disadvantage of its high cost. For this reason considerable work is under way with the goal of replacing platinum in fuel-cell electrodes with less-expensive materials. Because both catalysis and electrocatalysis are poorly understood in detail, the probability of finding replacements for platinum cannot be assessed at present. For this reason, fundamental investigations into the nature of catalytic and electrocatalytic processes in fuel cells are also being carried out.

It is beyond the scope of this chapter to review catalysis and electrocatalysis in greater detail, and for this the reader is referred to the literature.[28-30]

4.   *The Complete Fuel Cell—Power and Weight Relations*

The current widespread interest in fuel cells for packaged-energy uses as defined in Sec. 1 is due in part to their weight advantage over conventional power sources such as batteries or motor-generator sets. In a package consisting of a battery of fuel cells and a supply of fuel required to deliver electric power p for a length of time t, the operating voltage per cell E_a is, within certain limits, an adjustable parameter. The proper selection of E_a minimizes the weight of the total system for producing $M = pt$ watt-hours at a constant rate of p watts.†

† For a more general calculation of the type presented here, see Jon Van Winkle and W. N. Carson, Jr.[31]

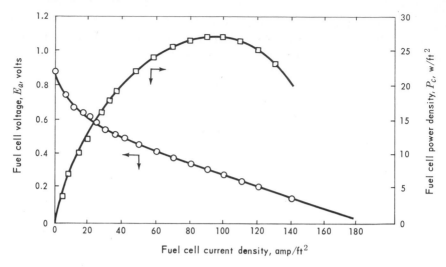

Fig. 2-10. *Performance curve of a propane fuel cell at 175°C.*

The manner in which the total weight of system varies with the parameter E_a will be illustrated by the example of a propane-air cell for which the performance curve is presented in Fig. 2-10.† Figure 2-10 is the usual plot of E_a and power density as a function of current density. Vertical lines connect the value of E_a with the corresponding value of power density.

Values of the energy density of propane fuel in watt-hours per pound have been presented in Table 2-1 (p. 47). In the following discussion, the weight of tanks and accessories will be assumed to be equal to the weight of fuel necessary for the mission.

It is next necessary to relate to E_a the *specific weight* of the *fuel system* W_f° (fuel plus tankage and auxiliaries) in pounds per watt-hour and the *specific weight* of *fuel battery* W_c° in pounds per watt. In the case of the fuel system, W_f° is given by $1/E_a D_E\ddagger \times 2$ (cf. Table 2-1). The factor 2 comes from the allowance for tankage and auxiliaries. Because of the complex form of the relation between power density and E_a for a fuel cell, W_c° cannot be expressed by a simple equation except in special cases and is best represented graphically.

The graph of Fig. 2-11 presents the variation of W_c° and W_f° with E_a. There is a minimum in W_c° at the maximum power point of the cell, while W_f° decreases monotonically as E_a increases. Of course, points above the

† Performance data of the propane fuel cell from W. T. Grubb and C. J. Michalske.[32]
‡ D_E is the number of watt-hours per pound a fuel would produce if it oxidized at 1 volt in a fuel-air fuel cell at 100 percent current efficiency (see Table 2-1).

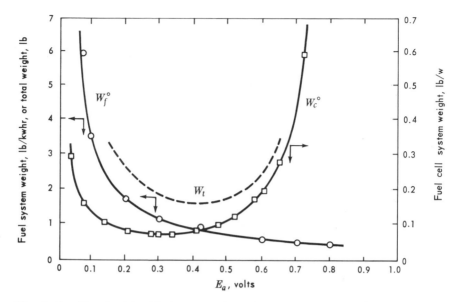

Fig. 2-11.   *Plot of weight of fuel system, weight of fuel battery, and total weight as a function of E_a.*

observed open-circuit voltage of the cell have no practical significance.   In plotting W_c°, it has been assumed that the fuel battery weighs 2 lb/ft² of active cell area.

The total weight of the system W_t for supplying $M = pt$ watt-hours at a constant rate of p watts is given by

$$W_t = pW_c^\circ + ptW_f^\circ \tag{2-25}$$

A useful alternative form for this equation is

$$W_t = \frac{M}{t} W_c^\circ + M \cdot W_f^\circ \tag{2-26}$$

In Eq. (2-26) the first term on the right is the weight of the fuel battery, and the second term is the weight of the fuel system.   The weight of fuel battery varies inversely with the time of discharge (assuming a constant rate of discharge).

A quantity often used to characterize conventional batteries is the energy density or number of watt-hours available per pound of battery. For the fuel battery plus fuel system, this quantity is given by

$$\frac{M}{W_t} = \frac{1}{W_c^\circ/t + W_f^\circ} \tag{2-27}$$

This quantity is a very strong function of t, the time of discharge, and for a given value of t it has a maximum at a particular value of E_a.

The value of E_a which gives minimum W_t or maximum energy density for the system can be determined graphically. In Fig. 2-11 the dashed line indicates the value of W_t in pounds for a 10-watt cell with fuel sufficient to produce 1,000 whr at constant rate ($t = 100$ hr). For this case, W_t minimizes at $E_a = 0.42$ volt. For other values of t, different values of E_a give minimum total weight. The numbers in Table 2-2 illustrate this point. Each value of E_a for minimum system weight has been determined graphically as above. It can be seen from Table 2-2 and Fig. 2-10 that the best value of E_a approaches the point of maximum power density at very short discharge times and approaches the open-circuit potential of the fuel c ll at very long discharge times.

Table 2-2. *Minimum System Weight and Corresponding E_a Values for $M = 1,000$ whr as a Function of Time of Discharge t in Hours for a Propane-Air Fuel Cell and Fuel System†*

t, time of discharge, hr	E_a for minimum W_t, volts	Minimum weight, lb	Energy density M/W_t, whr/lb
0.1	0.32	720	1.39
1	0.32	73	13.7
10	0.33	8.3	120
100	0.42	1.7	590
1,000	0.57	0.73	1370
10,000	0.68	0.53	1890

† The assumption of 100% fuel utilization has been made.

Ordinary batteries possess energy densities in the range of about 10 to 50 whr/lb. The energy-density values in Table 2-2 show why the choice between batteries and fuel cells is in favor of batteries for short-time applications and in favor of fuel cells for missions of long duration.

5. Fuel Cells—Present Status

5-1. General

The previous sections have dealt with the advantages of fuel cells, their principles of operation, and some of the problems which require solution before practical fuel batteries can be achieved. The latter comprise a large number of scientific, engineering, and manufacturing problems. To a large extent, the pace of fuel-cell effort has been such that two or more of these problem areas have been investigated concurrently and not successively, as a more leisurely approach would permit. Hence the status of fuel cells is complex and rapidly changing, and a really complete status report on fuel cells would be out of date before it appeared in print. The present section will not, therefore, attempt to cover the field completely and will not necessarily be complete with respect to original literature. Instead, we will describe examples of the most important types of fuel cells and indicate their state of development.

The classification will be roughly in order of increasing temperature of operation, and the cells are somewhat arbitrarily grouped according to operating temperature as low-temperature ($<300°C$) and high-temperature ($>300°C$). This distinction on the basis of temperature is not entirely arbitrary. The low-temperature electrolyte systems contain water, and the major conducting ions are usually either hydrogen or hydroxyl ions. With such electrolytes, temperatures to nearly 300°C are available, using, for example, concentrated KOH as an alkaline electrolyte or concentrated H_3PO_4 as an acidic electrolyte. Above 300°C the most important fuel-cell electrolytes are fused salt mixtures, notably alkali metal carbonates, where carbonate ion transfer predominates, or doped zirconia ceramics, in which oxide ions are mobile.

It will be noted that major advances are being made toward the long-term goal of practical, direct hydrocarbon cells. However, it will be equally clear that we are much nearer to practical application of cells employing alternative, more reactive fuels—particularly hydrogen.

Most of the work with highly reactive fuels is based upon low-temperature aqueous electrolyte cells. With regard to the hydrocarbons the situation is more diverse. The low-temperature cells show considerable promise, but much attention is still being given to the higher-temperature devices employing molten carbonate and solid oxide electrolytes. In addition, work continues with systems coupling reformers to fuel cells.

The relatively new area of biochemical fuel cells is under investigation. Secondary, or regenerative, fuel cells are also receiving attention. These center largely on reversible hydrogen-oxygen and hydrogen-halogen cells, which can be coupled with solar cells or other systems and used for energy storage.

5-2. *Low-temperature Aqueous Electrolyte Fuel Cells (Including Ion-membrane Cells)*

Hydrogen-oxygen (air) cells. Because of its extreme reactivity, the simplicity of its electrochemical oxidation reaction, and compatibility with

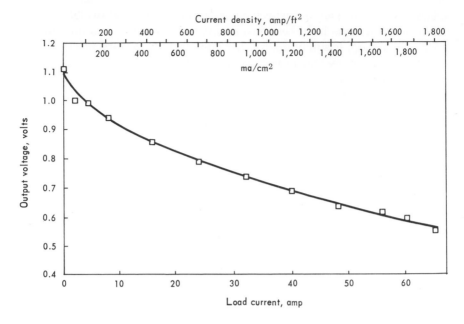

Fig. 2-12. *Performance curve for Bacon H_2-O_2 cell.*

both caustic and acidic systems, hydrogen is the most tractable fuel for fuel cells. It therefore is the one used in the most advanced fuel batteries available at present, including those planned for use in space applications such as the Gemini, Apollo, and Lunar excursion-module projects.

Bacon's classic investigations in the 1930s and 1940s laid groundwork for much of the present hydrogen-fuel-cell effort. He achieved high current densities by the use of pressurized systems to permit operation with aqueous KOH electrolytes at temperatures above 100°C.[15] Preferred conditions were 600 psi at 200°C with a 45 percent KOH electrolyte. Nickel anodes and lithiated nickel oxide cathodes that were relatively low in catalytic activity were used. Bacon used double-porosity electrodes (cf. Sec. 3) and pressure control to maintain the gas-electrolyte interfaces in the electrodes.

A performance curve for one of Bacon's best cells is shown in Fig. 2-12. It represents the best performance for a hydrogen-oxygen cell that has ever been reported. Bacon was also the first to demonstrate a battery on the scale of a few kilowatts. A photograph of his 5-kw unit appears in Fig. 2-13. It consisted of 40 series-connected cells in a "filter press" arrangement. The schematic diagram of Fig. 2-14 shows the complete system and

Fig. 2-13.   *Five-kilowatt Bacon battery.*

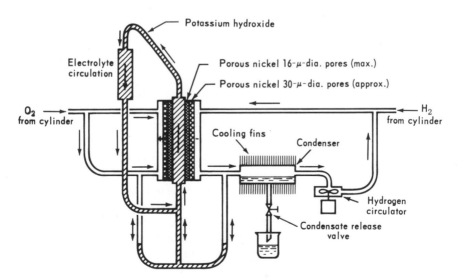

Fig. 2-14.   *System for pressure and water control in a Bacon battery.*

indicates the means for removing product water. While differing in detail, many later systems are quite similar in principle.

Because of difficulties with gasketing, pressure control, and other factors associated with the high-pressure operation, industrial interest never developed, and Bacon's work was discontinued in 1961. Many of his basic concepts are now being applied by Pratt and Whitney to fuel batteries for the Apollo and Lunar excursion-module projects, as well as terrestrial applications.[33,34] Using dual-porosity electrodes and a more concentrated caustic electrolyte (85 percent KOH), their cells operate at 250°C but at pressures of only 1 to 2 atm. Current densities of over 250 amp/ft^2 at 0.9 volt have been obtained.

Another type of alkaline H_2–O_2 fuel cell is that under development by the Union Carbide Corp.[34] It employs a 25 percent aqueous KOH electrolyte. The gas-electrolyte interface is maintained by controlling the wetting properties of catalyzed carbon electrodes of selected porosity.[17] Tubular and planar electrodes have been fabricated from porous carbon stock. Performance data indicated for 1-kw batteries based upon these electrodes are shown in Table 2-3.[35]

Table 2-3. *Performance of 1-kw Union Carbide Hydrogen-Oxygen Cells*

	Air-hydrogen (atm pressure 70°F)	Oxygen-hydrogen (atm pressure 70°F)	Oxygen-hydrogen (atm pressure 140°F)
Current density, amp/ft^2	33	50	50
Terminal voltage per cell	0.82	0.85	0.88
Watts/lb[†]	5	6.7	8.3
kw/ft^3	0.33	0.46	0.62

† Includes operational accessories but no fuel or oxidants.

Recently an improved electrode structure has been described.[36] Much thinner than the earlier porous carbon electrodes (10 to 15 mils versus 250 mils) it permits the design of more compact cells of higher power densities. A comparison of the sizes of 6 volt/20 watt versions of the thick- versus thin-electrode fuel batteries is shown in Fig. 2-15. Such cells have been life-tested for several thousand hours with but a small decline in performance.

Allis-Chalmers H_2–O_2 cells, while also employing a caustic electrolyte, differ in that the electrolyte is immobilized by a thin asbestos matrix.[37] This permits the use of thin electrodes without great structural strength.

Fig. 2-15. *Comparison of two Union Carbide Corp. 6-volt 20-watt fuel-cell batteries. Battery on left made from thin electrodes; battery on right made from ¼-in.-thick electrodes. (Photo courtesy of Union Carbide Corp.)*

Sintered nickel plates catalyzed with platinum and palladium have been used, and recently a nickel boride–hydrogen electrode has been described.[25] In this type of cell it is necessary to control the volume of the electrolyte. This controls the position of the gas-liquid interface and is accomplished by regulating the rate of evaporation of product water. Because the vapor pressure over the electrolyte decreases as the solution concentrates, the system is somewhat self-regulating. Hydrogen-oxygen batteries of this type rated at 50 watts and 1 kw have been designed for space applications.[38] The former is rated at 30 watts/lb, and with auxiliaries at 18 watts/lb; or 3.0 kw/ft³ and 1.1 kw/ft³.

In Europe, Justi has been active for many years in the development of hydrogen-oxygen cells.[16] He has contributed an important electrode structure known as the *double-skeleton* (DSK) electrode. It consists of a Raney metal catalyst (e.g., nickel or silver) in a supporting sintered metal structure. Again the electrolyte is KOH, and because of the high activity of Raney catalysts, the electrodes deliver current densities on hydrogen

Fig. 2-16.   *Battery of eight fuel cells operating on hydrogen and oxygen at ambient temperature powering two automobile headlights.*   (*Photo courtesy of Varta AG, Frankfurt/Main, Germany.*)

of several hundred amperes per foot squared at ambient temperature with little polarization.   Fabrication procedures involve high pressures at elevated temperatures and special leaching procedures to activate the electrodes.

An extensive development effort based on Justi's work is under way at Varta in Frankfurt/Main, Germany.   Figure 2-16 shows a room-temperature hydrogen-oxygen fuel battery which delivers electrical energy to two automobile headlights.   The battery contains anodes of the DSK structure and proprietary cathodes containing silver.[39]   It operates at room-temperature ambient.

Shell, Ltd., in England has described a cell employing either alkaline or acidic electrolytes and still another type of electrode structure.[40]   A porous plastic is used for the support structure.   Upon this is deposited a thin conducting layer of silver or gold thickened by subsequent electro-deposition.   The electrode is activated by a final deposit of catalyst.   In operation the plastic is wetted by the electrolyte.   The catalyst layer faces

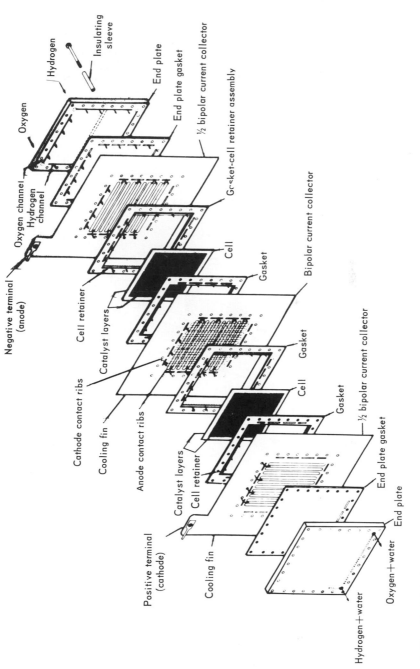

Fig. 2-17. *Exploded view of ion-exchange-membrane fuel cells assembled in series.*

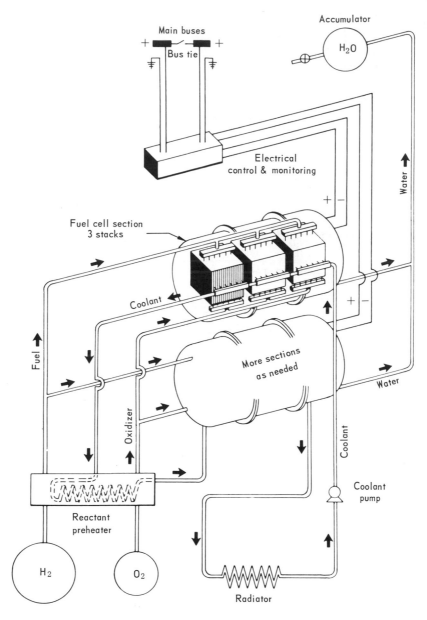

Fig. 2-18. *Schematic of fuel-battery system for Project Gemini.*

Fig. 2-19. *Gemini fuel-battery section showing cutaway cell and manifolding. (Photo courtesy of General Electric Co. Direct Energy Conversion Operation.)*

the gas. Small batteries demonstrating capability of the structure have been constructed.

Also falling into the category of low-temperature systems are fuel cells employing ion-exchange membranes as electrolytes. Such cells have been previously reviewed.[41] The Direct Energy Conversion Operation of the General Electric Co. has developed a battery of this type for space and many other applications.[42] A 2-kw battery (peak load rating) is planned for the two-man orbiting vehicle of the Gemini project. The membranes contain acidic groups (sulfonic acid groups) linked directly to a polymer network and hence are not leached from the system by the product water. Also, since the membranes have a fixed capacity for water, they reject liquid product water, which may be used for drinking.

General construction of an ion-exchange-membrane battery[43] is shown in the exploded view of a small unit (10 watts) in Fig. 2-17.   As in Bacon's battery, the individual cells are connected in series.   Gases are manifolded internally through appropriate ports in plates and gaskets.   Ribbed current-collector plates also separate the individual cells and aid in heat transfer.   The active catalyst upon which the electrode reactions occur is integrally bonded to the opposite surfaces of the membrane electrolyte. The individual cell units of the Gemini battery are similar to the above in principle.

The overall system for Gemini is shown diagrammatically in Fig. 2-18 and a view of a fuel-cell tank assembly is seen in Fig. 2-19.   The system consists of six individual batteries or *stacks* which are each made up of 32 cells.   The stacks are assembled further into groups of three which are sealed in a protective tank.   Fuel and oxygen are supplied from a cryogenic system.   As shown in Fig. 2-18, appropriate heat exchangers are included in the system, and means are provided for purging the system of impurities that may accumulate.   Product water is removed for drinking purposes with a suitable wicking arrangement.

Other types of ion-exchange-membrane fuel cells include types in which an aqueous electrolyte is contained between two membranes each of which supports an electrode on one surface.[44,45]   Efforts to develop inorganic membranes for fuel cells have resulted in some success.   The most promising type thus far is based upon zirconyl phosphate systems.[46] The electrolytic conductivity of such membranes, however, tends to be insufficient for practical operation, and generally some free acid, e.g., phosphoric acid, is therefore incorporated into the membranes.

Hydrazine and ammonia cells.   Hydrazine, H_2NNH_2, represents another highly reactive fuel.   Its disadvantages are toxicity and high cost. It has the advantage, however, of being a liquid fuel rather than a gas requiring high pressure or cryogenic storage.   Its high solubility in aqueous electrolytes provides for ready accessibility to the fuel anode, but this is a mixed blessing since fuel must be prevented from reaching the cathode. Otherwise undesirable, direct oxidation can occur without the production of electrical energy.   This is both wasteful of fuel and detrimental to cathode performance.

On balance, hydrazine is an interesting fuel, at least for interim specialty applications.   The Allis-Chalmers Co. has indeed engineered a 3-kw hydrazine-oxygen battery[47] and used it to power a demonstration golf cart (Fig. 2-20).

In structure the cells are similar to their "capillary membrane" (matrix) hydrogen cells, but here the asbestos membrane not only contains the electrolyte but also reduces transport of hydrazine to the cathode.

Fig. 2-20. *Experimental golf cart built by the Research Division of Allis-Chalmers in 1962. The cart is powered by a 60-cell 3-kw hydrazine-oxygen fuel-cell module.* (*Photo courtesy of Allis-Chalmers, Research Division.*)

Porous nickel activated with palladium or nickel boride has been used as the anode. The oxygen cathode is catalyzed with silver. Performance curves for an individual cell are shown in Fig. 2-21.

In operation the fuel is dissolved in a circulating portion of the 25 percent KOH electrolyte and fed to the anode chambers of the cells.

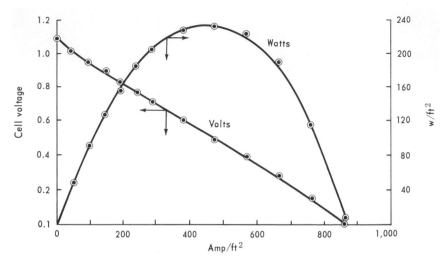

Fig. 2-21. *Performance curves for hydrazine-oxygen cell.   Electrode area, 7.50 in.²; temperature, 70°C.*

Circulation of the fuel-electrolyte solution permits the ready addition of make-up fuel and also aids in the removal of the nitrogen formed in the oxidation reaction.   The make-up fuel is stored as relatively stable hydrazine hydrate.   Scrubbers containing sulfuric acid are incorporated into the vent lines from both fuel and oxygen electrodes to eliminate hydrazine from the waste gases exhausted to the atmosphere.

Nominal operating temperature of the golf-cart battery is 70°C. To bring the unit to start-up temperature, external heaters are used. Warm-up times of the uninsulated system are 45 to 60 minutes, but once at temperature the unit is self-sustaining, and, in fact, radiators are used for cooling when the unit is on load.   These features illustrate some of the problems encountered with cells operating at elevated temperatures. Engineering experience with hydrazine batteries will be helpful in solving such problems for other systems.

About 80 percent of the hydrazine has been converted into electric current in individual cells.   Some loss is attributed to autodecomposition of the hydrazine on the anode catalyst and some to direct oxidation at the cathode.   An overall energy efficiency of 40 percent has been reported.

Hydrazine is also receiving attention by others.   Shell, Ltd., has successfully operated cells similar to their hydrogen-oxygen units on hydrazine.[48]   The general mode of operation is similar to that of Allis-Chalmers.   In this case the porous plastic (Porvic) base of the electrode serves to reduce transport of the fuel to the oxygen electrode.

Chloride Technical Services, Ltd., have also described work in this field.[49] They circulate the caustic electrolyte containing the dissolved fuel but cause it to flow through the anode structure and into the electrolyte gap between anode and cathode, from which it then returns to an external reservoir. A view of a battery containing four hydrazine electrodes and five oxygen electrodes in a conventional, polystyrene battery case is shown in Fig. 2-22. Based upon single-cell performance, data ratings of 8.6 watts/lb and 0.8 kw/ft^3 have been estimated.[50]

Ammonia cells have not advanced as far as those based upon hydrazine.

Fig. 2-22. *Hydrazine-oxygen battery. (Photo by permission of Chloride Technical Services, Ltd., England.)*

As a fuel ammonia is attractive because it is reactive, less expensive than hydrazine, and easily stored as a liquid in pressure tanks. Because it is gaseous under ambient conditions, exhaust gases from the battery would contain some ammonia unless removed by scrubbing or some other treatment. Like hydrazine, ammonia is compatible with caustic electrolytes. Performance data for single cells have been published.[23,51] Information about batteries is not yet generally available.

Alcohol cells.   Cells employing methanol as the fuel are of considerable interest because of its low cost, storability as a liquid, and moderate reactivity. Some higher alcohols have also been considered. Methanol cells and batteries have not been developed as far as those using hydrogen and hydrazine.

Much emphasis to date has been placed upon cells employing potassium hydroxide electrolytes which are converted to carbonates by the CO_2 produced by the anode reaction. Because of the low solubility of potassium bicarbonate, such electrolytes have limited life before they require replacement. Such systems are therefore limited to specialty applications. For example, Vielstich has described an alkaline methanol battery which is designed to provide power for signal lights on buoys.[52]

Acidic electrolytes are also of importance because they are CO_2-rejecting. Considerable study of this type of system has been carried out at the Esso Research and Engineering Co. Performance data for anodes and single cells have been reported.[53,54]

The direct, nonelectrochemical oxidation of methanol at the cathode of such a cell can be a major problem. It not only is wasteful of fuel and detrimental to the performance of the oxygen cathode, but also it can cause formation of carbon dioxide product gas in the electrolyte chamber, leading to operating problems and difficulties during standby periods.

A compromise must be made between the concentration of dissolved fuel which gives high performance at the methanol anode and that which can be tolerated at the cathode for the above reasons. Proper design of the fuel-electrolyte flow pattern can also alleviate the problem of direct oxidation at the cathode.

Using this approach, laboratory cells at Esso have operated at 60 ma/cm^2 at 0.4 volt on methanol and air. The operating temperature is 60°C. Results have been sufficiently encouraging that engineering research studies have been initiated.[54] Actual performance data on methanol-air batteries have not been reported as yet, but such units have been built and tested. Figure 2-23 is a photograph of a six-cell battery of methanol-air cells each of 50-in.^{2} active area.

In most of the alcohol cells reported to date the fuel is highly soluble,

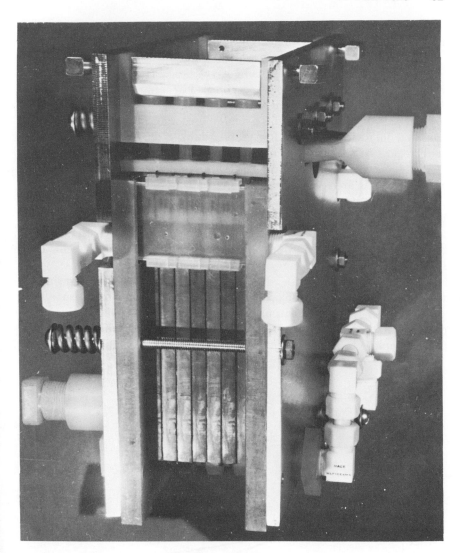

Fig. 2-23. *Six-cell assembly of a methanol-air battery.* (*Photo courtesy of Esso Research and Engineering Corp.*)

and precautions must be taken to prevent excessive migration of fuel to the cathode, where direct oxidation can occur. In a methanol cell recently reported, however, advantage is taken of the "salting out" effect of concentrated cesium carbonate on methanol. The use of this electrolyte permits operation with methanol on a porous gas electrode and thereby largely circumvents the migration problem.[24] Because of the high solubility of the carbonates of cesium, problems from precipitation are not encountered with this CO_2-rejecting electrolyte.

Hydrocarbon cells. Work has not yet progressed to the point where large-scale batteries incorporating direct low-temperature oxidation of hydrocarbons have been achieved. Considering the fact, however, that concerted study of the anodic oxidation reactions of hydrocarbons was initiated only within the last few years, results to date encourage optimism with regard to the ultimate realization of such low-temperature devices. Because of the great importance of these fuels, the present status of the research in this area will be indicated in some detail.

The current-voltage curves in Fig. 2-24a for methane and propane in complete fuel cells employing platinum-black electrodes and a phosphoric acid electrolyte at 150°C are illustrative of performances that can be achieved at present.[55,56] Similar reactivities in anode half-cells have recently been reported using sulfuric acid electrolyte at 100°C.[57]

Of importance at least equal to the current-voltage relationships is the stoichiometry of the oxidation reactions. It has now been amply demonstrated that with platinum-catalyzed electrodes over a wide range of operating conditions the oxidation of saturated hydrocarbons is essentially complete to CO_2.[32,57–64]

Because of the complexity of the systems involved, it is important to

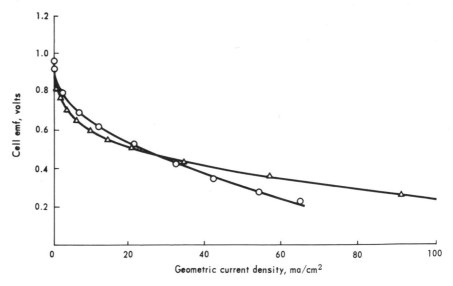

Fig. 2-24. *Polarization curves for methane and propane fuel cells at 150°C. Electrodes, platinum; electrolyte, 85 percent phosphoric acid;* ○, *methane;* △, *propane.*

consider the behavior of hydrocarbons in somewhat greater detail. As already noted in earlier sections, many steps must be involved in the overall reaction. These include transport, sorption, the breaking of C—H and C—C bonds, the making of C—O bonds, and the formation of hydrogen ions. These steps can be affected by such important variables as the electrolyte composition, the electrocatalyst, the temperature, and the hydrocarbon structure.

Work with sulfuric acid and potassium hydroxide cells at 25°C has indicated that among the elemental materials, platinum black is the most active catalyst for all hydrocarbons.[26] To date no conflicting evidence has been reported. Because of its activity, considerable work has been done with platinum (both supported and unsupported) with several electrolytes.[26,32,55—69] The field of oxide catalysts is relatively untouched, but it has been disclosed that cobalt molybdate is active toward hydrocarbons.[27] No promotion was observed when a wide variety of oxides were admixed with platinum in phosphoric acid cells, even though many of the oxides enhanced the performance of carbon monoxide.[70] Evaluation of electrocatalysts continues as a most important aspect of hydrocarbon-fuel-cell programs because of the urgency of eliminating the platinum or at least markedly reducing the amounts presently required.[71]

The effect of the electrolyte is complex. Most hydrocarbons electrooxidize on platinum-black electrodes in acidic cells, and with certain fuels no differences due to anion effects have been detected among perchloric, sulfuric, and phosphoric acids.[59] In similar alkaline cells the performance of unsaturates is at least as good as in acidic cells. Saturates, however, do not support appreciable load currents on platinum black in alkaline cells.[26] Because of the carbonate problem, the poorer performance in alkaline cells is not of practical importance. It may, however, have important bearing on theoretical understanding of the systems.

Important effects of fuel structure have been noted. In acidic cells unsaturates are capable of supporting high current densities even at low temperatures, e.g., 65°C. Saturated hydrocarbons reach a region of unstable performance at relatively low current densities even at temperatures as high as 90°C.[26,59,61,66] In some cases voltage oscillations of rather long period are observed.[57,61] At 150°C and higher the unstable region is suppressed and high performance is achieved[32] using phosphoric acid as electrolyte.

The molecular weight of the fuel is important regardless of structural type, and a maximum performance is seen with C_3 and C_4 hydrocarbons.[69] In higher-temperature phosphoric acid cells it has been found that straight-chain saturates perform best. Even methane performs quite well.[56] Branching or cyclization reduces performance somewhat, and the introduction of unsaturation is a further deterrent, probably due to side reactions.[69]

The use of a concentrated phosphoric acid electrolyte permits operation at atmospheric pressure, even at elevated temperatures, because of the low vapor pressure (activity) of the contained water. If the water activity is suppressed excessively, poor performance is obtained. This results from the fact that the water is the source of the oxygen for the formation of CO_2 at the anode.

Even at 25°C and on open circuit much chemistry occurs on the electrode surface. Thus methane has been found in the gas phase when ethane and propane have been equilibrated.[72,73] Generally, formation of these gaseous species is suppressed when a cell is on load.[73] Just as cracking products are formed, so are higher-molecular-weight species and other strongly adsorbed species. These tend to remain on the electrode surface[72,73] and may contribute to inducing the oscillations mentioned above. Such materials would be expected to be removed by oxidation as the potential of the fuel electrode rose (cell potential fell). This would make additional catalyst sites available for the primary cell reaction until the less reactive materials again accumulated.

In summary, present information emphasizes the following important points:

1. The uniqueness of platinum among simple catalysts
2. The pronounced influence of the electrolyte (acidic versus alkaline)
3. The completeness of oxidation
4. The parallels between some of the surface reactions on open circuit and some seen in heterogeneous catalysis

It is clear that much additional information is still required, particularly with regard to the mechanisms of the direct hydrocarbon anode reactions. The many programs presently under way should provide this knowledge. Meanwhile, considerable effort continues to be devoted to high-temperature fuel-cell systems for the electrooxidation of carbonaceous fuels.

Biochemical fuel cells. There has been an increasing interest in cells which employ microorganisms for converting the energy of various substances into electrical energy. This is a special subject not closely related to ordinary types of fuel cells. The field is in a very early stage of development.

There are two main types of biochemical fuel cells, those which directly convert an oxidizable material into electrical energy by a biochemical mechanism and those in which microorganisms produce a fuel for an ordinary fuel cell by their action on various starting materials. For example, production of hydrogen from glucose solutions by various types of bacteria has been investigated.[74,75]

With biochemical cells the possibility exists of obtaining electrical energy from the oxidation of a wide variety of substances. Many materials have been proposed as potential fuels, such as garbage, sewage, sugars, sawdust, grasses, and leaves.

Biochemical systems have also been proposed for utilizing aqueous oxygen containing ions as cathode reactants. Such ions as sulfate and carbonate might be obtained from sea water and utilized in underwater fuel-cell systems.[76]

Significant effort on biochemical fuel cells has only recently been initiated, and it is too early to assess the importance of such systems in the overall fuel-cell picture. For details on biochemical fuel cells, the literature[74-79] should be consulted.

Regenerative fuel cells (secondary fuel cells). Certain types of fuel cells may be recharged; that is, the anode and cathode reactants can be regenerated by electrolysis of the electrolyte. When this is done, the fuel cell becomes an energy-storage device. Under proper conditions of use, the regenerative fuel cell can possess much higher energy density than conventional secondary batteries. Hydrogen-oxygen fuel cells are the type of fuel cell most commonly considered for regenerative operation.

Werner von Braun[80] foresees the possible application of regenerative fuel cells as power stations on the moon. The abundance of solar energy makes it desirable to consider solar batteries for recharging the fuel cells. It is considered possible that the water needed for electrolysis to produce the necessary hydrogen and oxygen could come from water of hydration thought to be present in some lunar minerals.[81]

Regenerative fuel cells have received relatively less attention to date than primary fuel cells. They have been considered a mode of operation for most of the low-temperature hydrogen-oxygen cells under investigation. The efficiency of such systems is limited by the irreversibility of the oxygen electrode. Consequently, alternative cathode systems such as the bromine-bromide couple[82] have been considered for regenerative cells because of their better reversibility.

Limited studies of regenerative operation of hydrogen-oxygen fuel cells have been reported by a number of investigators.[44,82-88] High-temperature systems have usually not been considered for regenerative applications because of the obvious disadvantage of either maintaining cells at operating temperature during long standby periods or tolerating long start-up times.

5-3. High-temperature Fuel Cells

Fused-carbonate fuel cells. The type of fused-salt electrolyte most commonly employed in fuel cells is fused alkali carbonate. Single-alkali metal carbonates have melting points somewhat higher than is desirable, but a number of lower-melting mixtures are available. For example, the following have been employed in fuel cells:[89] Li Na CO_3 (mp 510°C), Li K CO_3 (mp 710°C), Li Na K$(CO_3)_{3/2}$ (mp 410°C), and Li Na K Ca$(CO_3)_{5/2}$ (mp 360°C).

With such electrolytes the carbonate ion is the current carrier in the cell as well as the sole source of oxygen for the anode half-reaction. Because of this it is of interest to note that CO_2 is formed at the anode even when pure hydrogen is the fuel:

$$H_2 + CO_3^{--} \rightarrow H_2O + CO_2 + 2e$$

When a hydrocarbon fuel, for example, methane, is used, additional carbonate is consumed by the oxidation reaction

$$CH_4 + 4 CO_3^{--} \rightarrow 2 H_2O + 5 CO_2 + 8e$$

In order to prevent depletion of carbonate in the electrolyte, with ensuing polarization and/or solidification of the electrolyte, it is necessary to add make-up CO_2 at the cathode, where the half-reaction is

$$O_2 + 2 CO_2 + 4e \rightarrow 2 CO_3^{--}$$

The source of this CO_2 can be the anode off-gas, a portion of which can be recycled to the cathode feed. This, of course, introduces some complications into cell operation. With smaller units that are unable to sustain the required operating temperature, a portion of the fuel not consumed electrochemically would be burned to maintain the cell temperature. This offers another source of CO_2 for the cathode reaction.

A fused carbonate is a CO_2-rejecting electrolyte; it is therefore suitable for oxidizing both hydrogen and carbonaceous fuels. The temperatures of operation are sufficiently high to permit rapid electrochemical oxidation of a variety of fuels. It is also convenient in the temperature range of fused-carbonate cells to combine them with gasifiers or converters ahead of the fuel cell by which coal, natural gas, or heavy hydrocarbons are pre-converted into electrochemically reactive gas mixtures. When fused-carbonate cells are operated directly upon hydrocarbon fuel feeds, water is usually added to the fuel stream to prevent carbon deposition in the cell.[90]

Fused-carbonate fuel cells have been operated directly on a diversity of fuels including hydrogen, carbon monoxide, methanol, methane, propane, petroleum ether, kerosine, and white gasoline. In most cases, except for hydrogen, water is fed into the cells along with the fuel. It is generally felt that a reaction of the fuel with water to produce hydrogen and CO or CO_2 occurs at the anode of the cell, and that CO and/or hydrogen are the species actually undergoing electrochemical oxidation. This differs markedly from the direct electrochemical oxidation of hydrocarbons which occurs in low-temperature, acid-electrolyte cells. It has the consequence that various fuels show similar performance in fused-carbonate cells, and because of the high temperatures of operation, activation polarization is largely absent. Fused-carbonate cells tend to have an almost linear voltage–current-density relation. The sources of polarization at the electrodes of fused-carbonate fuel cells have been investigated.[91] Activation overvoltage was found to be very small at both electrodes.

Early work on fused-carbonate cells is due to Baur et al.[92] More recent efforts have been stimulated by the work of Broers[93] and by E. Gorin's patents[94] on integrating-carbonate fuel cells with gasifiers to produce electricity from coal or natural gas. Research effort has been under way in the Netherlands by Broers and Ketelaar,[95,96] in France by O. Bloch and coworkers,[97] and in England by Chambers et al.[98] In the United States fused-carbonate cells have been investigated in several laboratories, including those of the Texas Instrument Co.,[99–101] the Institute of Gas Technology,[102] the Westinghouse Electric Corp.,[103] and the General Electric Co.[104]

The cell structures have varied somewhat from one investigator to another. The fused carbonate has usually been immobilized in a porous magnesia matrix or combined with powdered magnesia in what is called a paste electrolyte. Alternatively, the double-layer type of electrode structure originated by F. T. Bacon[15] has been employed in free electrolyte cells. The type of structure has not been observed to have a profound effect upon performance.[98] Lifetime at high temperatures is always a problem, but a number of investigators have reported lifetimes in the order of a thousand hours or more for fused-carbonate cells.

The extensive investigations of fused-carbonate fuel cells can be only incompletely covered within the scope of this writing. Table 2-4 summarizes some of the results obtained with various fuels in various cells under various conditions of operation. Most of the cells of Table 2-4 have an approximately linear relation between voltage and current density so that approximate performance at other load points can be estimated by interpolation of the data given in the table.

Today's most advanced systems for utilizing hydrocarbon fuels in high-temperature carbonate fuel cells employ a converter ahead of the fuel cells. This has the advantage of greater flexibility and permits separately optimizing conditions in the converter and in the cells.

Table 2-4. Representative Data on High-temperature Fused-carbonate Fuel Cells

Fuel	Oxidant	Anode	Cathode	Alkali carbonates used as electrolyte	Temperature, °C	Open-circuit voltage, volts	Current density, amp/ft^2, at 0.7 volt cell potential	References
H_2 96%, H_2O 4%	O_2 91%, CO_2 9%	Pt	Ag	Li, Na, K	500	1.1_8	65	95, 96
$CH_4 + H_2O$	Air + CO_2	Ni	Ag	Li, Na, K	775	0.9_8	45	95, 96
CO 75%, CO_2 25%	Air + CO_2	Fe + Ni + Cu	Ag	Li, Na, K	720	0.9_7	50	95, 96
H_2	Air (+ CO_2)	Silverized ZnO	Silverized ZnO	Li, Na	550	1.1	60	98
H_2	Air (+ CO_2)	Silverized ZnO	Silverized ZnO	Li, Na	690	1.2	85	98
Kerosine	Air (+ CO_2)	Silverized ZnO	Silverized ZnO	Li, Na	640	1.0_5	25	98
CH_4	Air (+ CO_2)	Silverized ZnO	Silverized ZnO	Li, Na	585	1.0_5	15	98
H_2 + some H_2O	$O_2 + CO_2$	Ni	Ag	Li, Na, K	600	1.3_0	30	104
H_2 + some H_2O	$O_2 + CO_2$	Ni	Au	Li, Na, K	600	1.2_5	20	104
CO	$O_2 + CO_2$	Stainless steel	Ag	Li, Na, K	610	0.9_5	10	104
H_2	Air + 10% CO_2	Ni	Ag	Li, Na	700	1.2_0	55	105
H_2	Air + 10% CO_2	Ni	Lithiated NiO	Li, Na	700	1.2_2	45	105
Kerosine	Air + 20% CO_2	—	—	Li, Na	650	0.9_0	15	101
White gasoline		—	—	Li, Na	650	1.0_0	40	101
H_2	O_2 + 67% CO_2	Ni	Ag	Li, Na, K	580	1.2_5	135	103
Steam reformed CH_4	O_2 + 67% CO_2	Ni	Ag	Li, Na, K	580	1.1_0	80	103
H_2	Air + CO_2 + H_2O	Pd foil	Ag	Li, Na, K	600	0.8_8	35	102
Steam reformed CH_4	Air + CO_2 + H_2O	Pd foil	Ag	Li, Na, K	600	0.7_9	10	102

Fig. 2-25a. *An interior view of an experimental 2-cell molten-carbonate fuel battery with 1.33 ft² of active area per cell. This unit is part of a fuel-cell system developed by Texas Instruments, Inc. (Photo courtesy of Texas Instruments, Inc.)*

Texas Instruments, Inc., has undertaken the development of a system for converting logistic fuels, such as JP-4 jet fuel and other hydrocarbon fuels, into electrical energy using a partial-oxidation preconverter and a high-temperature carbonate fuel battery. The cells used in this system are really small modules consisting of several cells in parallel. Figure 2-25a is a photograph showing a battery of two such modules. The performance of a single module on hydrogen is shown in Fig. 2-25b and on reformed propane in Fig. 2-26. The cell used in this system consists of a fused-carbonate mixture immobilized in a magnesium oxide matrix on opposite faces of which sintered electrodes have been applied by a flame-spray technique. According to a published report,[106] over 400 such cells have been tested and a large number have exceeded 2,000 hours of continuous operation on hydrogen and air.

A system producing 72 watts of continuous power from JP-4 jet-engine fuel has been successfully operated.[106] The partial-oxidation unit converts the JP-4 into a stream having the following typical dry composition:

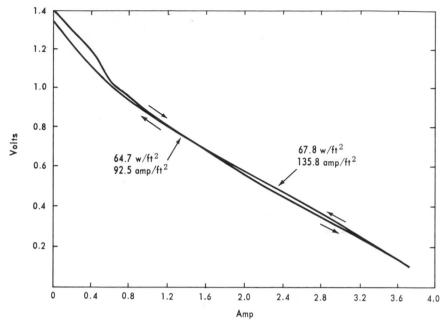

Fig. 2-25b. *Operating characteristics of molten-carbonate fuel cell on hydrogen and oxygen. Cell no. 289, 5 days operating; temperature, 600°C; fuel flow, 480 cc/min H_2.*

	Volume, %
Nitrogen	38
Hydrogen	30
Carbon monoxide	23
Methane	3
Ethylene	1
Carbon dioxide	5

The partial-oxidation converter is fed with fuel, air, and steam.

The Institute of Gas Technology has operated a battery of 10 fused-carbonate cells on methane preconverted in a steam reformer.[102] A part of the methane feed is burned to maintain the converter and the fuel battery at operating temperature. The burner flue gas containing excess air and CO_2 supplies the oxidant gas for the battery cathodes by natural convection. A schematic diagram of this system is presented in Fig. 2-27. Performance curves for this battery operating on hydrogen and on reformed natural gas are shown in Fig. 2-28.

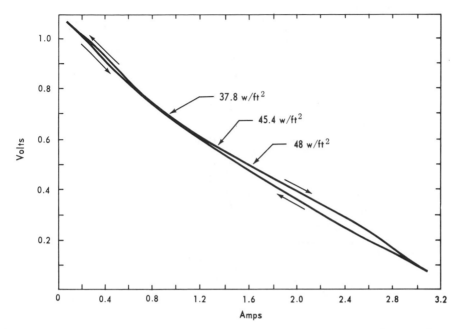

Fig. 2-26. *Performance of molten-carbonate fuel cell on propane-steam reformate. Performance of cell no. 316 after 21 hr of continuous operation on reformed propane at 600°C. Propane flow, 1.2 × 10⁻³ mole/min.*

Oxide-ion fuel cells. High-temperature fuel-cell effort has also been directed toward the investigation of fuel cells in which the electrolyte conducts by oxide-ion migration. This is the type of cell which was used for illustration earlier in this discussion and, for the case of carbon as fuel, is shown schematically in Fig. 2-3, page 45.

The major advantages of the oxide-ion ceramic electrolyte over fused carbonates lie in the elimination of two problems inherent in the latter system: (1) the necessity of maintaining an essentially fluid electrolyte in a high-temperature fuel cell and (2) the requirement of supplying CO_2 along with oxygen to the cathode of the cell. The price that is paid for these advantages is operation at higher temperatures. The presently known oxide-ion conductors become sufficiently conducting for high-performance fuel cells only at about 1000°C and higher.

An early version of this type of fuel cell by Baur and Preis[107] incorporated as the electrolyte a material known much earlier and employed in the Nernst glower,[108] a popular infrared radiation source still widely used today in infrared spectrometers. This material is a high-temperature cubic

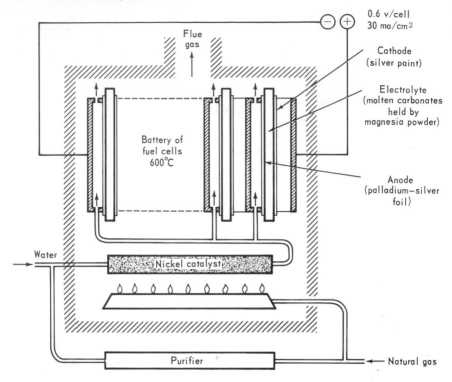

Fig. 2-27.   *Schematic representation of a molten-carbonate fuel battery developed by the Institute of Gas Technology operating on reformed natural gas.*

form of zirconium oxide, ZrO_2, which has been stabilized in the face-centered cubic (fluorite) crystal structure by the addition of yttrium oxide, Y_2O_3, in the amount of about 15 mole percent.   Today's high-temperature oxide-ion fuel cells employ either the above or a similar material in which calcium oxide CaO in the amount of about 15 mole percent is added to stabilize the zirconia in the cubic structure.   In either case, the addition of cations of lower valence than zirconia leads to the presence of oxide-ion vacancies in the structure and causes it to conduct by oxide-ion migration. Negligible electronic conductivity occurs as long as oxygen is present to permit the formation of O^{--} ions.

It is not surprising that at temperatures around 1000°C, there is practically no activation polarization at either electrode in this type of fuel cell.   Diffusion polarization is also not likely with such an electrolyte, and the voltage drop under load is simply linear with current density. The slope reproduces the ohmic-resistance loss in the electrolyte as accurately as it can be measured by other methods.   The manner in which this

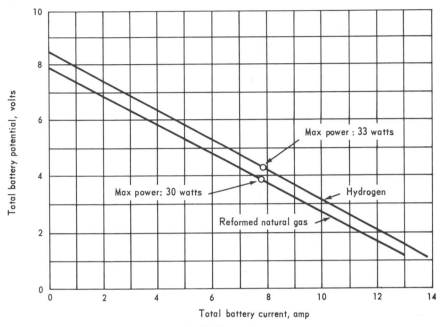

Fig. 2-28.   *Performance of 10-cell IGT fuel battery.*

resistance varies with temperature dictates the acceptable minimum temperatures of operation.

The effect of temperature has been studied by Weissbart and Ruka,[109] who obtained from the cell O_2, Pt || $(ZrO_2)_{0.85}$ $(CaO)_{0.15}$ || Pt, H_2/H_2O the results shown in Fig. 2-29. The relation between voltage and current density is linear. It appears that this cell must be operated at or above 1000°C to achieve performance in the range of practical interest.

The ratio of reactant to product in the anode affects both the performance under load and the open-circuit emf, as shown in Fig. 2-30. The emf for this cell calculated from the free energy of formation of water at 900°C is 0.94 volt, very close to the value for line (3) of Fig. 2-30, for which the ratio of H_2 to H_2O partial pressures is near unity. The open-circuit emf varies with the logarithm of this ratio as required by the Nernst equation.

In line with other high-temperature fuel cells the operating characteristic is not very sensitive to the type of fuel, and, in particular, hydrocarbons are thought to be converted in the cell by reaction with water (usually fed with the hydrocarbon to prevent carbon deposition) into other gases such as CO and H_2. Performance of the cell of Weissbart and Ruka on a

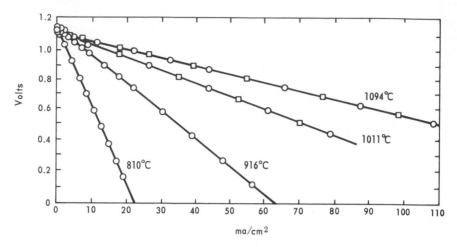

Fig. 2-29. *Current-voltage behavior of the cell*

$$O_2, Pt \,||\, (ZrO_2)_{0.85}(CaO)_{0.15} \,||\, Pt, H_2/H_2O$$

at O_2 pressure $\cong 730$ mm and $H_2/(H_2 + H_2O) \cong 0.973$ for four temperatures. $\bigcirc$, increasing current; $\square$, decreasing current.

methane-plus-water mixture at 20 percent conversion of the methane is shown in Fig. 2-31.

As in the case of fused-carbonate fuel cells, it is advantageous to integrate the fuel cell with a converter. A study of such a system has been carried out by Binder et al.[110] A cross-section diagram of their cell is shown in Fig. 2-32. The electrodes in the cell are of porous platinum bonded to opposite faces of the calcium oxide–stabilized zirconia electrolyte. The converter contains as the catalytic surface a rolled-up nickel screen. In this system a hydrocarbon gas or vapor is preconverted into mixtures containing hydrogen and carbon monoxide which are electrochemically oxidized in the fuel cell.

The voltage–current-density behavior of this system on several fuel feeds is shown in Fig. 2-33. Again here, except for slight effects near zero current density, the drop in voltage under load is due to ohmic-resistance loss in the electrolyte.

An interesting structure for oxide-ion electrolyte fuel cells has been described by Archer et al.[111,112] of the Westinghouse Laboratories. It is referred to as the *bell and spigot* design. Each cell is a hollow cylinder coated inside and outside with porous platinum. The cells are shaped so that it is possible to join them into a battery of cells connected in series with the physical form of a gas-tight cylindrical tube. Into this tube is fed a fuel gas, and the outside cathode surface of the tube is surrounded

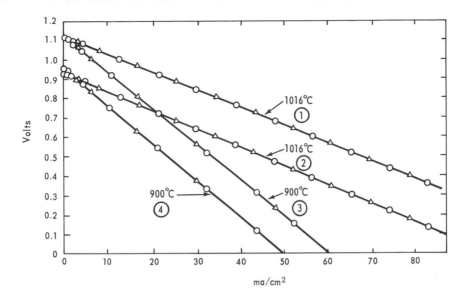

Fig. 2-30. *Current-voltage behavior of the cell*

$$O_2,Pt||(ZrO_2)_{0.85}(CaO)_{0.15}||Pt,H_2/H_2O$$

at two temperatures for two H_2/H_2O ratios. $\bigcirc$, *increasing current;* $\triangle$, *decreasing current.* O_2 *pressure* $\cong 731$ mm. $H_2/(H_2 + H_2O) \cong 0.97$ *for curves (1) and (3);* $H_2/(H_2 + H_2O) \cong 0.54$ *for curves (2) and (4).*

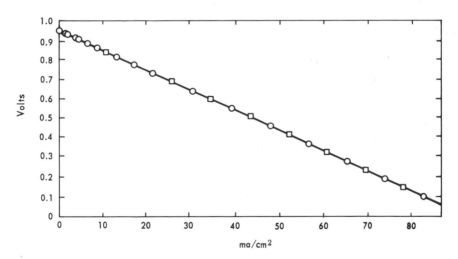

Fig. 2-31. *Current-voltage behavior of the cell*

$$O_2,Pt||(ZrO_2)_{0.85}(CaO)_{0.15}||Pt,CH_4/H_2O$$

Composition of inlet fuel gas: CH_4, 3.8%; H_2O, 2.1%; N_2, 94.1%. *Temperature,* 1015°C. $\bigcirc$, *increasing current;* $\square$, *decreasing current.* O_2 *pressure,* 731 mm.

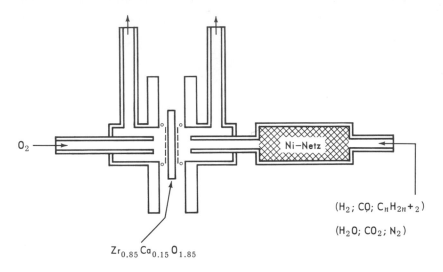

$Zr_{0.85}Ca_{0.15}O_{1.85}$

O_2

Ni–Netz

$(H_2; CO; C_nH_{2n+2})$

$(H_2O; CO_2; N_2)$

Fig. 2-32. *Schematic diagram of solid electrolyte fuel cell with converter developed at Battelle Institute, Frankfurt/Main, Germany.*

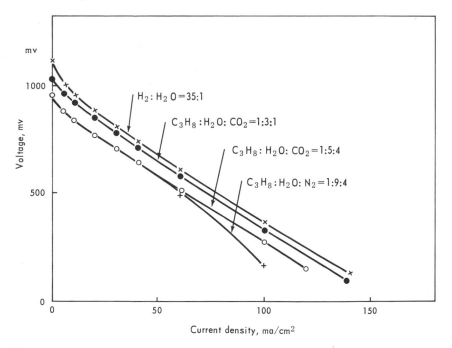

$H_2: H_2O = 35:1$

$C_3H_8: H_2O: CO_2 = 1:3:1$

$C_3H_8: H_2O: CO_2 = 1:5:4$

$C_3H_8: H_2O: N_2 = 1:9:4$

Fig. 2-33. *Performance of cell in Fig. 2-32 on several fuels.*

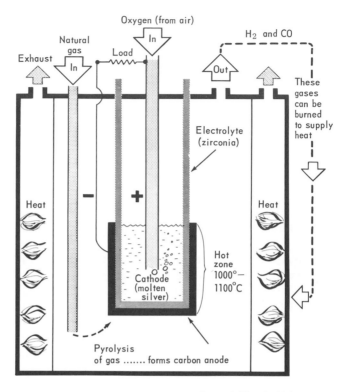

Fig. 2-34. *Principle of operation of General Electric high-temperature fuel cell operating on air and natural gas.*

by an oxygen-containing atmosphere. Thus while the cells are electrically in series, the gases are fed to all the cells in parallel.

Operating on hydrogen and oxygen a power density of 125 watts/lb is reported based on only the weight of active portion of the cells. Lifetimes on the order of 1,000 hours for some small 20-cell batteries have been reported.[112] The electrolyte used in these cells is zirconium oxide stabilized with 15 mole percent yttrium oxide.

An oxide-ion fuel cell not employing platinum electrodes has been reported by Carter, Rocco, Spacil, and Tragert[113,114] of the General Electric Research Laboratory. In this cell, which contains an electrolyte made of zirconia, the anode is formed of carbon deposited from natural gas (mostly methane) fed into the anode chamber of the cell. The cathode is molten silver through which oxygen is bubbled. The output of the cell is electric energy plus a hydrogen and carbon monoxide mixture that can be burned to keep the cell at temperature. Current density of 150 amp/ft² at 0.7 volt is reported and cells have operated at lower current densities for up to 3,000 hours without deterioration.   Figure 2-34 is a diagram showing the principle of operation of the cell.

6.   Summary and Conclusions

Fuel cells as a class of energy converters have been considered generally from the point of view of thermodynamics which sets the ultimate limitation on energy density, from the point of view of kinetics of electrochemical reactions and transport processes which set practical limits on energy density and are subject to improvement, and from the point of view of the state of development of representative types of fuel cells.   Of essentially equal importance to the future of fuel cells are economic considerations, which are outside the scope of this writing but form the subject of an extensive review.[115]

Most conclusions reached by the writers in the fuel-cell literature are temporal because of the rapidly changing and expanding nature of the field.   They seem out of place in a permanent volume such as the present one.   Only a few fundamental conclusions can be drawn, and among them are the following: Fuel cells will always be very complex in the chemical sense, and there will be many types of possible fuel cells in keeping with the wide diversity of chemical reactions that may be involved.   In this great array of possibilities, the practical success of some types of fuel cells has a high probability.

It is most likely that direct and economical conversion of coal into electrical energy by an electrochemical device will remain a problem of supreme technical difficulty.

Acknowledgments

The authors thank a number of their colleagues for helpful discussions and for critical review of the manuscript.   In particular, thanks are due to Drs. H. A. Liebhafsky, E. J. Cairns, and S. Gilman.

References

1.   *Selected Values of Physical and Thermodynamic Properties of Hydrocarbons and Related Compounds*, API. Project 44, pp. 445–448, 726–731, Carnegie Press, Carnegie Institute of Technology, Pittsburgh, Pa., 1953.
2.   Smith, J. M.: *Chem. Eng. Progr.*, **44**: 521–528 (1948).   See also *Natl. Bur. Std. U.S. Circ.* 500, Government Printing Office, 1952, p. 103.
3.   Thacker, C. M., H. D. Falkins, and E. L. Miller: *Ind. Eng. Chem.*, **33**: 588 (1941).

See also *Natl. Bur. Std. U.S. Circ.* 500, Government Printing Office, 1952, p. 54.

4. Niedrach, L. W., and H. R. Alford: *J Electrochem. Soc.*, **112:** 117 (1965).
5. Vetter, K. J.: *Elektrochemische Kinetik*, Springer-Verlag OHG, Berlin, 1961.
6. Austin, L. G.: *Proc. IEEE.*, **51:** 820 (1963).
7. Bockris, J. O'M.: *Modern Aspects of Electrochemistry*, Academic Press Inc., New York, 1954.
8. Winkelmann, D.: *Z. Elektrochem.*, **60:** 731 (1956).
9. Delahay, P.: *New Instrumental Methods in Electrochemistry*, Interscience Publishers (Division of John Wiley & Sons, Inc.), New York, 1954.
10. Liebhafsky, H. A., E. J. Cairns, W. T. Grubb, and L. W. Niedrach: chap. 10, in R. F. Gould (ed.), *Fuel Cell Systems* (Advances in Chemistry Series 47), ACS, Washington, 1965.
11. Schmid, A.: *Die Diffusionsgaselectrode*, Fred. Enke Verlag, Stuttgart, 1923.
12. Nobis, A.: dissertation, Dresden, 1909.
13. Weber, H. C., H. P. Meissner, and D. A. Sama: *J. Electrochem. Soc.*, **109:** 884 (1962).
14. Will, F. G.: *J. Electrochem. Soc.*, **110:** 145 (1963).
15. Adams, A. M., F. T. Bacon, and R. G. H. Watson: chap. 4, in Will Mitchell, Jr. (ed.), *Fuel Cells*, Academic Press Inc., New York, 1963.
16. Justi, E., and A. Winsel: *Kalte verbrennung Fuel Cells*, Franz Steiner, Wiesbaden, 1962.
17. Kordesch, K.: chap. 2, in G. J. Young (ed.), *Fuel Cells*, Reinhold Publishing Corporation, New York, 1960.
18. Haldeman, R. G., W. P. Colman, S. H. Langer, and W. A. Barber: chap. 10, in R. F. Gould (ed.), *Fuel Cell Systems* (Advances in Chemistry Series 47), ACS, Washington, 1965.
19. Carman, P. C.: *Flow of Gases through Porous Media*, Academic Press Inc., New York, 1956.
20. Scheidegger, A. E.: *The Physics of Flow through Porous Media*, The Macmillan Company, New York, 1957.
21. Oswin, H. G., and S. M. Chodosh: chap. 18, in R. F. Gould (ed.), *Fuel Cell Systems* (Advances in Chemistry Series 47), ACS, Washington, 1965.
22. Baker, B. S., L. G. Marianowski, John Meek, and H. R. Linden: 145th Meeting ACS, Division of Fuel Chemistry, preprints of symposium on fuel cell systems, 1963, pp. 209–222.
23. Eisenberg, M.: *Proc. 18th Ann. Power Sources Conf.*, Atlantic City, N.J., May, 1964.
24. Cairns, E. J., and D. C. Bartosik: *J. Electrochem. Soc.* **111:** 1205 (1964).
25. Jasinski, R.: *Proc. 18th Ann. Power Sources Conf.*, Atlantic City, N.J., May, 1964.
26. Grubb, W. T.: *Proc. 16th Ann. Power Sources Conf.*, Atlantic City, N.J., May, 1962, pp. 31–34.
27. Thompson, C. E.: U.S. Patent no. 3,116,169 (1963).
28. Heath, C. E., and W. J. Sweeney: in Will Mitchell, Jr. (ed.), *Fuel Cells*, pp. 65–128, Academic Press Inc., New York, 1963.

29. Young, G. J., and R. B. Rozelle: in G. J. Young (ed.), *Fuel Cells*, vol. I, pp. 23–33, Reinhold Publishing Corporation, New York, 1960.
30. Cohn, G.: *Proc. 17th Ann. Power Sources Conf.*, Atlantic City, N.J., May, 1961, pp. 12–16.
31. Van Winkle, Jon, and W. N. Carson, Jr.: *Electrochem. Technol.* **1:** 18–22 (1963).
32. Grubb, W. T., and Carol J. Michalske: *J. Electrochem. Soc.*, **111:** 1015 (1964).
33. Gregory, D. P.: "Hydrogen-Oxygen Cells of the Bacon Type," lecture to the U.C.L.A. course on electrochemical energy conversion, Aug. 6, 1963.
34. Shaw, R. H., and R. A. Thompson: ARS Space Power Systems Conference, Santa Monica, Calif., ARS Paper no. 2560–62, Sept. 25–28, 1962.
35. Kordesch, K. V.: chap. 8, in Will Mitchell, Jr. (ed.), *Fuel Cells*, Academic Press Inc., New York, 1963.
36. Clark, M. B., W. G. Darland, and K. V. Kordesch: *Proc. 18th Ann. Power Sources Conf.*, Atlantic City, N.J., May, 1964, p. 11.
37. Wynveen, R. A., and T. G. Kirkland: *Proc. 16th Ann. Power Sources Conf.*, Atlantic City, N.J., May, 1962, p. 24.
38. Jasinski, R. J., and T. Kirkland: "Fuel Cells—A State-of-the-Art Report," *Mech. Eng.*, March, 1964, p. 51.
39. Anonymous, *Fuel Cell Progr.*, **2**(9):1 (April, 1964).
40. Williams, K. R.: U.S. Patent no. 3,116,170, Dec. 31, 1963.
41. Niedrach, L. W., and W. T. Grubb: chap. 6, in Will Mitchell, Jr. (ed.), *Fuel Cells*, Academic Press Inc., New York, 1963.
42. Schanz, J. L., and E. K. Bullock: ARS Space Power Systems Conference, Santa Monica, Calif., ARS Paper no. 2561–62, Sept. 26–28, 1962.
43. Cairns, E. J., and D. L. Douglas: U.S. Patent no. 3,134,696, May 26, 1964.
44. Juda, W., C. E. Tirrell, and R. M. Lurie: *Progr. Astron. Rocketry*, **3:** 445–460 (1961).
45. Lurie, R. M., C. Berger, and R. J. Shuman: chap. 11, in G. J. Young (ed.), *Fuel Cells*, vol. II, Reinhold Publishing Corporation, New York, 1963.
46. Dravnieks, A., D. B. Boies, and J. I. Bregman: *Proc. 16th Ann. Power Sources Conf.*, Atlantic City, N.J., May, 1962, p. 4.
47. Tomter, S. S., and A. P. Antony: in *Fuel Cells*, p. 22, *Chem. Eng. Progr. Tech. Manual*, Am. Inst. of Chem. Engrs., New York, 1963.
48. Williams, K. R., J. W. Pearson, and W. J. Gressler: Fourth International Symposium on Batteries, Brighton, Eng., October, 1964, preprint.
49. Guillibrand, M. I., and G. R. Lomax: Third International Symposium, on Batteries, Bournemouth, England, October, 1962, preprint.
50. Barak, M.: in *Fuel Cells*, p. 79, *Chem. Eng. Progr. Tech. Manual*, Am. Inst. of Chem. Engrs., New York, 1963.
51. Wynveen, R. A.: chap. 12, in G. J. Young (ed.), *Fuel Cells*, vol. II, Reinhold Publishing Corporation, New York, 1963.
52. Vielstich, W.: *Proc. 4th Intern. Symp. on Batteries*, Brighton, England, Pergamon Press, New York, 1964.

53. Tarmy, B. L.: *Proc. 16th Ann. Power Sources Conf.*, Atlantic City, N.J., May, 1962, p. 29.
54. Heath, C. E.: *Proc. 18th Ann. Power Sources Conf.*, Atlantic City, N.J., May, 1964, p. 33.
55. Grubb, W. T., and L. W. Niedrach: *J. Electrochem. Soc.*, **110**: 1086 (1963).
56. Grubb, W. T., and Carol J. Michalske: *Nature*, **201**: 287 (1963).
57. Binder, H., et al.: 125th Electrochemical Society Meeting, Toronto, *J. Electrochem. Soc.*, **111**: 78C (1964), abstract.
58. Buck, R. P., L. R. Griffith, R. T. MacDonald, and M. J. Schlatter: *Proc. 15th Ann. Power Sources Conf.*, Atlantic City, N.J., May, 1961, p. 16.
59. Grubb, W. T., and L. W. Niedrach: *Proc. 17th Ann. Power Sources Conf.*, Atlantic City, N.J., May, 1963, p. 69.
60. Oswin, H. G., A. J. Hartner, and F. Malaspina: *Nature*, **200**: 256 (1963).
61. Schlatter, M. J.: chap. 22, in R. F. Gould (ed.), *Fuel Cell Systems* (Advances in Chemistry Series 47), ACS, Washington, 1965.
62. Wroblowa, H., B. J. Piersma, and J. O'M. Bockris: *J. Electroanal. Chem.*, **6**: 401 (1964).
63. Heath, C. E., and C. H. Worsham: in G. J. Young (ed.), *Fuel Cells*, vol. 2, p. 182, Reinhold Publishing Corporation., New York, 1963.
64. Schlatter, M. J.: *ibid.*, p. 190.
65. Vaucher, R., and O. Bloch: *Compt. Rend.*, **254**: 3676 (1962).
66. Niedrach, L. W.: *J. Electrochem. Soc.*, **109**: 1092 (1962).
67. Young, G. J., and R. B. Rozelle: in G. J. Young (ed.), *Fuel Cells*, vol. 2, p. 216, Reinhold Publishing Corporation, New York, 1963.
68. Griffith, L. R., and D. R. Rhodes: *Fuel Cells*, p. 32, *Chem. Eng. Progr. Tech. Manual*, Am. Inst. of Chem. Engrs., New York, 1963.
69. Grubb, W. T., and Carol J. Michalske: *Proc. 18th Ann. Power Sources Conf.*, Atlantic City, N.J., May, 1964, p. 17.
70. Niedrach, L. W., and I. Weinstock: *Electrochemical Technology*, **3**: 270 (1965).
71. Liebhafsky, H. A., and Cairns, E. J.: *Proc. 1962 Pacific Energy Conversion Conf.*, San Francisco, Calif., December, 1962.
72. Niedrach, L. W.: *J. Electrochem. Soc.*, **111**: 1309 (1964).
73. Grubb, W. T.: *J. Electrochem. Soc.*, **111**: 1086–1088 (1964).
74. Blanchard, G. C., and M. J. Allen: *Proc. 17th Ann. Power Sources Conf.*, Atlantic City, N.J., May, 1963, pp. 59–64.
75. May, P. S.: *Proc. 18th Ann. Power Sources Conf.*, Atlantic City, N.J., May, 1964, pp. 1–3.
76. Rohrbach, G. H., W. R. Scott, and J. H. Canfield: *Proc. 16th Ann. Power Sources Conf.*, Atlantic City, N.J., May, 1962, pp. 18–22.
77. Shaw, M: *Proc. 17th Ann. Power Sources Conf.*, Atlantic City, N.J., May, 1963, pp. 53–56.
78. Brake, J., W. Momyer, J. Cavallo, and H. Silverman: *ibid.*, pp. 56–59.
79. DeZubay, E. A., and E. B. Schultz, Jr.: *Ind. Res.*, **3**(4): 19–27 (1961).
80. *Fuel Cell Progr.*, **2**(6): 1 (January, 1964).
81. Hendel, F. J.: *Ind. Eng. Chem.*, **56**: 29–31 (1964).

82. Adams, A. M., F. T. Bacon, and R. G. H. Watson: *op. cit.*, pp. 190–192.
83. Glass, W. B., and G. H. Boyle: chap. 15, in R. F. Gould (ed.), *Fuel Cell Systems* (Advances in Chemistry Series 47), ACS, Washington, 1965.
84. Ludwig, F. A.: *Progr. Astron. Rocketry*, **3**: 425–444 (1961).
85. Bone, J. S., and M. D. Read: *ibid.*, pp. 461–468.
86. Bone, J. S., S. Gilman, L. W. Niedrach, and M. D. Read: *Proc. 15th Ann. Power Sources Conf.*, Atlantic City, N.J., May, 1961, pp. 47–50.
87. Justi, E., and A. Winsel: *Naturwiss.*, **47**: 299–300 (1960).
88. Justi, E., M. Pilkuhn, W. Scheibe, and A. Winsel: *High Drain Hydrogen Diffusion Electrodes Operating at Ambient Temperature and Low Pressure*, pp. 208–214, Academy of Sciences and Literature (Mainz), Komm.-Verlag Franz Steiner, Wiesbaden, 1959.
89. Peattie, C. Gordon: *Proc. of the IEEE.*, **55**: 801 (1963).
90. Cairns, E. J., G. J. Holm, and A. D. Tevebaugh: *J. Electrochem. Soc.*, **110**: 1025 (1963).
91. Trachtenberg, I.: *J. Electrochem. Soc.*, **111**: 110–113 (1964).
92. Baur, E., W. D. Treadwell, and G. Trümpler: *Z. Elektrochem.*, **27**: 199–209 (1921).
93. Broers, G. H. J.: thesis, University of Amsterdam, Netherlands, 1958.
94. Gorin, E.: U.S. Patent nos. 2,570,543 (1951); 2,581,650 (1952); and 2,581,651 (1952).
95. Broers, G. H. J., and J. A. A. Ketelaar: in G. J. Young (ed.), *Fuel Cells*, pp. 78–94, Reinhold Publishing Corporation, New York, 1960.
96. Broers, G. H. J.: Dechema Monograph, **38**: 277–303 (1960).
97. Degobert, P., and O. Bloch: *Bull. Soc. Chim. France*, pp. 1887–1891 (1962).
98. Chambers, H. H., and A. D. S. Tantram: in G. J. Young (ed.), *Fuel Cells*, pp. 94–109, Reinhold Publishing Corporation, New York, 1960.
99. Peattie, C. G., B. H. Barbee, K. W. Kreiselmaier, R. R. Neuman, S. G. Parker, and T. R. Perry: "Operating Characteristics of a High-temperature Fuel Cell," presented at the Spring Meeting, The Electrochemical Soc., Inc., Los Angeles, Calif., May 6–10, 1962.
100. Peattie, C. G., I. Trachtenberg, B. H. Barbee, K. W. Kreiselmaier, S. G. Parker, and A. H. White: "Factors Involved in the Use of a High-temperature Fuel Cell as a Space Power Source," presented at the Space Power Systems Conference, ARS, Santa Monica, Calif., ARS Paper no. 2565-52, Sept. 25–28, 1962.
101. Peattie, C. G., B. H. Barbee, K. W. Kreiselmaier, S. G. Parker, I. Trachtenberg, and A. H. White: "Performance Data for Molten-electrolyte Fuel Cells Operating on Several Fuels," *Proc. 1962 Pacific Energy Conversion Conf.*, San Francisco, Calif., Aug. 12–16, 1962.
102. Marianowski, L. G., John Meek, E. B. Schultz, Jr., and B. S. Baker: *Proc. 17th Ann. Power Sources Conf.*, Atlantic City, N.J., May, 1963, pp. 72–75.
103. Sandler, Y. L.: *J. Electrochem. Soc.*, **109**: 1115 (1962).
104. Douglas, D. L.: in G. J. Young (ed.), *Fuel Cells*, Reinhold Publishing Corporation, New York, 1960.
105. Gorin, E., and H. L. Recht: *Chem. Eng. Progr.*, **55**: 51–58 (1959).

106. Truitt, J. K.: in *Fuel Cells*, pp. 1–5, *Chem. Eng. Tech. Manual*, Am. Inst. of Chem. Engrs., New York, 1963.
107. Baur, E., and H. Preis: *Z. Elektrochem.*, **43**: 727–732 (1937).
108. Nernst, W., and W. Wild: *Z. Elektrochem.*, **7**: 373–376 (1900).
109. Weissbart, J., and R. Ruka: *J. Electrochem. Soc.*, **109**: 723–726 (1962).
110. Binder, H., A. Kohling, H. Krupp, and G. Sandstede: *Electrochim. Acta*, **8**: 781–793 (1963).
111. Alles, J. J., W. A. English, L. Elikan, and R. L. Zabradnik: chap. 24, in R. F. Gould (ed.), *Fuel Cell Systems* (Advances in Chemistry Series 47), ACS, Washington, 1965.
112. Archer, D. H., et al., *Proc. 18th Ann. Power Sources Conf.*, Atlantic City, N.J., May, 1964, p. 36.
113. General Electric Co. Research Laboratory, press release, Dec. 26, 1962.
114. *Chem. Eng. News*, **41**: 47, Jan. 14, 1963.
115. Adams, David R., et al.: *Fuel Cells, Power for the Future*, Fuel Cell Research Associates, P.O. Box 157, Cambridge, Mass., 1960.

Symbols

α transfer coefficient in the kinetic expression for an electrochemical reaction

γ surface tension

C concentration (with various subscripts)

D diffusion coefficient

δ thickness of diffusion layer

D_E energy density of a fuel

E cell emf (with various subscripts to indicate reversible emf, emf under load, etc.)

E efficiency

η overvoltage (with various subscripts to indicate the type)

$\mathcal{F}$ Faraday constant

F symbol for a fuel molecule

ΔG Gibbs free-energy change

ΔH enthalpy change

i current (with various subscripts)

k rate constant (with various subscripts)

M energy requirement of a mission

n number of electrons involved in oxidation of a molecule of fuel

n_t number of electrons involved in transfer step

P pressure (with various subscripts)

ϕ liquid-solid contact angle

p power

Q_H heat input to heat engine

R gas constant

s surface-roughness-factor radius

ΔS entropy change

T absolute temperature (with various subscripts)

t time

θ surface coverage (a fraction of total surface covered with a given species)

W work

W_c° specific weight of fuel battery (pounds per watt)

W_f° specific weight of fuel system (pounds per kilowatt-hour)

W_t total weight

w number of molecules of oxygen to oxidize one molecule of fuel

x number of molecules of carbon dioxide produced from one molecule of fuel

y number of molecules of water produced from one molecule of fuel

z number of molecules of inert gas produced from one molecule of fuel

3

THERMOELECTRIC POWER GENERATION

Steven I. Freedman

1. INTRODUCTION

During the last decade considerable interest has been focused on the problem of creating useful thermoelectric devices. Thermoelectric generators and refrigerators have been developed, and much knowledge has been gained of the thermoelectric properties of semiconductors. The rate of progress in the improvement of thermoelectric materials has tapered off recently, and the field has reached a plateau where additional gains are becoming expensive and painstaking. The basic theory of semiconductor thermoelectric power and heat and charge conduction has enticed the theoretical physicists to attempt to design improved materials. It is unfortunate that such goals have not met with success, as the goal of improved transistor design has. A crucial property, which so far has eluded attempts at improvement, is the mechanical strength of the highest-efficiency thermoelements. The best thermoelements, from the energy-conversion viewpoint, are those with the highest figure of merit Z. These materials seem to be approaching an empirical asymptote which enables thermopiles to operate at efficiencies up to one-sixth of Carnot. The maximum efficiency of a thermoelectric generator made from materials whose properties are independent of temperature and polarity will be shown to be

$$\eta = \frac{\Delta T}{T_h} \frac{\sqrt{1 + ZT} - 1}{\sqrt{1 + ZT} + T_c/T_h} \tag{3-1}$$

where

$$Z = \frac{\alpha^2}{\rho k} \tag{3-2}$$

Missile and Space Division, General Electric Company, Philadelphia, Pennsylvania.

The Seebeck coefficient α is the ratio of the open-circuit voltage developed to the temperature difference. The Seebeck voltage arises because of the thermal diffusion of electrons and holes. In a material with free electrons, the thermal motion of the charge carriers is greater at the hot end of the material. The thermal diffusion of the electrons builds up an excess of electrons at the cold end of the n-type material. This charge density creates an emf which, in the steady state, balances the thermal-diffusion driving force. When materials with low electrical conductivities are used, the internal reflux of electrons to the hot end is at a low rate and higher open-circuit voltages can be developed than in materials with greater electrical conductivities. It is to be expected, therefore, that semiconductor materials should make superior thermoelements to those made from metals. Indeed this is so. In addition, semiconductors can be made with positive "holes" as charge carriers which develop an emf of opposite sign to that of materials with free electrons. The best thermoelements are made from n-type and p-type semiconductors. Combustion-heated thermoelectric generators containing thermopiles made from the best available semiconductors have operated at efficiencies between 10 and 12 percent. While improvements in this figure can be expected, it is highly unlikely that thermoelectric generators will be able to compete with existing powerplants in applications other than those of modest power level where long-duration, maintenance-free operation is essential.

The origins of thermoelectricity date back to 1821 when Seebeck reported some experiments to the Prussian Academy of Sciences regarding the deflections of a compass created by placement adjacent to circuits made with dissimilar materials. Seebeck continued his work and arranged his materials in a thermoelectric series. It was unfortunate that he or contemporary investigators did not attempt to generate power. Since the electromagnetic laws, dealing with flowing currents and their generation of magnetic fields, were drawing the attention of the intellectual elite, Seebeck attempted to relate the earth's temperature differences and its magnetic field. If a thermoelectric generator had been built using the bismuth and antimony available at the time, such a generator could have produced power at an efficiency comparable to the best steam engines of the period.

The next discovery, by Peltier in 1834, was the reversible heat interaction accompanying the passage of a current through the junction of dissimilar materials. In 1838 Lenz demonstrated that water could be frozen with a bismuth-antimony thermocouple and that the ice could be melted by the reversal of the current.

Thermoelectricity remained an unexplained collection of data until Lord Kelvin, in 1854, discovered the relationship between the Seebeck voltage and the Peltier heat. The profound ability of Lord Kelvin can be appreciated by noting that he predicted the existence of a third thermo-electric effect, the Thomson heat, and then proceeded to measure it. His analysis was remarkable when one considers that the second law of thermo-dynamics had been discovered only four years previously.

Thermoelectricity was then applied to the measurement of tempera-tures by thermocouples and energy fluxes (thermal and solar) by thermo-piles. Some attempts were made, by Weston in 1888 and by Coblentz in 1913, to generate power by use of solar-heated thermopiles. A Sun Electric Generator Company was founded in 1910.

The first modern attempt at solar thermoelectric power generation was by Telkes. In the late 1930s Telkes studied PbS–ZnSb thermocouples. Later, in 1953, after the study of numerous thermoelement combinations, an efficiency of 3.35 percent was demonstrated using concentrated solar power. The thermoelements which achieved this were positive type ZnSb (Sn,Ag,Bi) and a negative alloy of 91 percent Bi + 9 percent Sb. This efficiency is 7 percent of Carnot. The figure of merit of this material must have been at least 0.9×10^{-3} °K^{-1}, about 40 percent of that of the best material available today.

The next discovery was by Joffe, who in 1956 discovered that PbTe and PbSe were superior thermoelement materials. Joffe and his co-workers had studied the use of semiconductors as thermoelements for many years and had developed several thermoelectric devices for use in remote areas. One such device was a combination kerosene lantern and thermoelectric generator. At this time it was discovered that the semiconductors with electron concentrations adjusted to about 10^{19}/cm^3 possessed figures of merit superior to better- and poorer-conducting materials. The materials which exhibit the highest thermoelectric efficiencies today are n-type PbTe and p-type BiTe–SbTe. The discovery of the tellurides and selenides enabled generators to be built which operated at efficiencies of 10 percent. Almost all the present-day thermoelectric materials are either tellurides or selenides.

Recent developments have produced silicon-germanium-alloy thermo-elements. These materials are capable of operating at higher temperatures, up to 1950°F, than the tellurides, which can be used up to 1250°F but have a figure of merit which is presently only about two-thirds that of the tellurides. Figure 3-1 shows the progress which has been made in thermo-electric-power-generation materials.

Another application of thermoelectricity is in refrigeration. Since the Peltier heat is reversible, thermoelement junctions can be used to remove heat by passing current through them in the appropriate direction. Since the efficiency of thermoelectric modules is independent of their size, small

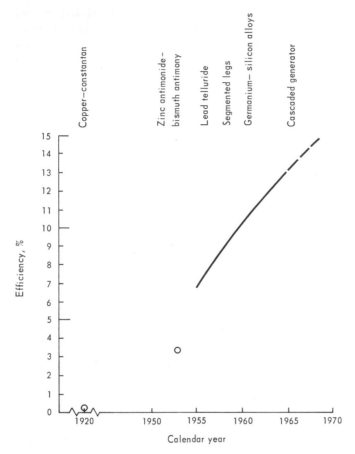

Fig. 3-1. *Progress in the development of thermoelectric materials.*

refrigeration units can be built where vapor-compression machinery cannot be effectively miniaturized. Some special-purpose refrigeration devices have been made to freeze small medical samples. The reversibility aspect of the Peltier heat has suggested that it be tried in situations where heating and cooling are both required at the same location, as in baby-bottle refrigerators and heaters, hostess carts with hot trays and small refrigerators, and constant-temperature-reference baths.

Present-day technology has not resulted in many commercial applications of thermoelectricity. While many refrigeration devices have been demonstrated, there are very few refrigeration models being offered for general sale. Many companies offer thermoelectric-refrigeration modules, but the costs have been too high for general commercial refrigeration.

The vapor-compression machines used in current refrigerators are more efficient, are less expensive, and have an extremely long mean time to failure. Thermoelectric-refrigeration equipment will have to offer real performance gains before it can begin to compete in the open market. Much interest exists in thermoelectric refrigeration because many of the problems associated with the use of semiconductor materials at elevated temperatures are not present.

The most developed application of thermoelectricity is modest-size power-generation units. Thermocouple-powered gas-burner controls are being produced in commercial quantities and are a standard component in many furnaces. The initial thermoelectric effort in the United States was supported by the gas industry, which needed a reliable control unit to sense the presence of the pilot flame and shut off the gas flow when the pilot flame was extinguished in the absence of any outside source of power. This requirement led to the development of commercial lead telluride thermocouples by Fritts. In addition to their use in gas-burner controls, the thermocouples are also sold individually and assembled in gas-heated thermopiles which supply the needs of those who desire portable, silent, and maintenance-free d-c power. Low-power-rating units are also in service in military and civilian applications in remote areas, such as cathodic protection of pipelines, remote automatic weather stations and buoys, signal lights, and battery-charging sets. One of the more impressive applications is the reactor and radioisotope-heated thermoelectric generators delivering power in space. The operational features, together with the ability to make small generators whose efficiency is essentially independent of power level, have resulted in today's limited market for thermoelectric generators. This market exists in spite of high cost per watt and low efficiency, when compared with the use of internal-combustion engines for standby power. Economic studies have shown that in the range between 1 watt and 1 kilowatt, gas-fired thermoelectric generators can be more economical than either batteries, solar cells, or internal-combustion engines. It is expected that future improvements in the efficiency and thermal stability of thermoelectric materials will broaden the applications, both on ground and in space.

2. Phenomenological Description of the Thermoelectric Effects

2-1. Classical Thermodynamic Analysis

The science of thermoelectricity is based on three thermodynamic interactions and their relationships. These phenomena are the Seebeck,

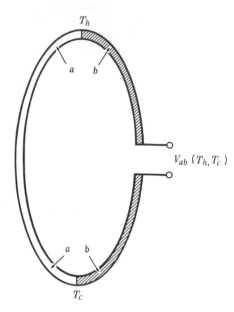

Fig. 3-2. *Seebeck-voltage coefficient.*

Peltier, and Thomson effects.   Each of these effects is reversible.   The
Seebeck voltage is the open-circuit voltage produced when two dissimilar
conductors are connected in a single loop, in such a manner that the two
connections between the materials are at different temperatures.   The
Seebeck coefficient is defined as

$$\alpha_{ab}(T) \equiv \lim_{\Delta T \to 0} \frac{\Delta V_{ab}}{\Delta T} = \frac{dV_{ab}}{dT} \tag{3-3}$$

Figure 3-2 illustrates the Seebeck effect.

The Peltier heat is the heat generated or absorbed at the junction of
two dissimilar materials when a current passes through them.   Figure 3-3
illustrates the Peltier effect.   The Peltier coefficient is defined as

$$\pi_{ab}(T) \equiv \frac{Q_{ab}}{I} \tag{3-4}$$

The third effect, the Thomson heat, occurs when a current flows in a
conductor which has a temperature gradient, as illustrated in Fig. 3-4.
The Thomson coefficient of a material is defined as

$$\tau_a(T) \equiv \lim_{\Delta T \to 0} \frac{\Delta Q_a / I}{\Delta T} \tag{3-5}$$

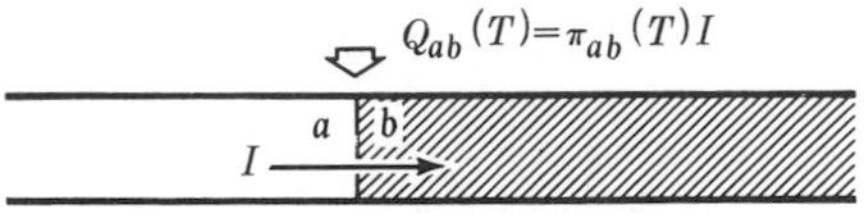

$$Q_{ab}(T) = \pi_{ab}(T) I$$

Fig. 3-3. *Peltier-heat coefficient.*

In addition to these three thermoelectric effects which occur in conductors, two other familiar thermodynamic processes take place; these are Joule heating and heat conduction. Both of these effects are irreversible; the Joule heating

$$Q = I^2 R \qquad\qquad (3\text{-}6)$$

or

$$\frac{Q}{\text{vol}} = \frac{J^2}{\sigma} \qquad\qquad (3\text{-}7)$$

is an irreversible effect. A heat flux exists when a temperature gradient is present in a material, and is given by

$$\mathbf{q} = -\mathbf{k}\cdot\boldsymbol{\nabla}T \qquad\qquad (3\text{-}8)$$

The heat flux is a vector and is not necessarily parallel to the direction of the temperature gradient. It is the tensor properties of the thermal conductivity of anisotropic materials which led Onsager to formulate the law of symmetry of the coefficients of coupled irreversible phenomena. This theory has led to an extensive development of the science of irreversible thermodynamics, also referred to as the thermodynamics of the steady state.[1-3] An excellent review of the thermodynamics of thermoelectricity can be found in Domenicali's article,[4] where much attention is paid to tensor effects in anisotropic materials. This article will be concerned only with isotropic material where all thermodynamic properties are scalar. In addition only one-dimensional geometries will be examined, since the practical devices developed to date have found that no advantage is to be

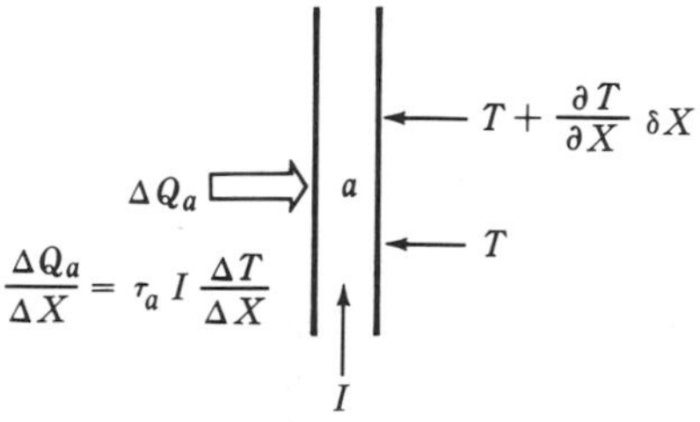

$$T + \frac{\partial T}{\partial X}\,\delta X$$

$$\Delta Q_a$$

$$a$$

$$T$$

$$\frac{\Delta Q_a}{\Delta X} = \tau_a I \frac{\Delta T}{\Delta X}$$

$$I$$

Fig. 3-4. *Thomson-heat coefficient.*

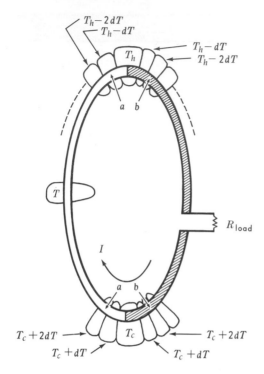

Fig. 3-5. *Thermoelectric circuit exchanging heat with heat reservoirs which are in local equilibrium with the thermoelectric material.*

gained by using two- and three-dimensional gradients. In applications involving magnetic fields the tensor properties of the medium, as well as the three-dimensional nature of the problem, must be considered.

The Kelvin relationships between the thermoelectric properties are obtained by applying the first and second laws of thermodynamics to a thermoelectric circuit which is in local thermal equilibrium with its environment. Figure 3-5 shows such a system.

The relationships between the thermoelectric coefficients were first obtained by Lord Kelvin in 1854 using classical thermodynamics and the assumption that the heat interactions accompanying the reversible thermoelectric effects could be separated from those due to the irreversible processes. Much debate has occurred over the validity of this assumption. The accuracy of the result has been proven by the measurements of the Thomson heat and the subsequent derivation of the Kelvin relations based on the methods of irreversible thermodynamics. The argument for the separation of the reversible and irreversible heat interactions lies in the physical observation that the reversible heat interactions are evaluated for an incremental charge transfer through the circuit and do not affect the temperature distribution. Hence, the entropy production in the steady state by irreversible means can be subtracted from the complete equation. Since the incremental charge can be arbitrarily small and the ratio of the local Joule heating to local reversible heat (Peltier or Thomson) is in the ratio of I^2/I, the irreversible effects due to Joule heating can be neglected in the limit as the current approaches zero.

During the operation of the circuit various reversible heat interactions occur between the material of the circuit and its environment. Applying the first law to the circuit,

$$dU = dQ + dW \tag{3-9}$$

Since no temperatures or voltages are changing with time, $dU = 0$. The work done by the system is the time integral of the power delivered to the load.

$$dW = IV_{ab}\, dt \tag{3-10}$$

and

$$dQ = I\left\{\pi_{ab}(T_c) - \pi_{ab}(T_h) + \int_{T_c}^{T_h} (\tau_a - \tau_b)\, dT\right\} dt \tag{3-11}$$

The first law becomes

$$V_{ab} = \pi_{ab}(T_h) - \pi_{ab}(T_c) - \int_{T_c}^{T_h} (\tau_a - \tau_b)\, dT \tag{3-12}$$

Taking the limit as T_c approaches T_h and dividing by dT yields

$$\frac{dV_{ab}}{dT} = \frac{d\pi_{ab}}{dT} - (\tau_a - \tau_b) \tag{3-13}$$

where

$$\frac{d\pi_{ab}}{dT} = \lim_{\Delta T \to 0} \frac{\pi_{ab}(T_h) - \pi_{ab}(T_c)}{\Delta T} \tag{3-14}$$

and

$$\Delta T = T_h - T_c \tag{3-15}$$

It is convenient to introduce the Seebeck coefficient, Eq. (3-3). Applying the second law to the reversible heat interactions, one obtains

$$dS = I\left\{\frac{\pi_{ab}(T_c)}{T_c} - \frac{\pi_{ab}(T_h)}{T_h} + \int_{T_c}^{T_h} (\tau_a - \tau_b)\frac{dT}{T}\right\} dt \tag{3-16}$$

where the entropy transfer due to the Thomson effect is

$$dS = I \int \tau \frac{dT}{T} \, dt \qquad (3\text{-}17)$$

Since all these heat interactions are reversible,

$$dS = 0 \qquad (3\text{-}18)$$

and again taking the limit as T_c approaches T_h,

$$\frac{d}{dT}\left[\frac{\pi_{ab}(T)}{T}\right] - \frac{\tau_a - \tau_b}{T} = 0 \qquad (3\text{-}19)$$

or, by differentiation,

$$\frac{d\pi_{ab}}{dT}(T) = \tau_a - \tau_b + \frac{\pi_{ab}}{T}(T) \qquad (3\text{-}20)$$

Comparison of Eqs. (3-3), (3-13), and (3-20) shows that the Seebeck coefficient and its derivative are given by

$$\alpha_{ab}(T) = \frac{\pi_{ab}}{T}(T) \qquad (3\text{-}21)$$

and

$$\frac{d\alpha_{ab}}{dT} = \frac{\tau_a - \tau_b}{T} \qquad (3\text{-}22)$$

Kelvin's discovery of the Thomson heat was based on predictions calculated from the above equation. Subsequent measurements have supported the Kelvin relations and, therefore, the assumptions on which they are based. It is to be noted that the assumption of constant Seebeck coefficient implies zero net Thomson heat. Such a model is convenient for analyzing and optimizing simple thermoelectric devices. It is impossible to have both the Seebeck coefficient and the Peltier heat independent of temperature.

It is often convenient to think in terms of an electron gas flowing in the conductors when trying to visualize the thermoelectric processes. The physically analogous model of a thermoelectric circuit is a two-phase system in a pipe-enclosed loop, as shown in Fig. 3-6.

In the hydraulic analog shown the working fluid absorbs and rejects heat during liquid-vapor phase changes. In a thermoelectric circuit the electrons similarly absorb and reject heat while crossing the interfaces between the n and p material. The metallic pipe transfers the working

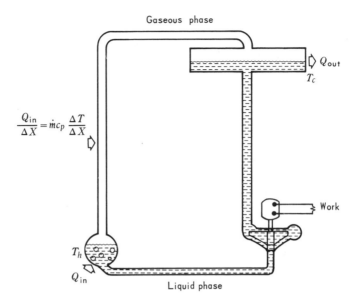

Fig. 3-6. *Two-phase hydraulic analogy of thermoelectric circuit.*

fluid and conducts heat. The heat conduction is usually negligible in comparison with the heat conducted along the pipe wall.

The heat conduction through the pipe walls can be made small in comparison with energy transported by the working fluid. In contrast, in electron "pipes" the cross-sectional area conducts both electricity and heat, and any attempt to reduce the thermal conductance will simultaneously increase the electrical resistance. It will be shown that the optimum geometry of thermoelectric legs is such that the RK product (resistance $\times$ conductance) is minimum. Such an optimization is also useful in designing leads for thermionic diodes where heat-conduction losses must be traded off against voltage drop.

The relationship between the temperature dependence of the pressure and the heat of vaporization in the hydraulic analog is the Clapeyron .relation

$$\frac{dp}{dT} = \frac{h_{fg}}{Tv_{fg}} \tag{3-23}$$

which is derived from the Maxwell relation

$$\left(\frac{\partial p}{\partial T}\right)_v = \left(\frac{\partial s}{\partial v}\right)_T \tag{3-24}$$

These equations for fluid properties are to be compared with the Kelvin relation

$$\alpha_{ab} = \frac{dV_{ab}}{dT} = \frac{\pi_{ab}}{T} \qquad (3\text{-}21)$$

The voltage is analogous to the fluid work per unit mass $p \, \Delta v$, and the Peltier heat corresponds to the heat of vaporization (phase change) per electron. The Thomson heat is the specific heat of the charge carriers in their respective phases, which is analogous to the specific heat of the fluid. The work produced when the charge carriers pass through the voltage drop in the load is analogous to the work done on the turbine by the fluid when it passes from the high-pressure side to the low-pressure side.

2-2. Irreversible Thermodynamic Analysis

The science of irreversible thermodynamics is concerned with systems which are operating in such a manner that they are entropy sources. The process of heat conduction through a finite temperature difference is such a case. In the steady state an amount of entropy.

$$dS_h = \frac{dQ}{T_h} \qquad (3\text{-}25a)$$

is transferred to a bar connected to a heat reservoir at T_h. The other end of the bar transfers this heat to a lower-temperature heat reservoir at T_c. All other surfaces of the bar are considered to be adiabatic. The entropy transferred from the bar to the second heat reservoir is

$$dS_c = \frac{dQ}{T_c} \qquad (3\text{-}25b)$$

These quantities of heat are identical according to the first law. The net entropy interaction between the bar and the two heat reservoirs is

$$dS_{\text{net}} = dQ \left(\frac{1}{T_c} - \frac{1}{T_h} \right) \qquad (3\text{-}26)$$

$$= dQ \, \frac{\Delta T}{T_h T_c} > 0$$

Since the bar does not experience a change in state, the net change is an increase in entropy of the universe. The other irreversible processes similarly result in entropy production.

The present limitations of the science of irreversible thermodynamics are such that only small departures from equilibrium can be studied.

Note that the majority of engineering applications involve elements whose thermodynamic states represent only small departures from equilibrium. Most of the work in this field has been confined to analyses of steady-state processes, where the material being studied is in local thermochemical equilibrium. The effects of the irreversible processes are confined to perturbations in the distribution functions of the active species. These perturbations are equivalent to thermodynamic fluctuations in the distribution of energy among the particles. The thermodynamic properties necessary for the description of the irreversible processes, conductivities, viscosities, and diffusion coefficients can be derived from the regression of these fluctuations. So far these analyses have been limited to linear processes, partially because the linear model has been so successful. The linear laws of the rate processes include:

Fourier's law of conduction

$$\mathbf{q} = -\mathbf{k} \, \nabla T \qquad\qquad\qquad\qquad (3\text{-}8)$$

Fick's law of diffusion

$$\dot{\mathbf{n}} = -\mathbf{D} \, \nabla C \qquad\qquad\qquad\qquad (3\text{-}27)$$

Newton's law of viscosity

$$\tau = -\mu \, \nabla V \qquad\qquad\qquad\qquad (3\text{-}28)$$

Ohm's law of conduction

$$\mathbf{J} = -\sigma \, \nabla \phi \qquad\qquad\qquad\qquad (3\text{-}29)$$

Irreversible thermodynamics seeks to relate these processes to the coupled processes such as thermal diffusion, thermoelectricity, thermomagnetism, and others. Thermoelectric processes will be the only ones discussed here. For descriptions of the other related phenomena the reader is referred to Domenicali's article, Ref. 4.

The basic assumptions of linear irreversible thermodynamics are that the fluxes $\mathbf{J}_i$ can be expressed in terms of the driving-potential gradients X_j by a linear law

$$\mathbf{J}_i = L_{ij}\mathbf{X}_j\dagger \qquad\qquad\qquad\qquad (3\text{-}30)$$

where

$$\mathbf{X}_j = \nabla \phi_j \qquad\qquad\qquad\qquad (3\text{-}31)$$

† The Einstein convention of summation of repeated indices is used.

and that the rate of entropy production can be written in terms of conjugate forces and fluxes as

$$\dot{S} = \mathbf{J}_i \cdot \mathbf{X}_i \tag{3-32}$$

These assumptions are supplemented by Onsager's law of reciprocal relations, namely, that when the forces and fluxes are chosen such that the above relationship is satisfied,

$$L_{ij} = L_{ji} \tag{3-33}$$

The scalar electrical conductivity is an example of a diagonal term of the L_{ij} matrix.

The energy and particle fluxes crossing a plane are denoted by $\mathbf{J}_u$ and $\mathbf{J}_n$. The second law is used to relate changes in entropy with changes in energy and particle number for an open system of fixed volume.

$$T \, dS = dU - \mu_i \, dN_i \tag{3-34}$$

where μ is the electrochemical potential. The rate of change of entropy accompanying a transfer of charge and energy into a region is obtained by evaluating the rate of change of the extensive properties in the Gibbs equation (3-34).

$$\frac{\partial S}{\partial t} = \frac{1}{T} \frac{\partial U}{\partial t} - \frac{\mu_i}{T} \frac{\partial N_i}{\partial t} \tag{3-35}$$

The law of conservation of particles states that the rate of change of particles plus the net flux out equals zero.

$$\frac{\partial N}{\partial t} + \mathbf{\nabla} \cdot \mathbf{J}_n = 0 \tag{3-36}$$

Similarly, the first law can be stated in the form

$$\frac{\partial U}{\partial t} + \mathbf{\nabla} \cdot \mathbf{J}_u = 0 \tag{3-37}$$

where $\mathbf{J}_u$ accounts for both heat and work interactions and U, therefore, is the internal energy. Combining these terms with the second law yields

$$\frac{\partial S}{\partial t} = -\frac{1}{T} \mathbf{\nabla} \cdot \mathbf{J}_u + \frac{\mu}{T} \mathbf{\nabla} \cdot \mathbf{J}_n \tag{3-38}$$

which can also be written in the form

$$\frac{\partial S}{\partial t} + \mathbf{\nabla} \cdot \left(\frac{\mathbf{J}_u - \mu \mathbf{J}_n}{T} \right) = \mathbf{J}_u \cdot \mathbf{\nabla} \left(\frac{1}{T} \right) - \mathbf{J}_n \cdot \mathbf{\nabla} \left(\frac{\mu}{T} \right) \tag{3-39}$$

Thus the term

$$\frac{\mathbf{J}_u - \mu \mathbf{J}_n}{T} \equiv \mathbf{J}_S \tag{3-40}$$

can be thought of as the entropy flux. The right-hand side of Eq. (3-40) is dS/dt, or $\dot{S}$. Since the net entropy-production rate is the sum of the entropy change in the material and the net entropy flux crossing the boundary,

$$\dot{S} = J_i X_i = \mathbf{J}_u \cdot \boldsymbol{\nabla} \left(\frac{1}{T} \right) - \mathbf{J}_n \cdot \boldsymbol{\nabla} \left(\frac{\mu}{T} \right) \tag{3-41}$$

The conjugate potentials can be identified as $1/T$ and $-\mu/T$.[5] The linear phenomenological equations can now be written.

$$\mathbf{J}_u = L_{uu} \boldsymbol{\nabla} \left(\frac{1}{T} \right) - L_{un} \boldsymbol{\nabla} \left(\frac{\mu}{T} \right) \tag{3-42}$$

$$\mathbf{J}_n = L_{nu} \boldsymbol{\nabla} \left(\frac{1}{T} \right) - L_{nn} \boldsymbol{\nabla} \left(\frac{\mu}{T} \right) \tag{3-43}$$

It is often more convenient to use the temperature and electrochemical potential as the driving forces, or

$$\mathbf{J}_u = \frac{-L_{uu} + \mu L_{un}}{T^2} \boldsymbol{\nabla} T - \frac{L_{un}}{T} \boldsymbol{\nabla} \mu \tag{3-44}$$

$$\mathbf{J}_n = \frac{-L_{nu} + \mu L_{nn}}{T^2} \boldsymbol{\nabla} T - \frac{L_{nn}}{T} \boldsymbol{\nabla} \mu \tag{3-45}$$

Eliminating $\boldsymbol{\nabla}\mu$ from the energy-flux equation by use of the particle-flux equation yields

$$\mathbf{J}_u = \frac{L_{un}}{L_{nn}} \mathbf{J}_n + \left(L_{uu} - \frac{L_{un} L_{nu}}{L_{nn}} \right) \boldsymbol{\nabla} \left(\frac{1}{T} \right) \tag{3-46}$$

The thermal conductivity is defined for a sample without any electrical current flowing through it by

$$(\mathbf{J}_u)_{J_n=0} = -\mathbf{k} \cdot \boldsymbol{\nabla} T \tag{3-47}$$

It can be seen that

$$k = \left(\frac{\mathbf{J}_u}{\boldsymbol{\nabla} T} \right)_{J_n=0} = \left(L_{uu} - \frac{L_{un} L_{nu}}{L_{nn}} \right) \frac{1}{T^2} \tag{3-48}$$

The isothermal electrical conductivity is similarly defined by Ohm's law:

$$(\mathbf{J}_n)_T = -\boldsymbol{\sigma} \cdot \boldsymbol{\nabla} \mu \tag{3-49}$$

Therefore

$$\sigma = \frac{L_{nn}}{T} \tag{3-50}$$

The rate of entropy production is evaluated using Eq. (3-41).

$$\dot{S} = (\mathbf{J}_u - \mu \mathbf{J}_n) \cdot \nabla \left(\frac{1}{T}\right) - \frac{\mathbf{J}_n}{T} \cdot \nabla \mu \tag{3-51}$$

The isothermal Joule effect, the Ohmic heating, is the only isothermal process since no heat conduction can occur without a temperature gradient. The rate of heat generation is

$$(T\dot{S})_T = -(\mathbf{J}_n)_T \cdot \nabla \mu \tag{3-52}$$

However

$$(\mathbf{J}_n)_T = -\frac{L_{nn}}{T} \nabla \mu = -\sigma \cdot \nabla \mu \tag{3-53}$$

Therefore

$$(T\dot{S})_T = \frac{J_n{}^2}{\sigma} \tag{3-54}$$

which is always positive regardless of the direction of $\mathbf{J}_n$.

The Peltier coefficient is defined by Eq. (3-4) and can be obtained from the linear phenomenological equations

$$\pi = \left(\frac{J_u}{J_n}\right)_T \tag{3-55}$$

Use of Eqs. (3-44) and (3-43) for $(J_u/J_n)_T$ yields

$$\pi = \frac{L_{un}}{L_{nn}} \tag{3-56}$$

Use of Eq. (3-50) for L_{nn} shows that

$$L_{un} = \sigma T \pi \tag{3-57}$$

The phenomenological laws can now be written in terms of coefficients obtained from continuum thermodynamics.

$$\mathbf{J}_u = (kT^2 + \sigma T\pi^2) \, \nabla \left(\frac{1}{T}\right) - \sigma T\pi \, \nabla \left(\frac{\mu}{T}\right) \tag{3-58}$$

$$\mathbf{J}_n = \sigma T\pi \, \nabla \left(\frac{1}{T}\right) - \sigma T \, \nabla \left(\frac{\mu}{T}\right) \tag{3-59}$$

The coupling of the thermoelectric effects can be illustrated by transforming to new variables $\mathbf{J}_s$ and $\mathbf{X}_s$. $\mathbf{J}_s$ is the entropy flux. $\mathbf{X}_s$ is the driving potential for the entropy flux.

$$\mathbf{J}_s = \frac{\mathbf{J}_u - \mu \mathbf{J}_n}{T}$$

$$= L_{ss} T \, \mathbf{\nabla}\left(\frac{1}{T}\right) - \frac{L_{se}}{T} \, \mathbf{\nabla}\mu \tag{3-60}$$

and

$$\mathbf{X}_s = T \, \mathbf{\nabla}\left(\frac{1}{T}\right) \tag{3-61}$$

The electrical current is now written as $\mathbf{J}_e$†

$$\mathbf{J}_e = L_{es} T \, \mathbf{\nabla}\left(\frac{1}{T}\right) - \frac{L_{ee}}{T} \, \mathbf{\nabla}\mu \tag{3-62}$$

and

$$\mathbf{X}_e = - \frac{\mathbf{\nabla}\mu}{T} \tag{3-63}$$

Evaluating the electrical conductivity shows that

$$L_{ee} = L_{nn} \tag{3-64}$$

Eliminating $\mathbf{\nabla}\mu$ results in

$$\mathbf{J}_s = \left(L_{ss}T - \frac{L_{se}L_{es}T}{L_{ee}}\right) \mathbf{\nabla}\left(\frac{1}{T}\right) + \frac{L_{se}}{L_{ee}} \mathbf{J}_e \tag{3-65}$$

The thermal conductivity is again evaluated.

$$k = L_{ss} - \frac{L_{se}L_{es}}{L_{ee}} \tag{3-66}$$

The rate of entropy production is written in terms of the new forces and fluxes.

$$\dot{S} = \mathbf{J}_s \cdot \mathbf{X}_s + \mathbf{J}_e \cdot \mathbf{X}_e \tag{3-67}$$

L_{es} is evaluated using Eq. (3-62) when $\mathbf{J}_e = 0$.

$$L_{es} = \alpha \sigma T \tag{3-68}$$

---

† $\mathbf{J}_e = \mathbf{J}_n$; however, since $\mathbf{X}_e = \mathbf{X}_n$, new symbols are introduced for the coefficient.

Using the phenomenological relations

$$\mathbf{J}_s = L_{ss}\mathbf{X}_s + L_{se}\mathbf{X}_e \tag{3-69}$$

$$\mathbf{J}_e = L_{es}\mathbf{X}_s + L_{ee}\mathbf{X}_e \tag{3-70}$$

to eliminate J_s and X_e, one obtains the entropy-production rate

$$\dot{S} = \left(L_{ss} - \frac{L_{se}L_{es}}{L_{ee}}\right)\frac{(\nabla T)^2}{T^2} + \frac{J_e^2}{L_{ee}} + \left(\frac{L_{se} - L_{es}}{L_{ec}}\right)\mathbf{J}_e \cdot \mathbf{X}_s$$

$$= \frac{k(\nabla T)^2}{T^2} + \frac{J_e^2}{\sigma T} + \frac{(L_{se} - L_{es})}{L_{ee}}\mathbf{J}_e \cdot \mathbf{X}_s \tag{3-71}$$

The first term is the entropy production per unit volume due to the heat flux alone, as can be shown from Eq. (3-34).

$$(\mathbf{J}_s)_{J_n=0} = \frac{\mathbf{J}_u}{T} = \frac{\mathbf{q}}{T} \tag{3-72}$$

since

$$\mathbf{q} = (\mathbf{J}_u)_{J_n=0} \tag{3-73}$$

For constant heat flux $\mathbf{q}$, the net entropy flux per unit volume is

$$\nabla \cdot (\mathbf{J}_s)_{J_n=0} = \mathbf{q} \cdot \nabla \left(\frac{1}{T}\right) = -\frac{\mathbf{q}}{T^2} \cdot \nabla T \tag{3-74}$$

$$\dot{S} = \frac{k(\nabla T)^2}{T^2} \tag{3-75}$$

Similarly, the $J^2/\sigma T$ term can be identified as the entropy production due to Joule heating. The remaining term is the coupling term, ignored by Kelvin. It is seen that Onsager's law states that this term must be zero, since

$$L_{es} = L_{se} \tag{3-33}$$

Hence, Kelvin's hypothesis that the entropy production due to the irreversible effects need not consider coupled phenomena is justified, since inclusion of these terms in the calculation does not alter the entropy-production rate.

A useful new concept can be obtained from the foregoing analysis, the entropy of transport. Define

$$\left(\frac{\mathbf{J}_s}{\mathbf{J}_e}\right)_T = \frac{L_{se}}{L_{ee}} \equiv S^* \tag{3-76}$$

Then

$$\mathbf{J}_e = -\sigma(S^* \nabla T + \nabla\mu) \tag{3-77}$$

and

$$\mathbf{J}_s = L_{ss} T \, \mathbf{\nabla} \left(\frac{1}{T} \right) - \sigma S^* \, \mathbf{\nabla} \mu \tag{3-78}$$

It is the entropy of transport which enters into the coefficient relating the coupling terms in the equations for the fluxes. It is fortunate that Onsager's law results in no additional entropy production owing to the simultaneous omission of both of these terms.

One may obtain the Seebeck coefficient by evaluating the open-circuit voltage of a thermocouple circuit. Since $J_e = 0$,

$$S^* \, \mathbf{\nabla} T = -\mathbf{\nabla} \mu \tag{3-79}$$

The open-circuit voltage is

$$\int_1^2 d\mu_a + \int_2^1 d\mu_b = -\int_{T_c}^{T_h} S_a^* \, dT - \int_{T_h}^{T_c} S_b^* \, dT \tag{3-80}$$

or

$$V_{ab} = -\int_{T_c}^{T_h} (S_a^* - S_b^*) \, dT \tag{3-81}$$

and

$$\alpha_{ab} = \frac{dV_{ab}}{dT} = S_a^* - S_b^* \tag{3-82}$$

Hence S_i is the absolute Seebeck coefficient.

It has been shown that the entropy of transport of a charge carrier in a particular phase is the absolute Seebeck coefficient for that phase. In addition the connection between Kelvin's hypothesis and Onsager's law of reciprocal relations has been demonstrated.

3. Electron-transport Theory

In the previous section the thermoelectric effects were described on a phenomenological basis. The Peltier, Seebeck, and Thomson coefficients, as well as the electrical and thermal conductivities, are material properties which can be related to the atomic structure of the material. Any real material is much too complicated to analyze completely. However, various simplified models of electronic processes in metals and semiconductors can be made which are useful in illustrating the physical origin of the thermoelectric effects. These models can identify various material parameters which are helpful in screening prospective thermoelectric materials.

A simplified model of the conduction process will be used in order to illustrate the physics of the transport of heat and electrical charge. Then the distribution function for the energy levels of an electron gas will be summarized. This distribution function will then be used to obtain the transport and thermoelectric coefficients. The sequence of topics in this section has been selected with the intent to educate those who are unfamiliar with the theories used in the prediction of transport properties. Unlike the case of ionized gases, the mean free time of an electron in a real metal or semiconductor cannot be obtained from first principles. If the mean free time were known, the thermal and electrical conductivities could be calculated directly.

3-1. *Mean-free-path Model of Transport Processes*

The simplest model of electrons in conductors is a dilute electron gas composed of rigid spheres. Analyses of such a model result in predictions of transport properties of the electron gas. Calculations of the thermoelectric properties require an accurate model of the allowable electron energy levels and, hence, a semiconductor model. The semiconductor energy bands are determined by the quantum-mechanical electron wave functions. While the simple conduction analysis does not predict absolute magnitudes of conductivities since the relaxation time or mean free path cannot be evaluated from first principles, the theory does give meaningful estimates of the ratio of thermal to electrical conductivities.

A simple model which suffices to explain the physical nature of the transport of heat by electrons in a solid is that based on the assumption that the electrons behave like a gas contained by the lattice. In such a model the random flux is $nc/4$, as in the case of an ordinary gas. The average of the projections of the trajectories made by the electrons in the interval between their last collision and when they cross an arbitrary plane perpendicular to the conduction direction is two-thirds of a mean free path. The simple electron-gas model is similar in most respects to the models of ordinary gases used in conventional kinetic-theory texts.

Assume an electron gas moving in a lattice. When an electric field E is established, the electrons will acquire a net velocity in the direction of the field which is superimposed on the thermal motion. The time between collisions is defined as τ. The acceleration of the electron in the direction of the field is $-eE/m$. The average increase in velocity in the direction of the field acquired between collisions becomes $-eE\tau/2m$. The current resulting from this drift velocity is

$$j = \frac{ne^2E\tau}{2m} \tag{3-83}$$

The conductivity is simply

$$\sigma = \frac{j}{E} = \frac{ne^2\tau}{2m} \tag{3-84}$$

It is to be noted that the conductivity is proportional to the density of free electrons and the time between collisions. The density of free (or conduction) electrons must be obtained from a statistical thermodynamic analysis of the probability of occupancy of the allowable energy levels.

The temperature of the electron gas in the region of a few mean free paths around the plane in question is

$$T(x) = T_0 + \left(\frac{dT}{dx}\right)_0 x \tag{3-85}$$

The net energy crossing an arbitrary plane in the gas is

$$q = \frac{n\bar{c}C_vT}{4} \left[T(x - \tfrac{2}{3}\lambda) - T(x + \tfrac{2}{3}\lambda)\right]$$

$$= -\frac{n\bar{c}C_v\lambda}{3}\frac{dT}{dx} \tag{3-86}$$

where C_vT is the energy per electron. The mean free path is related to the mean speed and mean free time:

$$\lambda = \bar{c}\tau \tag{3-87}$$

The thermal conductivity is defined by

$$k = -\frac{q}{\nabla T} \tag{3-8}$$

and is evaluated as

$$k = \frac{n\bar{c}^2\tau C_v}{3} \tag{3-88}$$

The ratio of thermal to electrical conductivity for this electron-gas model is then

$$\frac{k}{\sigma} = \frac{2m\bar{c}^2C_v}{3e^2} \tag{3-89}$$

If the electron gas is dilute enough, the specific heat and rms speed of the electrons can be evaluated with the classic expression

$$\frac{3}{2}k_BT = \frac{m\bar{c}^2}{2} \tag{3-90}$$

For this case the specific heat is

$$C_v = \tfrac{3}{2} k_B \tag{3-91}$$

If the difference between the rms and the mean speed is neglected, the ratio of the conductivities is

$$\frac{k}{\sigma} = 3 \left(\frac{k_B}{e} \right)^2 T \tag{3-92}$$

The Lorenz number is

$$L = \frac{k}{\sigma T} = 3 \left(\frac{k_B}{e} \right)^2 \tag{3-93}$$

which is about 10 percent lower than the measured value for pure metals. That the ratio of thermal to electrical conductivities of metals is a constant was first postulated by Wiedemann and Franz and is referred to as the Wiedemann-Franz law. Lorenz formulated the rule that the Wiedemann-Franz ratio is proportional to the absolute temperature. Drude and Lorentz later derived expressions for the Lorenz number from kinetic-theory considerations. The specific heat and mean speed of electrons in a metal cannot be obtained accurately from classical mechanics. When the correct values of these quantities are obtained from the Fermi-Dirac quantum statistics, the Lorenz number becomes

$$L = \frac{\pi^2}{3} \left(\frac{k_B}{e} \right)^2 \tag{3-94}$$

which is within $\tfrac{1}{2}$ percent of the observed room-temperature value for pure metals.[7] The thermal conductivity of semiconductors is composed of lattice-wave and electron-gas contributions. In metals the electron concentration is very large, and the electron-gas contribution to the thermal conductivity dominates. The electron concentration in the semiconductors of interest for thermoelectric applications is low enough so that the lattice contribution to the thermal conductivity is comparable to that of the electron gas. In semiconductors the ratio of the electronic contribution to the thermal conductivity to the electrical conductivity is still well approximated by the Lorenz number. The ratio of the conductivities is

$$\frac{k}{\sigma} = LT \left(1 + \frac{k_L}{k_e} \right) \tag{3-95}$$

In the section on device performance it will be shown that the condition for maximum generator efficiency is that the product RK be a minimum where the thermal conductance is given by

$$K = \left(\frac{kA}{L}\right)_n + \left(\frac{kA}{L}\right)_p \qquad (3\text{-}96)$$

and the electrical resistance is given by

$$R = \left(\frac{L}{\sigma A}\right)_n + \left(\frac{L}{\sigma A}\right)_p \qquad (3\text{-}97)$$

For a single thermoelement leg

$$RK = \frac{k}{\sigma} \qquad (3\text{-}98)$$

which can only be minimized by making $k_L \ll k_e$. Such material optimization must be consistent with obtaining large Seebeck coefficients and figures of merit.

3-2. *Statistical Thermodynamics of Semiconductors*

In order that the performance of semiconductor thermoelements can be analyzed, the distribution of electron kinetic energies must be obtained. In an ordinary metal this is given by the Fermi-Dirac distribution function

$$f_{0_{F.D.}}(E) = \frac{1}{e^{(E - E_F)/k_B T} + 1} \qquad (3\text{-}99)$$

where E_F is the Fermi energy, given by

$$E_F = E_{F_0}\left[1 + \frac{\pi^2}{12}\left(\frac{k_B T}{E_{F_0}}\right)^2 + \cdots\right] \qquad (3\text{-}100)$$

E_{F_0} is the Fermi level at $0°K$

$$E_{F_0} = \frac{h^2}{8m}\left(\frac{3n}{\pi}\right)^{2/3} \qquad (3\text{-}101)$$

and E is the electron kinetic energy.

When the number density n of electrons becomes low enough so that the allowable energy states are not densely populated, as is found for many semiconductors, the distribution function becomes Maxwellian.

$$f_{0_M}(E) = \left(\frac{2\pi m k_B T}{h^2}\right)^{3/2} e^{-(E - E_F)/k_B T} \qquad (3\text{-}102)$$

The conduction electrons travel in the lattice as a whole, rather than being attached to individual atoms. It is more convenient to describe the motion of the electrons in terms of their quantum wave functions than employ a particle-like analysis. The electrons would occupy discrete energy levels if the atoms were spaced far apart. However, as the interatomic distance is reduced, the electron energies are broadened and eventually form bands. When the Fermi level, the maximum electron kinetic energy in a metal at absolute zero, lies in the middle of an allowable energy band, the thermal excitation allows the electrons to flow freely within the lattice. When the Fermi level lies between the bands, conduction can only occur by two means, intrinsic and extrinsic conduction. The material is called an intrinsic semiconductor when the thermal excitation is sufficient to cause enough electrons to have energies over the Fermi level and up into the next highest vacant band (called the conduction band) to make the material conduct. The material is said to be extrinsic when impurities are present whose electron energies lie between the last filled band (valence band) and the conduction band, and can either give up an electron to a higher-energy conduction band or absorb an electron from a lower-energy valence band. This latter process of absorbing an electron from a lower-energy band results in a deficit of an electron which can then migrate throughout the lattice. Such an absence of a valence electron is called a hole.

The quantum-mechanical treatment of the electron energy levels in solids is attributed to Bloch.[8] Complete descriptions are to be found in standard texts on the theories of metals, the solid state, and semiconductors.[7,9,10] The allowable energy levels of the electron are given by the periodic solutions to Schrödinger's wave equation.

$$\frac{-\hbar^2}{2m} \Delta^2 \psi + V(\mathbf{r})\psi(\mathbf{r}) = E\psi(\mathbf{r}) \tag{3-103}$$

where ψ = wave eigenfunctions; E = allowable electron energies, eigenvalues; and V = electron potential energy.

The momentum is given by

$$p = i\hbar \, \nabla\psi \tag{3-104}$$

The force law in wave number space is

$$\mathbf{F} = \hbar \, \frac{d\mathbf{\kappa}}{dt} \tag{3-105}$$

For a free electron, $V(x) = 0$ and the eigenfunctions are

$$\psi_j = A e^{i\kappa x} \tag{3-106}$$

where κ is the quantum wave number,

$$\kappa = \frac{\sqrt{2mE}}{\hbar} \tag{3-107}$$

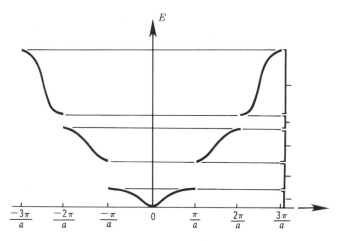

Fig. 3-7.   *Energy levels in a solid.*

and the energy is therefore given by

$$E = \frac{\hbar^2 \kappa^2}{2m} \tag{3-108}$$

Only the one-dimensional case will be treated here. The model of the electron-lattice potential is that of a periodic function. One of the areas of basic research in solid-state physics is the determination of this (three-dimensional) potential. For a periodic potential the coefficients of the eigenfunctions are also periodic functions with the same frequency. The energy levels show discontinuities at integral values of π/a where a is the lattice spacing. Typical energy levels are shown in Fig. 3-7. All the lattice sites are assumed identical. The superposition of the energy levels at a specific point is shown in Fig. 3-8. The energy levels are such that at the edge of each zone (referred to as Brillouin zones) $dE/d\kappa = 0$. The effective mass of the charge carrier is given by

$$m_{\text{eff}} = \frac{\hbar^2}{d^2 E / d\kappa^2} \tag{3-109}$$

Since $d^2 E / d\kappa^2$ changes sign between the bottom and top of the bands, it is seen that the effective mass changes sign also. The acceleration of the charge carrier is

$$\ddot{\mathbf{r}} = \frac{\mathbf{F}}{m_{\text{eff}}} \tag{3-110}$$

It becomes apparent that the change in sign of the effective mass is the manifestation of the change in sign of the charge carrier. When the

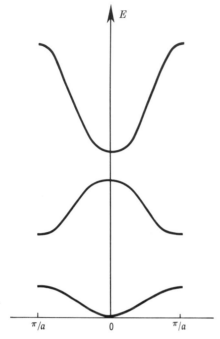

E

π/a 0 π/a

Fig. 3-8.   *Superimposed energy levels in a solid.*

effective mass is negative, the charge carrier moves in the opposite direction to that of an electron when an electric field is applied.   This is the origin of the "hole" into the conduction of heat or electricity.   The lowest unfilled band is called the conduction band.   Transport processes occur because the electrons in a conduction band are free to move in the entire lattice.   In insulators the energy gap between the valence and conduction band is too large for a significant number of electrons to be available for conduction.   Semiconductors have energy gaps from zero to about 3 ev. One electron volt of energy corresponds to a value of $k_B T$ of about $11,600°$K. Since the Maxwellian average kinetic energy is $3k_B T/2$, it is seen that semiconductors with high-enough conductivities so that the lattice thermal conductivity will not overshadow the electronic contribution to the thermal conductivity will have energy gaps of a few tenths of a volt.

3-3.   *Evaluation of the Transport Coefficients*

In order to obtain a more accurate expression for the thermal and electrical conductivities than is possible with a free path model and to obtain better understanding of the processes which occur when both temperature gradients and electric fields exist simultaneously, it is necessary to evaluate the heat flux and current using a model which accounts for the velocity distribution of the electrons and the energy dependence of the collision frequency. Such an analysis is based on the Boltzmann transport equation

$$\mathbf{F} \cdot \nabla_v f + \mathbf{V} \cdot \nabla_r f = \left(\frac{\partial f}{\partial t}\right)_{\text{collision}} \tag{3-111}$$

The assumption is made that the distribution function with temperature gradients and electric fields present is not very much different from the equilibrium distribution, and the collision term can be represented by a relaxation time τ.

$$\left(\frac{\partial f}{\partial t}\right)_{\text{collision}} = \frac{f_0 - f}{\tau} \tag{3-112}$$

where f_0 is the local isotropic distribution function. When only an electric field in the X direction is present, the Boltzmann equation reduces to

$$\frac{-eE}{m} \frac{\partial f}{\partial u} + u \frac{\partial f}{\partial x} = \frac{f_0 - f}{\tau} \tag{3-113}$$

Since the system is near equilibrium, the approximation can be made that $f = f_0$ for the terms on the left-hand side. In general the current is given by

$$j = -en \iiint_{-\infty}^{\infty} uf \, du \, dv \, dx \tag{3-114}$$

In the case where an electric field is present, the current is

$$j = -en \iiint_{-\infty}^{\infty} u \left(f_0 + \frac{\tau eE}{m} \frac{\partial f_0}{\partial u}\right) du \, dv \, dw \tag{3-115}$$

It is noted that

$$\iiint_{-\infty}^{\infty} f_0 \, du \, dv \, dw = 0 \tag{3-116}$$

since f_0 is isotropic. The integral can be evaluated by noting that $E = mc^2/2$.

$$4\pi c^2 \, dc = du \, dv \, dw$$
$$= \frac{4\pi \sqrt{2E}}{m^{3/2}} \, dE \tag{3-117}$$

and

$$j = \frac{ne^2E}{m}\frac{2}{3k_BT}\frac{\int_0^\infty E^{3/2}\tau(E)f_0\,dE}{\int_0^\infty E^{1/2}f_0\,dE} \tag{3-118}$$

where use was made of the Maxwellian, rather than the Fermi-Dirac, distribution function in evaluating $\partial f_0/dE$.

$$\frac{\partial f_0}{\partial E} = -\frac{f_0}{k_BT} \tag{3-119}$$

and

$$n = \iiint_{-\infty}^{\infty} f_0\,du\,dv\,dw = \int_0^\infty f_0 4\pi c^2\,dc$$

$$= \frac{4\pi\sqrt{2}}{m^{3/2}}\int_0^\infty f_0 E^{1/2}\,dE \tag{3-120}$$

For a dilute gas the average energy is

$$\langle E \rangle = \tfrac{3}{2}k_BT \tag{3-121}$$

where

$$\langle E \rangle = \frac{\iiint_{-\infty}^{\infty} Ef_0\,du\,dv\,dw}{\iiint_{-\infty}^{\infty} f_0\,du\,dv\,dw} = \frac{\int_0^\infty E^{3/2}\,dE}{\int_0^\infty E^{1/2}\,dE} \tag{3-122}$$

Then

$$j = \frac{ne^2E}{m}\frac{2}{3k_BT}\frac{\int_0^\infty E^{3/2}\tau(E)f_0\,dE \cdot \int_0^\infty E^{3/2}f_0\,dE}{\int_0^\infty E^{3/2}f_0\,dE \cdot \int_0^\infty E^{1/2}f_0\,dE} \tag{3-123}$$

Therefore

$$j = \frac{ne^2E\langle\tau\rangle}{m} \tag{3-124}$$

where the mean collision time $\langle\tau\rangle$ is defined by

$$\langle\tau\rangle \equiv \frac{\int_0^\infty E^{3/2}\tau(E)f_0\,dE}{\int_0^\infty E^{3/2}f_0\,dE} \tag{3-125}$$

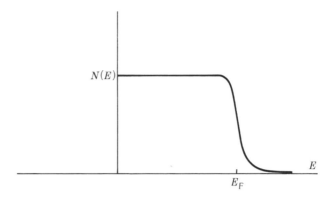

Fig. 3-9. *Fermi-Dirac energy distribution.*

The conductivity is

$$\sigma = \frac{ne^2}{m} \langle \tau \rangle \qquad (3\text{-}126)$$

in approximate agreement with the mean-free-path model.

In the above derivations use was made of the Maxwellian velocity distribution rather than the Fermi-Dirac function. The result is of the same form when use is made of the proper distribution function.

For a Fermi-Dirac distribution

$$\frac{\partial f_0}{\partial E} = \frac{-f_0(1 - f_0)}{k_B T} \qquad (3\text{-}127)$$

When a strong degeneracy exists, the distribution is that shown in Fig. 3-9. For $E < E_F, f_0 = 1$; and for $E > E_F, f_0 = 0$. The term $\partial f_0/\partial E$ is sizable only in the vicinity of E_F. Therefore

$$\int_0^\infty \tau(E) E^{3/2} \frac{\partial f_0}{\partial E} \, dE \simeq -\tau(E_F) E_F^{3/2} \qquad (3\text{-}128)$$

Also,

$$\int_0^\infty f_0 E^{1/2} \, dE \simeq \tfrac{2}{3} E_F^{3/2} \qquad (3\text{-}129)$$

Using Eq. (3-124), the current is evaluated as

$$j = \frac{ne^2 E}{m} \tau(E_F) \qquad (3\text{-}130)$$

The difference between the mean free time in a Maxwellian gas [(3-124) and (3-125)] and an electron gas with a Fermi-Dirac distribution is that the mean time between collisions for the Fermi gas is evaluated for electrons with energies near the Fermi level, rather than being averaged over the entire distribution function.

In the degenerate case, when the lower-energy quantum states are filled, and, as a consequence of the Pauli exclusion principle, the distribution is that given by the Fermi-Dirac function, only the electrons near the Fermi level can change their energy levels by means of collisions.   While all the electrons may contribute to the conduction process, the collision frequency is controlled by the random (thermal) transitions of the electrons near the Fermi level.   Whenever an electron near the Fermi level changes its quantum state, those electrons immediately below it also find it possible to change their states.   Thus a single collision of an electron near the Fermi level can act as a collision for a great many other (lower-energy) electrons.

The electrical conductivity is often written in terms of the mobility μ as follows:

$$\sigma = en\mu \tag{3-131}$$

This form is often convenient because

$$\mu = \frac{e\tau}{m} \tag{3-132}$$

Even when the number of charge carriers varies with impurity level, the mobility does not vary significantly.   Also, when both electrons and holes are present in the same material,

$$\sigma = e(n\mu_e + p\mu_h) \tag{3-133}$$

where p is the number density of holes.   When temperature gradients are present, an additional term $\partial f_0/\partial x$ enters into the distribution function:

$$f = f_0 + \tau e E \frac{\partial f_0}{\partial u} - \tau u \frac{\partial f_0}{\partial x} \tag{3-134}$$

The temperature gradient is related to the gradient of the distribution function.

$$\frac{df_0}{dx} = \frac{\partial f_0}{\partial T} \frac{\partial T}{\partial x} \tag{3-135}$$

and

$$\frac{\partial f_0}{\partial T} = T \frac{d}{dT} \left(\frac{E - E_F}{T} \right) \frac{\partial f_0}{\partial E} \tag{3-136}$$

and the distribution function is

$$f = f_0 + \tau u \frac{\partial f_0}{\partial E} \left[eE + T \frac{d}{dT} \left(\frac{E_F}{T} \right) \frac{dT}{dx} + \frac{E}{T} \frac{dT}{dx} \right] \tag{3-137}$$

The current is again

$$j = \iiint\limits_{-\infty}^{\infty} efu \; du \; dv \; dw \tag{3-114}$$

$$j = \frac{ne}{m} \left[eE + T \frac{\partial}{\partial x} \left(\frac{E_F}{T} \right) \right] \langle \tau \rangle + \frac{nE}{mT} \langle \tau E \rangle \frac{dT}{dx} \tag{3-138}$$

The heat flux is the flow of electron energy:

$$q = \iiint\limits_{-\infty}^{\infty} Ef \; du \; dv \; dw$$

$$= - \frac{n}{m} \left[eE + T \frac{\partial}{\partial x} \left(\frac{E_F}{T} \right) \right] \langle \tau E \rangle - \frac{ne}{mT} \langle \tau E^2 \rangle \frac{dT}{dx} \tag{3-139}$$

where the integrals are evaluated in the manner indicated in the section on isothermal electrical conduction [see Eq. (3-125)].

When no current flows, the combination of the electric field and spatial gradient of the Fermi level may be eliminated from the heat-flux equation by use of the electric-current equation. The result is

$$q = - \frac{n}{mT} \frac{\langle \tau \rangle \langle \tau E^2 \rangle - \langle \tau E \rangle^2}{\langle \tau \rangle} \frac{dT}{dx} \tag{3-140}$$

The thermal conductivity due to the electron mobility is

$$k = - \frac{n}{mT} \frac{\langle \tau \rangle \langle \tau E^2 \rangle - \langle \tau E \rangle^2}{\langle \tau \rangle} \frac{dT}{dx} \tag{3-141}$$

and the Lorenz number is

$$L = \frac{k}{\sigma T} = \left(\frac{k_B}{e} \right)^2 \frac{\langle \tau \rangle \langle \tau E^2 \rangle - \langle \tau E \rangle^2}{(k_B T \langle \tau \rangle)^2} \tag{3-142}$$

For a nondegenerate electron gas and for a power-law variation of

$$\tau = aE^{-s} \tag{3-143}$$

$$\langle \tau \rangle = \frac{a \Gamma(\frac{5}{2} - s)}{\Gamma \frac{5}{2}} \tag{3-144}$$

then

$$\langle \tau E \rangle = \frac{a k_B T \Gamma(\frac{7}{2} - s)}{\Gamma \frac{5}{2}} \tag{3-145}$$

$$\langle \tau E^2 \rangle = \frac{a (k_B T)^2 \Gamma(\frac{9}{2} - s)}{\Gamma \frac{5}{2}} \tag{3-146}$$

$$L = \left(\frac{k_B}{e}\right)^2 (\tfrac{5}{2} - s) \tag{3-147}$$

For a completely degenerate electron gas a more accurate evaluation of the mean collision time must be obtained, since if the averages are all merely the values at the Fermi level,

$$L = 0 \tag{3-148}$$

The integrals in the transport equations are evaluated with the Fermi-Dirac distribution function by expanding the expression for the collision frequency in powers of $(E - E_F)$,

$$\tau(E) = \tau(E_F) + (E - E_F)\tau'(E_F) + \tfrac{1}{2}(E - E_F)^2 \tau''(E_F) + \cdots \tag{3-149}$$

and integrating by parts. Thus

$$\int_0^\infty \tau(E) \frac{\partial f_0}{\partial E} dE = -\tau(E_F) - \frac{\pi^2}{6} (k_B T)^2 \tau''(E_F) + \cdots \tag{3-150}$$

since

$$\int_0^\infty \frac{\partial f_0}{\partial E} dE = -1 \tag{3-151}$$

$$\int_0^\infty (E - E_F) \frac{\partial f_0}{\partial E} dE = 0 \tag{3-152}$$

and

$$\int_0^\infty (E - E_F)^2 \frac{\partial f_0}{\partial E} dE = -\frac{\pi^2}{3} (k_B T)^2 \tag{3-153}$$

The Lorenz number becomes

$$L = \left(\frac{k_B}{e}\right)^2 \frac{\pi^2}{3} \tag{3-154}$$

3-4. Thermoelectric Coefficients

When a temperature gradient is present, the open-circuit field created by the thermal diffusion of the electrons is obtained from Eq. (3-141).

$$j = 0 = \frac{ne}{m}\left[eE + T\frac{d}{dx}\left(\frac{E_F}{T}\right)\right]\langle\tau\rangle + \frac{ne}{mT}\langle\tau E\rangle\frac{dT}{dx} \tag{3-138}$$

Therefore

$$eE = -\frac{1}{T}\frac{dT}{dx}\frac{\langle\tau E\rangle}{\langle\tau\rangle} - T\frac{1}{dx}\left(\frac{E_F}{T}\right) \tag{3-155}$$

or

$$eE = T\frac{d}{dT}\left[\frac{\langle\tau E\rangle - E_F\langle\tau\rangle}{T\langle\tau\rangle}\right]\frac{dT}{dx} \tag{3-156}$$

The Seebeck voltage increment along a differential length of conductor is

$$d\alpha = E\,dx = -\tau\,dT \tag{3-157}$$

where τ now refers to the Thomson coefficient. The Thomson coefficient is therefore

$$\tau = -\frac{T}{dT}\left(\frac{\langle\tau E\rangle - E_F\langle\tau\rangle}{eT\langle\tau\rangle}\right) \tag{3-158}$$

Since the Thomson and Seebeck coefficients are related by the Kelvin relation

$$\tau = \frac{T\,d\alpha}{dT} \tag{3-159}$$

the Seebeck coefficient for a material is

$$\alpha = \frac{E_F\langle\tau\rangle - \langle\tau E\rangle}{eT\langle\tau\rangle} \tag{3-160}$$

For an isotropic material having carriers with scattering laws of the form

$$\tau = aE^{-s} \tag{3-143}$$

the Seebeck coefficient is

$$\alpha = -\left(\frac{k_B}{e}\right)\left(\frac{5}{2} - s - \frac{E_F}{k_BT}\right) \tag{3-161}$$

Since (k_B/e) is about 120 μ/°K, the Seebeck coefficients of semiconductors are high. Typical values are between 100 μ/°K and 1 mv/°K, whereas typical metals have Seebeck coefficients between 1 and 10 μv/°K.

When the charge carriers are holes, the Seebeck coefficient is

$$\alpha = \frac{k_B}{e}\left(\frac{5}{2} - s + \frac{E_F}{k_BT} + \frac{\Delta E_{\text{gap}}}{k_BT}\right) \tag{3-162}$$

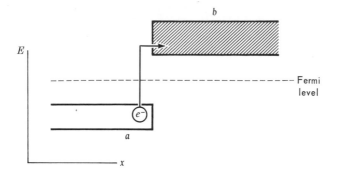

Fig. 3-10.   *Energy distribution at a p-n junction.*

A simpler, physical model to describe the Peltier coefficient is based on the energy diagram shown in Fig. 3-10.

In an ideal metal, one with a zero Seebeck coefficient, the conduction electrons are all at the Fermi level. In the semiconductor the average energy of the conduction electrons, above the bottom of the conduction band, is ΔE_e. The energy required to lift an electron from the Fermi level to that of the average conduction electron is

$$E = \Delta E_e - E_F \qquad (3\text{-}163)$$

The energy must be supplied to each electron as it transverses the junction. The Peltier heat is therefore $\pi = eE$. Since the Fermi level is below the band edge, E_F is negative. By comparison with the previous section it is seen that

$$\Delta E_e = (\tfrac{5}{2} - s)k_B T \qquad (3\text{-}164)$$

since

$$\alpha = \frac{\pi}{T} \qquad (3\text{-}165)$$

In order to calculate Peltier coefficients, one must know the position of the Fermi level relative to the band edges. In intrinsic semiconductors, the electrons and holes are created by thermal excitation of the electrons to energies over the edge of the conduction band. The electron-hole-pair production is a process similar to the ionization process of a gas. The number density of electrons is given by

$$n = 2 \int_0^\infty N_e P_e \, dE \qquad (3\text{-}166)$$

where P_e is the probability of finding an electron with energy E. For a Fermi-Dirac distribution

$$p_e = (e^{(E-E_F)/k_B T} + 1)^{-1} \tag{3-167}$$

Since few electrons are excited to the conduction band, one can approximate the high-energy tail of the Fermi-Dirac distribution by the Maxwellian distribution function. This is based on the assumption that $E - E_F \gg k_B T$.

$$p_e = e^{-(E_E - E_F)/k_B T} \tag{3-168}$$

The number of allowed energy levels per unit volume, N_e, is

$$n_e = \left(\frac{2\pi m_e k_B T}{h^2}\right)^{3/2} \tag{3-169}$$

The number of conduction electrons is

$$n = N_e e^{-E_F/k_B T} \tag{3-170}$$

Similarly. the hole density is

$$p = N_h e^{-(E_F + \Delta E_{\text{gap}})/k_B T} \tag{3-171}$$

where

$$N_h = \left(\frac{2\pi m_{\text{eff}} k_B T}{h^2}\right)^{3/2} \tag{3-172}$$

If no impurities are present, the electron and hole concentrations are equal and the Fermi level is given by

$$E_F = -\frac{\Delta E_{\text{gap}}}{2} + \frac{3}{4} k_B T \ln \frac{m_{\text{eff},h}}{m_e} \tag{3-173}$$

When the effective masses of the conduction electrons and holes are equal, the Fermi level is halfway between the band edges. This is approximately true for most semiconductors. However, some semiconductors have notably different effective masses. In indium antimonide the ratio of effective masses is almost 20, and the Fermi level is shifted toward the conduction band to a relative position of about one-quarter of the gap. The number density of electrons and holes must be equal when no impurities are present and the material is an intrinsic semiconductor. Then the electron and hole densities are given by

$$n = p = 2\left(\frac{2\pi k_B T}{h^2}\right)^{3/2} (m_e m_h)^{3/4} e^{-\Delta E_{\text{gap}}/k_B T} \tag{3-174}$$

When impurities are present in extrinsic semiconductors, the number density of conduction electrons in a band whose edge is adjacent to the energy level of the dopants is

$$n_c = \left(\frac{2\pi m k_B T}{h^2}\right)^{3/4} N_d e^{-\Delta E_d/2k_B T} \qquad (3\text{-}175)$$

where N_d is the dopant density and ΔE_d is the energy gap between the impurity level and the conduction band. The Fermi level is then

$$E_F = -\frac{\Delta E_d}{2} - \frac{k_B T}{2} \ln\left[\frac{4}{Nd}\left(\frac{2\pi m k_B T}{h^2}\right)^{3/2}\right] \qquad (3\text{-}176)$$

As the concentration of impurities increases, the Fermi level rises and approaches the edge of the conduction band. Impurities may also be added which accept electrons. When the energy levels of the acceptor impurities are near the edge of the valence band,

$$p = 2\left(\frac{2\pi m_h k_B T}{h^2}\right)^{3/4} N_a^{1/2} e^{-\Delta E_a/2k_B T} \qquad (3\text{-}177)$$

where ΔE_a is the energy gap between the acceptor impurity level and the edge of the valence band. The Fermi energy in the p-type extrinsic semiconductor is then

$$E_F = \frac{\Delta E_a}{2} + \frac{k_B T}{2} \ln\left\{\frac{1}{N_a}\left(\frac{2\pi m_h k_B T}{h^2}\right)^{3/2}\right\} \qquad (3\text{-}178)$$

The figure of merit of a semiconductor becomes

$$Z = \frac{\alpha^2}{\rho k} = \frac{(E_F\langle\tau\rangle - \langle\tau E\rangle)^2}{T\langle\tau\rangle(\langle\tau\rangle\langle\tau E^2\rangle - \langle\tau E\rangle^2)}\frac{1}{1 + k_L/k_e} \qquad (3\text{-}179)$$

where

$$1 + \frac{k_L}{k_e} = 1 + \frac{k_L}{L N_e e \mu e^{-E_F/k_B T}} \qquad (3\text{-}180)$$

The material parameters can be tailored to alter $\langle\tau\rangle$, $\langle\tau E\rangle$, $\langle\tau E^2\rangle$, and E_F. It is seen that the dimensionless group ZT is a function of the material properties, and it is reasonable to expect that in each temperature regime a material with the highest ZT can be found. The ratio of the lattice to electron contributions to the thermal conductivity increases as the number density of electrons decreases. The best materials are found with electron concentrations low enough to have high Seebeck coefficients but high enough so that the lattice thermal conductivity is tolerable.

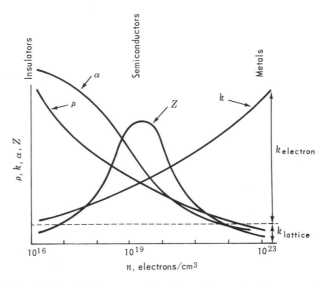

Fig. 3-11. *Relative properties of metals, semiconductors, and insulators.*

Lowering the lattice conductivity by alloying or by the introduction of appropriate impurities results in a lower thermal conductivity at a given electron density. These low-lattice-thermal-conductivity materials can then be doped for lower electron concentration and higher Seebeck coefficients, thereby improving the figure of merit. The variations with electron density of the properties which enter into the figure of merit are shown in Fig. 3-11 in relative proportions.

4. Thermoelectric-generator Performance

4-1. Constant-material-property Analysis

The thermoelectric generator operates as an electron-gas Rankine cycle, where the energy level of the electrons is raised at the thermocouple hot junction and lowered at the cold junction, in a manner analogous to the boiling and condensing processes in an ordinary steam powerplant. In the thermoelectric generator, however, the heat transfer along the conductors represents a large thermal loss, and an optimum ratio of heat conduction to electrical-resistance losses exists. A simplified analysis of a thermoelectric generator with constant-property materials will show this optimization.

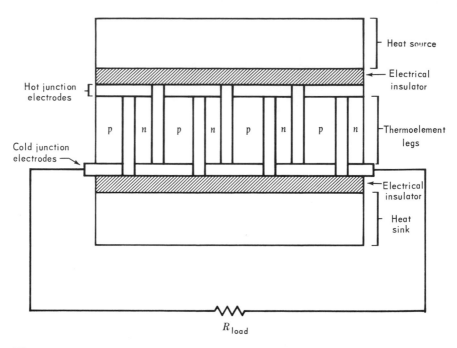

Fig. 3-12. *Thermopile.*

A schematic drawing of a thermopile is shown in Fig. 3-12. The heat input at the hot junctions is

$$Q = I\pi(T_h) + kA \frac{dT}{dx} \tag{3-181}$$

The Peltier coefficient is evaluated using the Kelvin relation as follows:

$$\frac{\pi}{T} = \alpha \tag{3-182}$$

If the Seebeck coefficient is independent of temperature, the Thomson coefficient will be zero and the differential equation for the temperature distribution is

$$\frac{kd^2T}{dx^2} + J^2\rho = 0 \tag{3-183}$$

where

$$J = \frac{I}{A} \tag{3-184}$$

The solution to this differential equation, with the boundary conditions

$$T(0) = T_h \tag{3-185a}$$

$$T(L) = T_c \tag{3-185b}$$

is obtained by the superposition of the homogeneous and inhomogeneous solutions subject to the above boundary conditions, the solution of which is

$$T(x) = T_c + \frac{(T_n - T_c)(L - x)}{L} = \frac{J^2 \rho x}{2k}(L - x) \tag{3-186}$$

The heat flux in the element is determined by the temperature gradient at $x = 0$.

$$q = -k\left(\frac{dT}{dx}\right)_0 = \frac{k\Delta T}{L} - \frac{J^2 \rho L}{2} \tag{3-187}$$

Thus it is seen that half the Joule heat appears at the hot end.

The overall conductance and resistance of the two legs of a thermocouple are

$$K = \left(\frac{kA}{L}\right)_n + \left(\frac{kA}{L}\right)_p \tag{3-188}$$

and

$$R = \left(\frac{\rho L}{A}\right)_n + \left(\frac{\rho L}{A}\right)_p \tag{3-189}$$

The heat input at the hot junction is the sum of the Peltier heat and the conduction heat, less half the resistive dissipation.

$$Q = I\alpha T_h + K\,\Delta T - \frac{I^2 R}{2} \tag{3-190}$$

where

$$\alpha = \alpha_n - \alpha_p \tag{3-191}$$

The electrical output is the product of the terminal voltage and the current. The terminal voltage is the Seebeck voltage less the internal losses.

$$P = I\alpha\,\Delta T - I^2 R \tag{3-192}$$

The efficiency is the ratio of power output to heat input.

$$\eta = \frac{P}{Q} = \frac{\alpha\,\Delta T - IR}{\alpha T_h + k\,\Delta T / I - IR/2} \tag{3-193}$$

The power generated can also be expressed as

$$P = I^2 R_L \tag{3-194}$$

The current is obtained by considering a circuit in which the Seebeck voltage drives the current through the internal and external resistances.

$$I = \frac{\alpha\,\Delta T}{R + R_L} \tag{3-195}$$

Defining the ratio of load to internal resistance as m,

$$m = \frac{R_L}{R} \tag{3-196}$$

In terms of the resistance ratio, the efficiency becomes

$$\eta = \frac{\Delta T}{T_h}\,\frac{m}{1 + m - \Delta T/2T_h + (1+m)^2 RK/\alpha^2 T_h} \tag{3-197}$$

The efficiency is obviously limited to values less than the Carnot efficiency. To maximize η, the product RK,

$$RK = \left[\left(\frac{kA}{L}\right)_n + \left(\frac{kA}{L}\right)_p\right]\left[\left(\rho\frac{L}{A}\right)_n + \left(\rho\frac{L}{A}\right)_p\right] \tag{3-198}$$

should be a minimum. Defining the ratio of the length-to-area ratios of the two legs as g,

$$g \equiv \frac{(L/A)_n}{(L/A)_p} \tag{3-199}$$

The RK product may be minimized with respect to g by straightforward differentiation.

$$\frac{d}{dg}(RK) = 0 = \frac{d}{dg}\left(k_n\rho_n + \frac{k_n\rho_p}{g} + k_p\rho_n g + k_p\rho_p\right) \tag{3-200}$$

with the result that, for the minimum value of the product RK,

$$g_{\text{opt}} = \sqrt{\frac{k_n\rho_p}{k_p\rho_n}} \tag{3-201}$$

The value of RK for the optimum value of g is then

$$(RK)_{\text{opt}} = (\sqrt{(\rho k)_n} + \sqrt{(\rho k)_p})^2 \tag{3-202}$$

The value of the efficiency for the optimum RK product is

$$\eta = \frac{\Delta T}{T_h}\,\frac{m}{1 + m - \Delta T/2T_h + (1+m)^2/ZT_h} \tag{3-203}$$

where

$$Z = \frac{\alpha^2}{(RK)_{opt}} \tag{3-204}$$

in terms of the material properties

$$Z = \frac{(\alpha_n - \alpha_p)^2}{(\sqrt{(\rho k)_n} + \sqrt{(\rho k)_p})^2} \tag{3-205}$$

and is called the figure of merit. For n- and p-type materials with equal values of their thermal and electrical conjunctivities and equal magnitudes of their Seebeck coefficients, the figure of merit becomes

$$Z = \frac{\alpha^2}{\rho k} \tag{3-2}$$

which is used as the expression for the figure of merit of a single material. The efficiency increases with increasing Z, and hence the best (constant-property) material to use is the one with the largest value of Z.

The optimum load resistance is obtained by differentiation of Eq. (3-197) with respect to m, yielding

$$\frac{m^2}{ZT_h} + \frac{1}{T_h}\left(\frac{\Delta T}{2} - \frac{1}{Z}\right) - 1 = 0 \tag{3-206}$$

Therefore

$$m_{opt} = \sqrt{1 + Z\bar{T}} \equiv M \tag{3-207}$$

where

$$\bar{T} = \frac{T_h + T_c}{2} \tag{3-208}$$

The maximum efficiency of the generator becomes

$$\eta = \frac{\Delta T}{T_h} \frac{M}{1 + M - \Delta T/2T_h + (1 + M)^2/ZT_h} \tag{3-209}$$

Equations (3-207) and (3-208) can be used to obtain a more convenient form of Eq. (3-209).

$$\eta = \eta_c \frac{M - 1}{M + \dfrac{T_c}{T_h}} \tag{3-210}$$

where η_c is the Carnot efficiency

$$\eta_c = \frac{\Delta T}{T_h} \tag{3-211}$$

in the limit as $T_c \rightarrow T_h$

$$\eta = \eta_c \frac{\sqrt{1 + ZT} - 1}{\sqrt{1 + ZT} + 1} \tag{3-212}$$

The optimum current is

$$I_{\text{opt}} = \frac{\alpha \, \Delta T}{R(1 + M)} \tag{3-213}$$

The net voltage is

$$V_{\text{net}_{\text{opt}}} = \frac{\alpha \, \Delta T M}{(M + 1)} \tag{3-214}$$

and the net power is

$$P_{\text{net}_{\text{opt}}} = \frac{M}{R} \left(\frac{\alpha \, \Delta T}{M + 1} \right)^2 \tag{3-215}$$

A material efficiency is often defined as

$$\epsilon = \frac{\sqrt{1 + ZT} - 1}{\sqrt{1 + ZT} + 1} \tag{3-216}$$

so that the efficiency of a thermoelectric generator operating on a differential temperature difference becomes

$$\eta = \eta_c \epsilon \tag{3-217}$$

Figure 3-13 shows the relationship between ZT and ϵ.

Maximum power is obtained at the usual matched impedance condition of $R_L = R$, or $M = 1/2$. The maximum power is

$$P_{\text{max}} = \frac{A_n + A_p}{4L} \left(\frac{\alpha \, \Delta T}{\sqrt{\rho_n} + \sqrt{\rho_p}} \right) \tag{3-218}$$

where the area ratio is

$$\left(\frac{A_n}{A_p} \right)_{P_{\text{max}}} = \sqrt{\frac{\rho_n}{\rho_p}} \tag{3-219}$$

The material properties entering into the expression for the maximum power are in the form of

$$\frac{\alpha^2}{(\sqrt{\rho_n} + \sqrt{\rho_p})^2} \tag{3-220}$$

Hence, a single element materials parameter useful for selecting materials for maximum power applications is α^2/ρ rather than the figure of merit

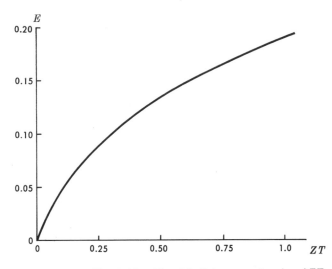

Fig. 3-13. *Material efficiency as a function of* ZT.

$\alpha^2/\rho k$ used for selecting materials for maximum efficiency applications. Clearly, when maximum power is desired and efficiency can be sacrificed, it is immaterial how much heat leaks through the thermoelement legs.

The efficiency at maximum power is

$$\eta_{P\max} = \frac{\Delta T}{T_h} \frac{1}{\frac{1}{2}(3 + T_c/T_h) + 16\rho^* k^*/\alpha^2 T_h} \tag{3-221}$$

where

$$\rho^* = \frac{\rho_n + \rho_p}{2} \tag{3-222}$$

and

$$k^* = \frac{k_n + k_p}{2} \tag{3-223}$$

4-2. Temperature-dependent Properties

The materials used in thermoelectric generators have, in general, properties which vary considerably with temperature. The major problem associated with evaluating the performance of generators with temperature-dependent properties is the determination of the temperature distribution in the legs. Once the temperature distribution is known, the heat flux can be obtained and also the resistance of each leg. The computation of the open-circuit voltage does not require knowledge of the temperature distribution. It is simply

$$V_{oc} = \int_{T_c}^{T_h} (\alpha_n - \alpha_p) \, dT \qquad (3\text{-}224)$$

The resistance of the legs is

$$R = \int_0^L \left[\left(\frac{\rho}{A}\right)_n + \left(\frac{\rho}{A}\right)_p \right] dx \qquad (3\text{-}225)$$

It is to be noted that $\rho(x)$ rather than $\rho(T)$ is needed.

The temperature distribution is obtained by solving the nonlinear differential equation

$$\frac{d}{dx}\left(k\,\frac{dT}{dx} \right) - \tau J\,\frac{dT}{dx} + \rho J^2 = 0 \qquad (3\text{-}226)$$

where $\rho(T)$, $k(T)$, and $\tau(T)$ are variable coefficients. The boundary conditions are

$$T(0) = T_h \qquad (3\text{-}227a)$$

$$T(L) = T_c \qquad (3\text{-}227b)$$

The Thomson coefficient is obtained from the Seebeck voltage using the Kelvin relation

$$\frac{d\alpha}{dT} = \frac{\tau}{T} \qquad (3\text{-}22)$$

The heat required at the hot junction is

$$Q = \alpha T_h I + \left(kA\,\frac{dT}{dx} \right)_n + \left(kA\,\frac{dT}{dx} \right)_p \qquad (3\text{-}228)$$

The temperature distributions in both legs must be determined in order to obtain the efficiency

$$\eta = \frac{I(V_{oc} - IR)}{Q} \qquad (3\text{-}229)$$

When the current flowing in the legs is zero, the heat flux can be obtained by integrating the differential equation for the temperature distribution [Eq. (3-187)]:

$$\int_0^L q \, dx = -\int_0^L k\,\frac{dT}{dx} \qquad (3\text{-}230)$$

or

$$qL = \int_0^L k \frac{dT}{dx} \, dx = \int_{T_c}^{T_h} k \, dT = \langle k \rangle \, \Delta T \qquad (3\text{-}231)$$

where $\langle k \rangle$ is the temperature-averaged thermal conductivity. In the absence of a current the heat flux becomes

$$Q = \langle k \rangle A \frac{\Delta T}{L} \qquad (3\text{-}232)$$

The overall resistance of the thermoelement leg can be easily obtained for the case of zero current.

$$R = \frac{1}{A} \int_{T_c}^{T_h} \rho(T) \frac{dx}{dT} \, dT = \frac{L}{kA} \Delta T \int_{T_c}^{T_h} \rho(T) k(T) \, dT \qquad (3\text{-}233)$$

$$R = \frac{\langle \rho k \rangle}{\langle k \rangle} \frac{L}{A} \qquad (3\text{-}234)$$

Thus

$$\langle \rho \rangle = \frac{\langle \rho k \rangle}{\langle k \rangle} \qquad (3\text{-}235)$$

When the current differs from zero, the use of these average properties still results in meaningful estimates of device performance. In order to calculate the efficiency of the generator more accurately, a solution (inevitably obtained with the assistance of a digital computer) to the differential equation is required. The form of the figure of merit which should be used with average material properties becomes

$$Z_{av} = \left(\frac{\alpha_n - \alpha_p}{\sqrt{(\rho k)_n} + \sqrt{(\rho k)_p}} \right)^2 \qquad (3\text{-}236)$$

It is to be noted that Z_{av} can vary considerably from the temperature average of $Z(T)$. In a specific case it was found that Z_{av} was $0.56 \, Z(T)$. The use of $Z(T)$ may lead to gross overestimates of generator efficiency.[11]

The efficiency of thermoelectric generators has been computed from knowledge of the temperature profiles obtained from numerical solutions to the temperature-distribution differential equation.[12] Results for various temperature-dependent material properties have shown that use of average material properties predicts efficiencies which are within about 6 percent of the exact values computed. This accuracy can be improved by evaluating the Thomson-heat interactions for the legs and making the approximation that half the Thomson heat appear as a Peltier heat at both the hot and cold junctions. Inclusion of this approximation generally

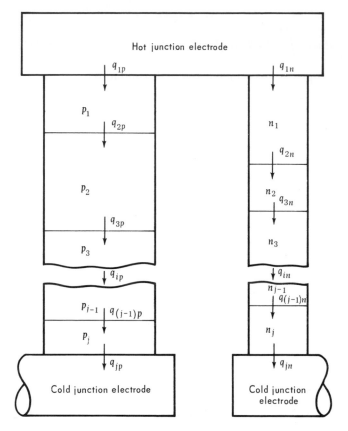

Fig. 3-14. *Segmented thermoelement.*

improves the accuracy of the prediction of thermoelement efficiency to 2 percent.[12a]   An upper limit on the device efficiency can be obtained by using the expression for the overall efficiency of an infinitely staged cascaded generator, which will be derived next.

$$\eta_\infty = 1 - \exp\left[-\int_{T_c}^{T_h} \epsilon(T) \frac{dT}{T}\right] \tag{3-237}$$

where $\epsilon(T)$ is evaluated at each temperature.

4-3. *Segmented and Cascaded Generators*

Since the values of the material properties vary considerably with temperature, the figure of merit is also strongly temperature-dependent.   When a

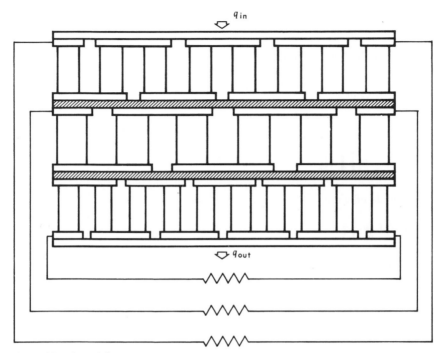

Fig. 3-15. *Cascaded generator.*

generator is designed to operate over a large temperature difference, it is often desirable to use different materials in different temperature regimes. This can be done in either of two ways, by cascading or segmenting. Segmented generators are built from legs made from different materials which are electrically and thermally connected and hence act in series. Cascaded generators are made by using the heat rejection from one generator to supply the thermal input to the next generator in the cascade. Segmented and cascaded generators are shown in Figs. 3-14 and 3-15.

The efficiency of the ith stage of a cascaded generator is

$$\eta_i = \frac{q_i - q_{i+1}}{q_i} = 1 - \frac{q_{i+1}}{q_i} \tag{3-238}$$

Hence

$$1 - \eta_i = \frac{q_{i+1}}{q_i} \tag{3-239}$$

The cascade efficiency is

$$\eta = 1 - \frac{q_j}{q_1} \tag{3-240}$$

where q_j is the heat rejected from the last stage.   Since

$$1 - \eta = \frac{q_j}{q_1}$$

$$= \frac{q_j}{q_{j-1}} \cdot \frac{q_{j-1}}{q_{j-2}} \cdots \frac{q_3}{q_2} \frac{q_2}{q_1}$$

$$= \prod_i (1 - \eta_i) \tag{3-241}$$

the cascade efficiency is

$$\eta = 1 - \prod_i (1 - \eta_i) \tag{3-242}$$

The maximum efficiency of the ith stage is

$$\eta_{max_i} = \epsilon(T) \frac{dT}{T} \tag{3-243}$$

The maximum efficiency of a cascaded generator is limited by

$$\eta_\infty = 1 - \prod_i \left(1 - G_i \frac{dT_i}{T}\right) \tag{3-244}$$

In the limit as $dT \to 0$

$$\prod_i \left[1 - \epsilon_i \left(\frac{dT}{T}\right)_i\right] \to 1 - \sum_i \epsilon_i \left(\frac{dT}{T}\right)_i + \sum_i \epsilon_i \left(\frac{dT}{T}\right)_i$$

$$\cdot \sum_j \epsilon_j \left(\frac{dT}{T}\right)_j + \cdots \tag{3-245}$$

The efficiency of an infinitely cascaded generator can be expressed as

$$\eta_\infty = 1 - \exp\left(\sum_i \epsilon_i \frac{dT}{T}\right) = 1 - \exp\left[-\int_{T_c}^{T_h} \epsilon(T) \frac{dT}{T}\right] \tag{3-237}$$

The difference between this exact expression and the approximation

$$\eta \approx \sum_i \epsilon_i \left(\frac{dT}{T}\right)_i = -\int_{T_c}^{T_h} \epsilon(T) \frac{dT}{T} \tag{3-246}$$

involves the reheat factor of multistage heat engines. The irreversible losses of one stage appear as an increase in the heat available in later stages.

For constant ϵ the efficiency is

$$\eta = 1 - \theta^\epsilon \qquad (3\text{-}247)$$

where

$$\theta = \frac{T_c}{T_h} \qquad (3\text{-}248)$$

The ZT product of the better materials is a maximum over a somewhat narrow temperature band. However, cascaded generators can be built which use each material at its maximum efficiency over the appropriate temperature drop. Figure 3-16 shows the theoretical efficiencies achievable with various values of ZT in multiply cascaded generators.

When cascaded generators are built, it is not necessary to have the same number of thermocouples in each stage of the cascade. The heat rejected by the first stage is

$$Q_{1_{\mathrm{rej}}} = N_1\left(\alpha_1 T_i I_1 + K_1\,\Delta T_1 + \frac{I_1^2 R_1}{2}\right) \qquad (3\text{-}249)$$

and is equal to the heat input to the second stage

$$Q_{1_{\mathrm{input}}} = N_2\left(\alpha_2 T_i I_2 + K_2\,\Delta T_2 - \frac{I_2^2 R_2}{2}\right) \qquad (3\text{-}250)$$

Equating the two heat-transfer rates results in an expression for N_2/N_1, the ratio of the number of couples in each stage.[13]

$$\begin{aligned}\frac{N_2}{N_1} = \frac{(A/L)_{p1}}{(A/L)_{p2}}\frac{\alpha_1\,\Delta T_1}{\alpha_2\,\Delta T_2}\frac{1+m_2}{1+m_1}&\sqrt{\frac{Z_1 k_{1P}\rho_{2p}}{Z_2 k_{2P}\rho_{1p}}}\\ &\times\frac{T_i+(1+m_1)/Z_1+\Delta T_1/2(1+m_1)}{T_i+(1+m_2)/Z_2-\Delta T_2/2(1+m_2)}\end{aligned} \qquad (3\text{-}251)$$

where the current in each level of the cascade is optimum, as obtained through use of Eqs. (3-195), (3-196), and (3-207). When it is desired to increase the output voltage by connecting the stages electrically in series, $I_1 = I_2$, the ratio of A/L in the two legs is given by[13]

$$\frac{(A/L)_{p1}}{(A/L)_{p2}} = \sqrt{\frac{Z_2 k_{2p}\rho_{1p}}{Z_1 k_{1p}\rho_{2p}}}\frac{\Delta T_2}{\Delta T_1}\frac{1+m_1}{1+m_2} \qquad (3\text{-}252)$$

and the ratio of the number of elements in each stage is

$$\frac{N_2}{N_1} = \frac{\alpha_1}{\alpha_2}\frac{T_i+(1+m_1)/Z_1+\Delta T_1/2(1+m_1)}{T_i+(1+m_2)/Z_2-\Delta T_2/2(1+m_2)} \qquad (3\text{-}253)$$

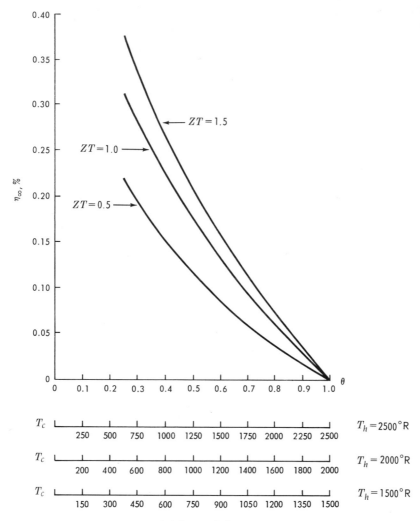

Fig. 3-16. *Efficiency of infinitely cascaded generators.*

All the design parameters not included in the above formulas are those previously obtained for an optimized generator.

When it is desired to produce a voltage in excess of the few tenths of a volt that a single thermocouple develops, a number of thermocouples are arranged electrically in series and thermally in parallel. Such an arrangement is referred to as a thermopile. The voltage developed is NV, and the optimum load is NR_L. The number of thermocouples required to produce a given power, at maximum efficiency is

$$N = \frac{P}{(A/L)_n} \frac{(m+1)^2}{m\alpha\,\Delta T^2} \sqrt{\frac{(\rho k)_n}{Z}} \qquad (3\text{-}254)$$

When the temperature range over which a generator is to be operated is such that figure-of-merit considerations indicate that two different materials should be used, the relative merits of segmented and cascaded geometries must be evaluated.   The main advantage in using a cascaded geometry appears when the optimum ratio of the number of thermocouples in the hot region to the number in the cold region differs widely from unity.   The advantages to the cascaded approach arise because of the ability to tailor independently in the stages the area, heat flux, current, and especially load resistance.   When a cascaded generator is designed, the temperature drop across the electrical interstage insulator must be included in the thermal analysis.   Often this loss in overall temperature difference is sufficient to offset the small gains to be obtained by cascading.   The problem of heat transfer and voltage drop in the electrical leads from the higher-temperature stage is another source of loss.   Often this loss is avoided by connecting the thermopiles in series so that the electrical leads from the higher-temperature thermopile are simply a replacement of two of the interstage insulators by conductors.

In analyzing generators with segmented legs, the intersegment Peltier heat must be accounted for.   Since the segmentation plane is the junction of two dissimilar materials, there is a Peltier-heat interaction at the junction.   The boundary conduction at the junction is

$$\left(k\frac{\Delta T}{L}\right)_i + \left(\rho\frac{J^2 L}{2}\right)_i = \left(k\frac{\Delta T}{L}\right)_{i+1} - \left(\rho\frac{J^2 L}{2}\right)_{i+1} + (\alpha_{i+1} - \alpha_1)T_i J$$

$$(3\text{-}255)$$

4-4. Off-design Performance

Ure and Heikes[11] have evaluated the apparent figure of merit when non-optimum thermocouple dimensions are used and have found that

$$Z_{\text{apparent}} = \frac{\alpha^2}{RK} \qquad (3\text{-}256)$$

When the ratio of the areas of the n and p legs differs from the optimum value by as much as 20 percent, the apparent figure of merit is only 1 percent smaller than the actual material value computed for the ideal case.   Since the properties of the materials may not be known exactly, and do vary with temperature, and fabrication considerations and tolerances exist, the thermocouple legs may not have the ideal dimensions. However, the variation of efficiency with changes in the ratio of electrical to thermal losses is sufficiently insensitive that reasonable care is adequate to avoid any significant penalty in efficiency.

When an n and p leg are combined into a thermocouple, the figure of merit of the couple is found, by Ure and Heikes,[11] to be

$$Z_{\text{couple}} = \left(\frac{\sqrt{Z_p} + \beta \sqrt{Z_n}}{1 + \beta} \right)^2 \tag{3-257}$$

where

$$\beta = \sqrt{\frac{\rho_n k_n}{\rho_p k_p}} \tag{3-258}$$

When materials with different values of ρk are used, the figure of merit of the couple may differ significantly from the average of the two materials. Since the ratio of the electrical conductivity to the electron-gas contribution to the thermal conductivity is given by the Wiedemann-Franz law, the ρk product is proportional to $1 + k_{\text{lattice}}/k_{\text{electron}}$. Overall couple performance is best obtained from materials with similar properties.

4-5.   *Thermoelectric Circuit*

The electrical circuit corresponding to a thermoelectric generator is shown in Fig. 3-17. The generator appears as a battery with an internal resistance. The output voltage, current, and power have previously been given. The maximum efficiency occurs when the impedance ratio is given by the optimum value found using Eq. (3-207).

$$R_L = R \sqrt{1 + ZT} \tag{3-259}$$

Materials which have the highest figures of merit require that the load resistance at maximum efficiency be between 30 and 40 percent larger than that required for maximum power. The point of maximum efficiency is always at a lower current than the maximum power point.

The dynamics of thermoelectric systems was studied by Gray.[41] While much of his work was devoted to refrigeration applications, the approaches are nonetheless valid for cases of power generation. Thermoelectric power generators are designed to operate under steady-state con-

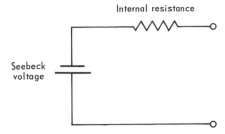

Fig. 3-17. *Thermoelement electric circuit.*

ditions. The chief utility of transient analyses is to obtain the time constants necessary to determine the dynamic response of the device. For moderate values of ZT the transient response of a thermoelectric generator is not greatly different from that of the thermal system alone. In refrigeration applications, where very large currents are being supplied, sizable departures from an ordinary transient thermal response can be found. Electrical and thermal analyses based on the methods presented in this chapter have been found completely adequate for the prediction of the performance of actual designs.

4-6. Metallic Thermoelements

Metallic thermoelements can be used to advantage when special requirements exist. Such demands include the need for ductile materials to permit the fabrication of high reliability thermopiles and for thermoelements of high L/A ratios which are needed for low-current high-voltage generators. The Seebeck coefficient of metallic thermoelements is low, typically of the order of 30 $\mu V/°F$. The thermal and electrical conductivities generally follow the Wiedemann-Franz law quite well. Since the Seebeck coefficient is about 10 percent of the value of that of the best semiconductors the figure of merit is very low. The ZT product is typically 0.01. The best efficiency of a metallic thermocouple is evaluated using Eqs. (3-216) and (3-217) and the first term in the series expansion of the square root terms.

$$\eta_{\text{low } ZT} = \eta_c \frac{ZT}{4} = \frac{Z\Delta T}{4} \tag{3-260}$$

For these materials and for small temperature differences the efficiency at maximum power is given by

$$\eta_{P\text{max, low } ZT} = \frac{Z\Delta T}{16} \tag{3-261}$$

5. *Thermoelectric Materials*

Many materials have been examined for use as thermoelements. Since the most promising materials have been extrinsic semiconductors, the total number of combinations of materials and dopants which have been evaluated is large. Many of the materials which are suitable for refrigeration applications below ambient temperature will not be considered here. The materials of major interest in the intermediate-temperature regime are the tellurides and selenides, especially lead, bismuth, and antimony. At higher temperatures the silicides and sulfides are suitable, and at still higher temperatures the oxides can be used. Most of the work on thermo-element materials for power generation has been aimed at materials for use below 1700°F, where nonrefractory structural materials can be used, and below 1200°F, where efficient combustion-heat sources and highly reliable radioisotope containers can be built. The advantages of higher-temperature operation have been apparent to the groups working on the development of thermoelectric materials, and the elusive goal of higher efficiency through larger temperature differences has attracted considerable attention. However, in the very-high-temperature regime, over 2500°F, thermionic diodes appear to be more efficient than thermoelectric materials. Much effort has been devoted to making reliable, long-lived, and stable thermoelements to operate at moderate temperatures.

The thermoelectric properties of many materials have been reported in the literature. Often only some of the properties of the materials have been measured and the others were computed on the basis of a highly plausible material model. The transport properties of semiconductors involve numerous complex facets, and often even the most plausible model for one property is inadequate for predicting other properties. A survey of the figure of merit of thermoelectric materials was published by White, Wedlock, and Blair[14] which included the available data through 1960. Since then, more accurate measurements have been made on many of the materials and the recommended values of the properties have been refined.

The material which is most often used in thermoelectric generators today is lead telluride. This material is sold in commercial quantities by the Minnesota Mining and Manufacturing Company, which also builds complete generators. The properties of commercial material differ somewhat from batch to batch and hence may differ from those reported here. The curves presented here show the properties for various levels of doping.[15] Commercial materials may have intermediate levels of doping. The Seebeck coefficient, thermal conductivity, electrical resistivity, and figure of merit of n- and p-type lead telluride are shown in Figs. 3-18 and 3-19.

Lead telluride is an intermetallic compound, the pure form of which melts at 922°C and contains 38.113 weight percent tellurium. The material can be made by melting the elements in a quartz container. The material has a metallic appearance. PbTe at elevated temperatures is handled in a slightly reducing atmosphere since the material oxidizes readily. Both lead and tellurium are soluble in PbTe to a few hundredths of a percent. Excess lead results in an n-type material while excess tellurium produces p-type properties. The density of PbTe is 8.25 g/cm^3. The carrier density required for a material with a large figure of merit is an order of magnitude greater than that obtainable with excess lead or tellurium only. Therefore, many dopants have been investigated in attempts to produce attractive materials. The data presented here are only for materials with one of n-type and one of p-type dopant. About 30 different dopants have been reported.[15,16] Lattice vacancies are believed to exist in stoichiometric PbTe, and the excess lead or tellurium fills the vacancies. The two outer p electrons of the lead atom filling a lead vacancy are free to enter the conduction band. Similarly, excess tellurium creates holes. Alkali metal dopants create holes since they have one less outer electron than lead; they therefore permit an increase in the excess tellurium. Likewise, halide dopants increase the electron density by allowing excess lead to supply electrons. Other n-type dopants include Bi_2Te_3, $TaTe_2$, $MnTe_2$, $ZrTe_2$, $TiTe_2$, Al_2Te_3, Ga_2Te_3, and UTe_2. At high temperatures PbTe begins to become intrinsic and the Seebeck coefficient and the figure of merit decrease.

The data presented in Figs. 3-18 and 3-19 show the properties of PbTe doped with PbI_2 (n-type) and Na (p-type). The Seebeck coefficient was measured with respect to copper. Since the mobility of the electrons is more than double the hole mobility, the onset of intrinsic ionization and the lowering of the figure of merit occur at lower temperatures in the p-type material than in the n-type material. The electrical resistivity similarly shows the onset of intrinsic conduction. The figure-of-merit data show that different doping levels produce maximum figures of merit at different temperatures. The more heavily doped materials provide the best figures of merit at the higher temperatures, as they are less sensitive to thermally activated charge carriers. The prospect of producing graded material, with the concentration of the dopant adjusted so that the maximum figure of merit is obtained at each location in the leg during operation, is an attractive one. A continuously doped PbTe thermopile could generate power at an efficiency of 12 percent when operating between 1100 and 1000°F. A thermopile made from material with a single level of doping would have an efficiency of only 10.2 percent.

The family of binary compounds made from bismuth, antimony, tellurium, and selenium have large figures of merit in the low-temperature

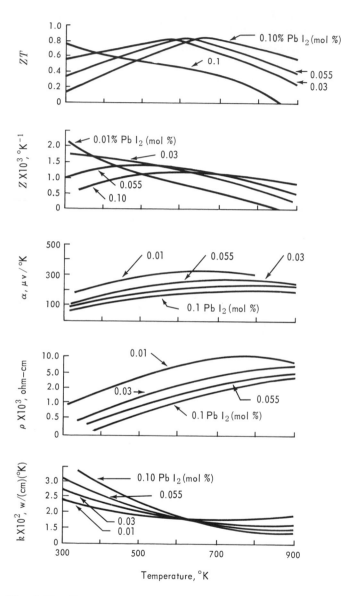

Fig. 3-18. *Temperature dependence of the thermoelectric properties of n-type PbTe.*

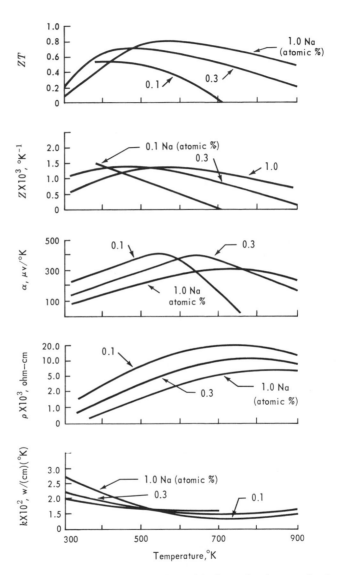

Fig. 3-19. *Temperature dependence of the thermoelectric properties of p-type PbTe.*

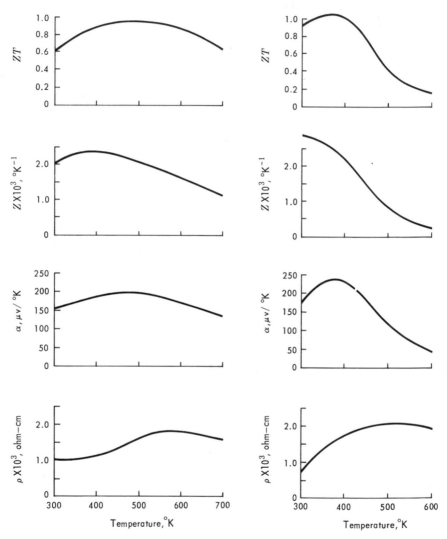

Fig. 3-20. *Temperature dependence of the thermoelectric properties of n-type 75% Bi₂Te₃–25% Bi₂Se₃.*

Fig. 3-21. *Temperature dependence of the thermoelectric properties of p-type 30% Bi₂Te₃–70% Sb₂Te₃ (2% excess Te).*

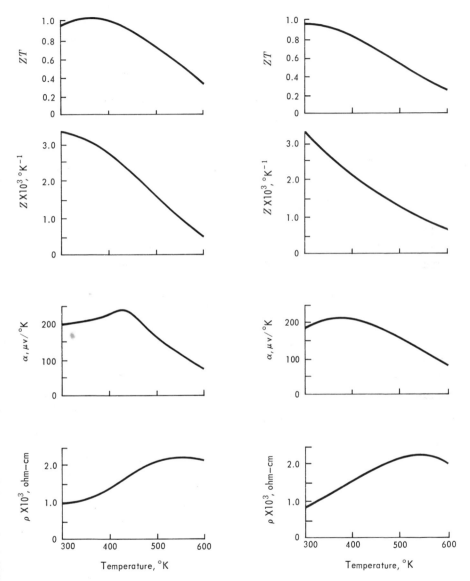

Fig. 3-22.   *Temperature dependence of the thermoelectric properties of p-type 25% Bi$_2$Te$_3$–75% Sb$_2$Te$_3$ (2.3% excess Te).*

Fig. 3-23.   *Temperature dependence of the thermoelectric properties of p-type 25% Bi$_2$Te$_3$–75% Sb$_2$Te$_3$ (1.75% excess Se).*

regime.   These materials are mainly used in refrigeration applications but are also suitable for use in the low-temperature section of a cascaded or segmented generator.   A review of the physics of these materials has been made by Heikes, Miller, and Ure.[17]   An extensive tabulation of the thermoelectric properties of these materials is given by Rosi, Hockings, and Lindenblad.[18]   The n-type material of most interest is 75% Bi_2Te_3–25% Bi_2Se_3 doped with CuBr or AgI. p-type materials with attractive properties can be made from bismuth-antimony telluride, containing between 20 and 30 percent (mole) bismuth telluride, and doped with about 2 weight percent excess tellurium or selenium.   Antimony telluride is normally a p-type material, and alloys of it with bismuth telluride produce p-type material.   Similarly bismuth selenide is normally an n-type material, and alloys of it with bismuth telluride understandably result in n-type material.   The properties of these alloys are shown in Figs. 3-20 to 3-23. These materials, like PbTe, start to become intrinsic at temperatures slightly higher than those at which the figure of merit becomes attractive. The Seebeck coefficient is seen to be a more sensitive parameter than resistivity with which to detect the onset of intrinsic behavior.   The figure of merit was calculated using a thermal conductivity computed from the sum of the electronic contribution to the thermal conductivity and the room temperature value of the lattice thermal conductivity.   Since the lattice conductivity generally decreases with temperature, it is believed that these values of Z are conservative.   The Westinghouse handbook[16] lists a somewhat higher value of Z than the RCA data show.[18]   Unalloyed Bi_2Te_3 is also a material with a high figure of merit.   Stoichiometric bismuth telluride, which melts at 585°C, is a p-type material.   Dopants which increase the hole concentration include Pb, Cd, Sn, and excess Bi. Alternatively excess Te or various halide dopants produce n-type material. Figure 3-24 shows the room-temperature figure of merit of Bi_2Te_3 as a function of electrical conductivity.[19]   The n-type material was doped with CuI, while excess Bi was used to dope the p-type material.   The electrical conductivity of Bi_2Te_3, doped to give a maximum figure of merit at room temperature, can be obtained from Fig. 3-24.

In addition to doping PbTe to achieve high figures of merit, SnTe may be alloyed with PbTe to produce a solid-solution alloy which has an attractive figure of merit.   The alloy with the most favorable properties is 75% PbTe–25% SnTe.   Its properties are shown in Fig. 3-25.   The figure of merit was based on a thermal conductivity which was the sum of the electronic contribution, calculated from the measured electrical conductivity, and the lattice conductivity, obtained from a T^{-1} scaling of the room-temperature value.

There are few materials with ZT products which are as large as those

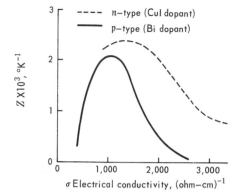

Fig. 3-24. *The figure of merit of Bi_2Te_3 as a function of electrical conductivity.*

obtainable with PbTe and which can be used at temperatures over 1300°F. The material which shows the best figure of merit in the 1300 to 1900°F range is an alloy of silicon and germanium. The advantage of using an alloy of these elements is that the lattice thermal conductivity can be reduced considerably without effecting any significant change in the electrical properties. The alloy has an attractive mechanical strength and a low coefficient of expansion. The material has been operated under temperature gradients of 900°C/cm for prolonged periods with no adverse effects on its properties. The low density of the alloy, 3.5 g/cm³, results in lighter-weight thermopiles than can be built with other materials. The properties of representative *n*- and *p*-type silicon-germanium alloys are shown in Fig. 3-26.[42] The proportions of the alloy vary, with the germanium content usually being between 20 and 30 percent. This variation is made in order to achieve the desired mechanical properties of the alloy, especially the thermal-expansion coefficient. The doping levels can be adjusted to result in the properties shown in Fig. 3-26. Doping levels can be used for which the maximum figure of merit is found to occur at other temperatures. Thermocouples made from germanium-silicon alloys have been successfully tested and operated in air and vacuum for extended periods.

Other alloys which have large ZT products include 95% GeTe–5% Bi_2Te_3[17] and 90% GeTe–10% $AgSbTe_2$.[18] Both of these alloys have slightly higher figures of merit than unalloyed GeTe. The maximum figure of merit of GeTe occurs at a higher temperature than the maximum in the alloys. GeTe might be used in applications where a multiply-segmented or cascaded generator is used. Unalloyed $AgSbTe_2$ can be used as an intermediate temperature leg. The properties of these *p*-type alloys and elements are shown in Figs. 3-27 and 3-28. The lattice thermal

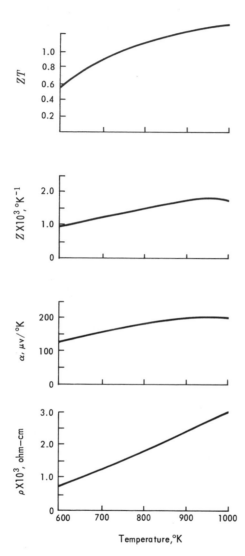

Fig. 3-25. *Temperature dependence of the thermoelectric properties of n-type 75% PbTe–25% SnTe.*

conductivity of AgSbTe$_2$ was assumed to be independent of temperature, while that of the 95% GeTe–5% Bi$_2$Te$_3$ was assumed to vary as $T.^{-1}$

Other high-temperature materials, in addition to the germanium-silicon alloy, are the III-V compounds InSb, InAs, and GaAs. The best of these materials is InAs, which may be alloyed with InP to shift the temperature at which maximum figure of merit occurs. Even with phosphorus dopant this material offers no thermodynamic advantage over the tellurides

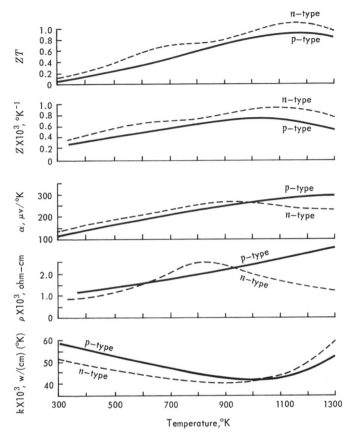

Fig. 3-26. *Temperature dependence of the thermoelectric properties of n- and p-type silicon-germanium.*

in the temperature range in which the tellurides can be operated. The properties of these materials are shown in Fig. 3-29.

The properties of ZnSb are also given here. While ZnSb material has been essentially replaced by PbTe, it is interesting to compare the properties of the grandfather of our present-day materials with those of the best materials modern science has been able to produce. The maximum ZT of ZnSb is about 0.6. The best stage efficiency of which ZnSb is capable is 11 percent of Carnot, which is not too bad when compared with the value of 17 percent, which is the best obtainable with PbTe. Figure 3-30 shows the properties of ZnSb doped to produce a maximum figure of merit.

Materials for use in very-high-temperature applications include the

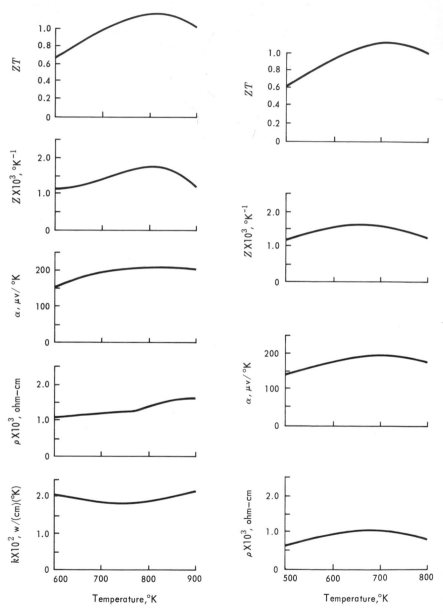

Fig. 3-27. *Temperature dependence of the thermoelectric properties of p-type 95% GeTe–5% Bi₂Te₃.*

Fig. 3-28. *Temperature dependence of the thermoelectric properties of p-type 90% GeTe–10% AgSbTe₂.*

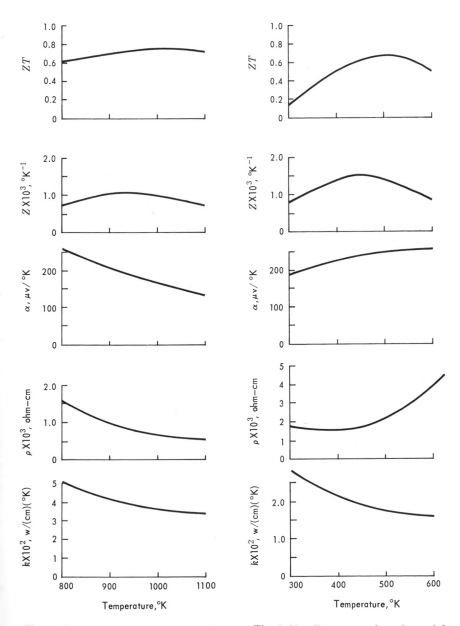

Fig. 3-29. *Temperature dependence of the thermoelectric properties of n-type $As_{0.9}P_{0.1}$.*

Fig. 3-30. *Temperature dependence of the thermoelectric properties of ZnSb.*

oxides, sulfides, and silicides.   At temperatures over 3000°F few materials are insulators, since thermal excitation at these temperatures is sufficient to make most ordinary insulators intrinsic semiconductors.   Some research has been done on the physical chemistry of materials which are semiconductors at these temperatures.   Since thermionic converters can operate at these temperatures at efficiencies as great as 25 percent of Carnot and no thermoelectric material has been found which operates at these temperatures and produces power at an efficiency even one-half that of the thermionic diodes, no extensive effort is being made to develop these materials.

In the temperature regime below which thermionic converters cease to be practical, about 2200°F in 1964, there are some materials which show promise for use in thermoelectric generators.   In addition to the silicon-germanium alloys there are the materials MCC-40, MCC-50, and MCC-60, under development at the Monsanto Research Corporation.[21] These materials have been examined with numerous dopants, and the data presented in Fig. 3-31 represent those properties obtainable as of the date of the reports.[22]   These materials successfully operated in vacuum at 1200°C (2192°F) during a 2,556-hour test.   Segmented couples made from MCC-40 and MCC-50 and MCC-40 and MCC-60 have been made.

In addition to the material described here other materials have been proposed for use between 1200 and 2000°F.   Compounds of cerium and sulfur, in various proportions, have been proposed for use as an n-type material.[23,24]   Manganese telluride, doped with sodium, in the form Na 0.01 Mn 0.99 Te, is an attractive p-type material, a figure of merit of 0.38×10^{-3} °K^{-1} being attained at 1200°K.   A comparison of the efficiency obtainable from various thermoelement legs is reported by Richards.[23]

It is impossible to predict what future discoveries will bring; however, a comparison of the local efficiencies of the various materials available today shows that these materials are approaching an asymptote of a stage efficiency which is 17 percent of Carnot.   This performance corresponds to a value of ZT of unity.   Even though kinetic-theory analyses of electrons and phonons in a semiconductor lattice show no explanation for this asymptote, it nevertheless appears to exit.   Few changes are expected in the effective mass of the charge carriers or in their mobility.   Alloying techniques have already been used to reduce the lattice thermal conductivity.   The expression for the ZT product contains the group $T^{5/2}m_{\text{eff}}^{3/2}\mu/k_{\text{lattice}}$.   Figure 3-32 shows the maximum figure of merit obtainable as a function of this variable.   New knowledge of methods of controlling the properties of semiconductors must be found in order to increase the efficiencies of thermoelectric generators.   Until such developments occur, much improvement can be obtained by segmenting, cascading,

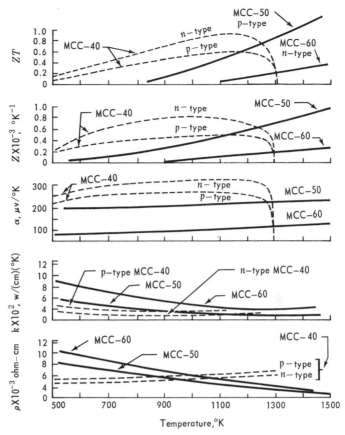

Fig. 3-31. *Temperature dependence of the thermoelectric properties of MCC-40, MCC-50, and MCC-60.*

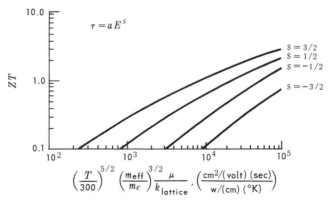

Fig. 3-32. *Upper limit of the ZT product as a function of charge-carrier mobility, effective mass, lattice conductivity, and temperature.*

and producing materials with graded doping levels. Such improvements, together with superior generator design, should result in an increased range of profitable applications of thermoelectric generators.

6. Technology of Thermoelectric Generators

Thermoelectric generators have been built which operate with solar, fossil fuel, radioisotope, and reactor heat sources. The earliest and first successful attempts at thermoelectric power production were with solar-heated generators. Telkes[25] built a solar concentrator which, coupled with a thermopile made from p-type zinc antimonide doped with tin, silver, and bismuth, and an n-type alloy of 94 percent bismuth and 6 percent antimony, generated power at an efficiency of 3.35 percent. The incident solar flux was concentrated by a condensing lens so that a temperature rise of 247°C was obtained during operation. The material used in the thermopile had a figure of merit of 0.9×10^{-3}, which is about 40 percent of that of the best materials available today. The course of thermoelectricity may have been quite different if Telkes had built combustion-heated thermoelectric generators instead of pursuing the elusive goal of practical solar-energy conversion.

Fossil-fueled thermoelectric generators were developed by Daniel-bek et al.[26] in Russia and by Fritts[27] here in the United States. Daniel-bek built a combination kerosene lantern and thermoelectric generator. Fritts's group first developed a thermocouple-powered gas-furnace safety valve and later a series of small generators for use in remote locations.[27] The SNAP-3 and SNAP-9 satellite thermoelectric-generator thermopiles were based on telluride technology.[28] Similar thermopiles were used in the SNAP-7 series generators which are deployed on buoys, in the ocean, and in polar regions.[43] Many groups currently are engaged in the development of portable power units for use in space and other remote locations.

Goldsmid[29] has done much of the developmental work on bismuth telluride and other low-temperature materials. Most of the early work on thermoelectric materials and devices can be found in Joffe's book,[30] which marked the turning point in thermoelectricity. Heikes and Ure were principal contributors to much of the research work on semiconductor thermoelements, sponsored mainly by the United States Navy. Other groups have also made contributions, but in more specific areas. The Atomic Energy Commission has built and placed in orbit isotope- and reactor-heated thermoelectric generators.[31,32,44] Space-power requirements have been summarized by Scott and Schulman.[33] Heat transfer and thermodynamic considerations for space power have been analyzed by

Freedman,[34] and Mackay[35] has summarized many of the nuclear requirements and capabilities for thermoelectric power production in space. Numerous papers describing thermoelectric modules and devices have been presented at the annual Power Sources Conferences.[37] Russian isotope and reactor thermoelectric generators were disclosed at the 1964 Atoms for Peace Conference in Geneva.[38,39]

The most severe technical problems are those associated with the metallurgical properties of the materials. First and foremost, the thermoelement material must be a chemically stable substance. Materials intended for long-lived service should be sufficiently annealed so that the metallurgical structure will not change with time. Often excess anion or cation material, beyond the solubility limit, is introduced into the melt and remains when the material solidifies. The properties of such substances will change with time as the excess material diffuses out of solution. Such behavior can lead to the erroneous conclusion that the compound itself is chemically unstable. Most moderate-temperature semiconductor thermoelements contain elements, such as tellurium, which are volatile and easily oxidizable. During the preparation of these substances oxygen must not contact the material. Similarly, the thermoelements must be operated in an inert atmosphere if temperatures of over a few hundred degrees centrigrade are to be experienced. At these temperatures the vapor pressure of the material and its dopants is sufficiently high to exclude operation in vacuum,[45] since the sublimation rates would be sufficient to degrade the material rapidly. Encapsulation in an inert atmosphere serves to reduce the diffusion rate, so that even though the vapor pressure is high, the net sublimation rate is low. When inert gas atmosphere is used, a high pressure is desirable, since the diffusion coefficient in gases is inversely proportional to the pressure. The pressure level is usually set by strength limitations of the encapsulating structure. The thermal conductivity of a gas is independent of the pressure level, so that no additional thermal losses are encountered because of the moderate pressure of the cover gas. High-molecular-weight rare gases have lower thermal conductivities than other inert vapors and hence are preferred.

It is important to ensure that any substance which contacts the thermoelements does not react with them. This requirement severely limits the choice of electrode material. Copper forms a Cu–PbTe eutectic at 500°C and therefore cannot be used at elevated temperatures with PbTe. Zinc and cadmium react directly with PbTe, replacing the lead in the molecular structure. Free-energy changes of possible reactions with electrode materials must be evaluated to ensure that no reaction of the thermoelements with the electrodes will occur. Similarly, the electrode must not dissolve the doping material, or the thermoelement will degrade owing to a leaching of the dopant. When solders are used, the chemical criteria for electrodes apply to the solder. The solder or electrode must not alter the carrier concentration or mobility. Care must be taken, before soldering to thermoelements, to remove the surface oxide layer, which is found soon after exposure of the thermoelements to air. Various solders, including bismuth-tin, have been found to be satisfactory for use with PbTe at modest temperatures. The recommended hot-junction-electrode material is iron, used with a spring-loaded contact. Moderate pressures of a few hundred pounds per square inch are sufficient to form an adequate contact junction. Very low contact resistances have been reported with this type of thermoelement-electrode junction.[15] At the hot-junction temperatures at which PbTe operates, 1000 to 1200°F,[27] the thermoelements plastically flow under pressure until an intimate contact is attained. Attempts may have been made to achieve bonded hot junctions, but none have been reported in the literature. Part of the difficulty in achieving successful hot-junction bonds is that thermal stresses are created by the differential expansion between the thermoelements and the electrode.

The silicon-germanium alloys have been operated for sufficiently long periods so that meaningful life data have been obtained. The material can be successfully bonded to tungsten, whose thermal expansion coefficient matches that of the alloy quite closely. Tungsten is not used as a hot-junction electrode for air operation because it oxidizes rapidly at elevated temperatures. Hot-junction electrodes have been made successfully from the silicon-germanium alloy itself, since the p- and n-type materials have almost identical crystallographic properties, and from other materials. Couples with this type of bonded hot junction are referred to as Air-Vac couples. The couples are placed in the thermopile with the hot junctions directly exposed to the heat source. Heat transfer to the hot junctions is by radiation, and in air it is augmented by conduction. The cantilevered structure is used in order to avoid differential thermal-expansion problems. Silicon-germanium-alloy thermoelements are being used in the SNAP-10A system. In this system the liquid-metal coolant from the reactor is circulated in the tubes of the radiator. Each radiator tube heats a silicon-germanium-alloy thermopile, the cold junctions of which radiate heat directly to space. Extensive materials evaluation and quality-control programs have been undertaken in conjunction with the SNAP-10A and other programs, and the properties of the silicon-germanium alloys being used are extremely reproducible.

The mass of thermoelements required is proportional to the product of the thermoelement length and area. The heat flux and power-producing capacity, however, are determined only by the A/L ratio. Ideally, very short thermoelements could be produced which would have an extremely large specific power. The factor that limits the length of thermoelements is the contact resistance. Both electrical and thermal contact resistances serve to degrade the thermopile performance. The degradation is more severe in fossil-fuel-fired than in radioisotope-heated thermoelectric generators, since the burner efficiency usually decreases with increasing flame temperature. Manufacturing tolerances also enter into the optimization of thermoelement length. Commercial thermoelements are made in sizes from $\frac{1}{2}$ in. o.d. by 1 in. to $\frac{1}{4}$ in. by $\frac{1}{4}$ in. Often the contact resistance is modeled in the form of an extra equivalent length, which conducts heat and dissipates electrical energy but has a zero Seebeck coefficient. Analyses have been made which evaluate the weight savings to be had from shorter thermoelement leg length and the penalty arising from having the "dead" resistance being a larger part of the overall leg resistance.

The heat-transfer rates which occur in thermoelements are greater than those normally associated with gas-phase heat-transfer equipment. Thermoelectric generators which operate in air use fins, or extended surfaces, to achieve economical cold-junction temperatures. In space, where radiation is the only possible process of heat rejection, fins are also used. In thermopiles using spring-loaded thermoelements, the loading member must be electrically insulated from the thermoelement. Since the spring loading occurs at the cold junction, the structural design must be such as to avoid interfering with the thermal path to the heat sink. The problem of minimizing the temperature drop from the cold junction to the heat sink, while maintaining electrical insulation between numerous spring-loaded thermoelements, is a difficult design task.

A symposium on thermoelectricity was held in 1961,[40] which summarized much of the experience gained in the preceding few years of active research. Considerable experience has been obtained in the synthesizing of improved thermoelectric materials and in the evaluation techniques. The art of the design of thermoelectric generators has progressed, and both commercial and military generators are being built. It is expected that gradual improvements will be made in the performance of thermoelectric materials and that this gain, along with design improvements, will result in a more widespread adoption of thermoelectric power generators.

References

1. deGroot, S. R.: *Thermodynamics of Irreversible Processes*, Interscience Publishers (Division of John Wiley & Sons, Inc.), New York, 1951.

2. Denbigh, K. G.: *The Thermodynamics of the Steady State*, Methuen & Co., Ltd., London, 1957.
3. Prigogine, I.: *Introduction to the Thermodynamics of Irreversible Processes*, Charles C Thomas, Publisher, Springfield, Ill., 1955.
4. Domenicali, C. A.: "Irreversible Thermodynamics of Thermoelectricity," *Rev. Mod. Phys.*, **26**: 237 (1954).
5. Hatsopoulos, G. N., and J. H. Keenan: "Thermodynamics of Thermoelectricity," chap. 15, in J. Kaye and J. A. Welsh (eds.), *Direct Conversion of Heat to Electricity*, John Wiley & Sons, Inc., New York, 1960.
6. Jeans, J.: *An Introduction to the Kinetic Theory of Gases*, Cambridge University Press, New York, 1959.
7. Wilson, A. H.: *Theory of Metals*, Cambridge University Press, New York, 1953.
8. Bloch, F.: *Z. Physik*, **52**: 555 (1928).
9. Kittel, C.: *Introduction to Solid State Physics*, John Wiley & Sons, Inc., New York, 1956.
10. Smith, R. A.: *Semiconductors*, McGraw-Hill Book Company, New York, 1959.
11. Ure, R. W., Jr., and R. R. Heikes: "Theoretical Calculations of Device Performance," chap. 15, in R. R. Heikes and R. W. Ure, Jr. (eds.), *Thermoelectricity: Science and Engineering*, Interscience Publishers (Division of John Wiley & Sons, Inc.), New York, 1961.
12. Sherman, B., R. Heikes, and R. Ure, Jr.: *J. Appl. Phys.*, **31**: 1 (1960).
12a. Cohen, R. W., and B. Abeles: "Efficiency Calculations of Thermoelectric Generators with Temperature Varying Parameters," *J. Appl. Phys.*, **34**: 1687 (1963).
13. Harman, T.: *J. Appl. Phys.*, **29**: 1471 (1958).
14. White, D. C., B. D. Wedlock, and J. Blair: "Recent Advances in Thermal Energy Conversion," *Proc. 15th Ann. Power Sources Conf.*, May, 1961.
15. Fritts, R. W.: "Lead Telluride Alloys and Junctions," chap. 10, in I. B. Cadoff and E. Miller (eds.), *Thermoelectric Materials and Devices*, Reinhold Publishing Corporation, New York, 1960.
16. Green, W. B. (ed.): *Thermoelectric Handbook*, Westinghouse Elec. Corp., Youngswood, Pa., 1962.
17. Heikes, R. R., R. C. Miller, and R. W. Ure, Jr.: "Survey of Known Thermoelectric Materials," chap. 13, in R. R. Heikes and R. W. Ure, Jr. (eds.), *Thermoelectricity: Science and Engineering*, Interscience Publishers (Division of John Wiley & Sons, Inc.), New York, 1961.
18. Rosi, F. D., E. F. Hockings, and N. E. Lindenblad: "Semiconducting Materials for Thermoelectric Power Generation," *RCA Rev.*, March, 1961.
19. Rosi, F., B. Abeles, and R. Jensen: *J. Chem. Solids*, **10**: 191 (1959).
20. Raag, V.: "Silicon-Germanium Thermocouple Development," *Proc. 17th Ann. Power Sources Conf.*, May, 1963.
21. Henderson, C. M., R. G. Ault, E. R. Beaver, G. B. Jankowsky, R. M. Jankowieki, and G. H. Rengrose: "High Temperature Thermoelectric Generator," ASD-TDR-62-896, October, 1963.

22. Henderson, C. M., and C. W. Glassburn: "High Temperature Thermoelectric Research," *IEEE Trans. on Aerospace*, no. 2, April, 1964.

23. Richards, J. D.: "Materials Selection Criteria for Thermoelectric Power Generation," *AIEE Proc., Pacific Energy Conversion Conf.*, 1962.

24. Egli, P. H.: "Thermoelectric Materials: The Present and the Potential," *AIEE Proc., Pacific Energy Conversion Conf.*, 1962.

25. Telkes, M.: "Solar Thermoelectric Generators," *J. Appl. Phys.*, **25:** 765 (1954).

26. Daniel-bek, V., A. Voronin, and N. Roginskaya: *Radio*, **2:** 24 (1954).

27. Fritts, R. W.: "The Development of Thermoelectric Power Generators," *Proc. IEEE*, May, 1963.

28. Fritts, R. W.: "Design Parameters for Optimizing the Efficiency of Thermoelectric Generators Using p-type and n-type Lead Telluride," *Trans. AIEE*, **78** *(Commun. and Electronics)*: 817 (1960).

29. Goldsmid, H. J.: *Applications of Thermoelectricity*, Methuen & Co., Ltd., London, 1960.

30. Joffe, A. F.: "Semiconductor Thermoelements and Thermoelectric Cooling," *Infosearch*, London, 1957.

31. Carpenter, R. T.: "Space Isotopic Power Sources," *Astronautics and Aerospace Eng.*, May, 1963.

32. Anderson, G. M.: "Nuclear Reactor Systems," *Astronautics and Aerospace Eng.*, May, 1963.

33. Scott, W. C., and F. Schulman: "Space Electrical Power," *Astronautics and Aerospace Eng.*, May, 1963.

34. Freedman, S. I.: "Heat Transfer Considerations in Space Power Supplies," chap. 15, in W. M. Rohsenow (ed.), *Developments in Heat Transfer*, The M.I.T. Press, Cambridge, Mass., 1964.

35. Mackay, D. B.: *Design of Space Powerplants*, Prentice-Hall, Inc., Englewood Cliffs, N.J., 1963.

36. Barmat, M.: "Direct Conversion Applied to Nuclear Heat Sources," chap. 18, in I. B. Cadoff and E. Miller (eds.), *Thermoelectric Materials and Devices*, Reinhold Publishing Corporation, New York, 1960.

37. *Proc. 13th to 18th Ann. Power Sources Conf.*, published and distributed by the PSC Committee, Red Bank, N.J., 1959 to 1964.

38. Vorinin, A. N., et al.: "Radioisotope Fueled Thermoelectric Generators," Third United Nations International Conference on the Peaceful Uses of Atomic Energy, Geneva, 1964.

39. Millionshchikov, M. D., et al.: "High Temperature Direct Conversion Reactor 'Romashka,'" Third United Nations International Conference on the Peaceful Uses of Atomic Energy, Geneva, 1964.

40. *Advances in Energy Conversion*, symposium on thermoelectric energy conversion, no. 1, 1961; no. 2, 1962.

41. Gray, P. E.: *The Dynamic Behavior of Thermoelectric Devices*, The M.I.T. Press, Cambridge, Mass., 1960.

42. "Thermal and Mechanical Characteristics—SiGe Material," RCA Direct Energy Conversion Department, Harrison, N.J., July, 1964.

42*a*.   Abeles, B., and R. W. Cohen: "Ge-S: Thermoelectric Power Generator," *J. Appl. Phys.*, **35**: 247 (1964).

42*b*.   Dismukes, J. P., L. Ekstrom, E. F. Steigmeier, I. Kudman, and D. S. Beers: "Thermal and Electrical Properties of Heavily Doped Ge-Si Alloys Up to 1300°K," *J. Appl. Phys.*, **35**: 2899 (1964).

43.   Corliss, W. R., and D. L. Harvey: *Radioisotope Power Generation*, Prentice-Hall, Inc., Englewood Cliffs, N.J., 1964.

44.   Wilson, R. F., J. E. Brunings, and G. S. Budney: "SNAP-10A-Prologue to Flight," *Nucleonics*, June, 1965, p. 44.

45.   Shakhtakhtinskii, M. K., A. A. Kulier, and G. B. Abdullaer: "Investigations of the Saturated Vapor Pressure of Some Selenides with Radioisotopes," *Proceedings of the Fourth All-Union Conference on Semiconductor Materials*," Consultants Bureau Enterprises, New York, 1963.

Symbols

A cross-section area

C concentration

c molecular speed

D diffusion coefficient

E energy, emf

e electron charge

f distribution function

g ratio of L/A in n and p material

h Planck's constant

$\hbar$ $h/2\pi$

h_{fg} enthalpy of evaporation

I current

J flux

J current density

K thermal conductance

k thermal conductivity

k_B Boltzmann's constant

L_{ij} coefficients in force-flux matrix

L Lorenz number, k/T

L length of thermoelement

M maximum efficiency value of m

m R/R_L

m mass of charge carrier

N number of thermocouples in a thermopile stage

N number of moles of a chemical species

n molar flux

P power

p hole density
p pressure
Q heat-transfer rate; also, total amount of heat
q heat flux
R resistance
r coordinate
S entropy
s energy-dependence factor in mean free time
T temperature
t time
U energy
u x-direction velocity
V potential energy; voltage; velocity
v y-direction velocity
V_{fg} change in specific volume during phase change
W work
w z-direction velocity
X generalized force
x coordinate
Z figure of merit

Greek

α Seebeck coefficient
ϵ material efficiency
η efficiency
θ temperature ratio, T_c/T_h
κ wave number
λ mean free path
μ electrochemical potential
μ mobility
μ viscosity
π Peltier coefficient
ρ resistivity
σ conductivity
τ mean free time
τ Thomson coefficient
ϕ potential
ψ wave function

Subscripts

ab difference between materials a and b
c cold

e electron
h hot
L lattice
n material with negatively charged carriers
p material with positively charged carriers
T isothermal
v isochor

Other

Δ difference
∇ divergence operator
d inexact differential

4

MAGNETOHYDRODYNAMIC POWER

GENERATION
George W. Sutton

1. INTRODUCTION

The magnetohydrodynamic (MHD) electrical power generator is based upon the Faraday effect, but until recently Faraday generators utilized conductors which are made of solid metal. However, the MHD generator is based on the concept of using flowing ionized gases or liquid metals as the moving conductor which has been heated by chemical or nuclear fuel. Thus, the MHD generator removes the intermediate step of the prime mover but can utilize working fluids at higher temperatures than are compatible with prime movers, since the MHD generator has no moving parts and therefore the level of mechanical stresses can be greatly reduced. This higher temperature can lead to increased conversion efficiencies or, in the case of closed cycles for space power, to a reduction in the size of the radiator.

At present, the primary interest is in d-c generators, because of problems associated with a-c generators (see Sec. 4-4); thus, in this chapter, we will introduce this subject by examination of the three d-c-generator geometries of most present interest; however, the linear channel and its variations will be emphasized. Next, the properties of partially ionized gases are given, because primary interest is in the use of ionized gases as the working fluid, although there is some interest in the use of two-phase fluids in which the liquid phase is a liquid metal (see Sec. 9). The theoretical performance of the linear geometry is then derived including the Hall effect and ion slip. This is considered first for a short section of a

AVCO-Everett Research Laboratory, Everett, Massachusetts.

d-c generator and includes a discussion of the continuous-electrode, seg-mented-electrode, and Hall geometries. In addition, the performance of the a-c induction generator is derived.

The factors which affect the overall generator efficiency are then con-sidered, and general expressions are derived for the polytropic efficiencies of the linear geometry. Compressible-flow theory is then applied to the linear geometry in order to obtain expressions for the overall performance. Finally, there is a discussion of the application of the MHD generator to various cycles and a description of the experimental results which have been achieved to date.

Most of the information in this chapter has been extracted from Ref. 1, to which the reader is referred for further details. However, this chapter has been brought up to date by inclusion of more recent results. The reader is also referred to general Refs. 2 to 5.

There are several different MHD-generator geometries presently under consideration. The chief requirement for any geometry is that there be a component of the gas velocity which is perpendicular to the magnetic field. The simplest geometries for accomplishing this are the linear (together with its many variations), vortex, and radial outflow (see Fig. 4-1). These are described qualitatively below, and the linear geometry is examined more thoroughly in the remaining sections of this chapter.

1-1. Linear MHD Generator—"Duct" or "Channel" Geometry

The simplest MHD-generator geometry is the "linear" geometry in which the gas flows through a linear duct or channel (see Fig. 4-1). The magnetic field is at right angles to the gas-flow velocity, which induces a Faraday electric field at right angles to both the flow velocity and magnetic field. If suitable electrodes are placed on either side of the channel and connected through an electrical load or resistance, current will flow through the gas, electrodes, and load. In addition to the Faraday electric field, the mag-netic field causes a Hall current to flow in the direction of fluid flow (see Sec. 4).

1-2. Vortex MHD Generator

In addition to the linear geometry with its many variations, there is also interest in the vortex, or spiral, geometry in which the gas is introduced tangentially into a cylindrical geometry and withdrawn along the surface of an inner coaxial cylinder (see Fig. 4-1). The magnetic field is in the

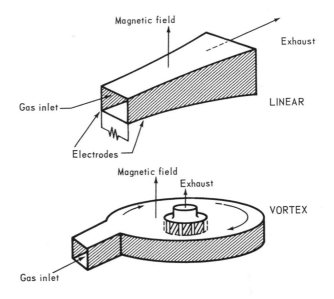

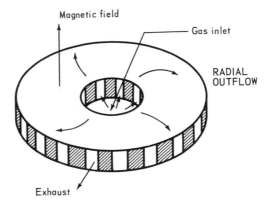

Fig. 4-1.   *MHD-generator geometries.*

axial direction, and the inner and outer cylinder are the two electrodes. When the diameter of the inner cylinder is much smaller than that of the outer cylinder, the gas makes several revolutions in the generator; thus, this geometry permits a long magnetic interaction length; or alternately, for a given interaction length, the vortex generator may have a more compact magnetic field.   On the other hand, the Hall currents tend to flow in the tangential direction.

1-3. Radial-outflow MHD Generator

A variation of the vortex generator is one in which the gas is injected radially outward from the inner cylinder. In this case, the Faraday current flows tangentially and the Hall current flows radially; the latter interacts with the magnetic field to rotate the flow, so that the flow becomes a spiral outward. This variation is essentially the same as the Hall geometry, with the gas flow deflected so that the Lorentz force caused by the Hall current is equal to the centrifugal force in the fluid.

2. Electrical Conduction in Gases

For MHD generators, a gas must be a conductor of electricity; that is, the gas must be ionized and also must be considered a continuum. Thus, the gas has a small mean free path or Larmor radius† with respect to the size of the apparatus, and, in addition, the Debye length d must be small, where

$$d = \sqrt{\frac{2K_0 kT}{\sum_s n_s Z_s{}^2}} \tag{4-1}$$

The Debye length is the distance over which space-charges can exist. When these conditions exist, the gas is considered to be a plasma.

The methods for calculating the percentage ionization are deferred to Sec. 3. In the present section it is assumed that the ionization is specified; and the appropriate relations between the current and electromagnetic fields are derived. For an MHD generator, electrons are mainly responsible for the conduction of electricity; negative ions generally reduce the electrical conductivity.

2-1. Scalar Electrical Conductivity

There exist several methods for theoretically calculating the scalar electrical conductivity of ionized gases. However, because electrons are mainly responsible for conduction, the Lorentz theory, which utilizes an expansion in terms of the ratio of the electron mass to the heavy-particle mass, is most applicable. This theory[6] gives the following expression for the scalar electrical conductivity in the absence of a magnetic field due to electron motion:

---

† The Larmor radius is the radius of gyration of a charged particle in a magnetic field.

$$\sigma = \frac{4\pi e^2}{3kT_e} \int_0^\infty \frac{f_0 c^4 \, dc}{\nu(c)} \tag{4-2}$$

where $f_0(c)$ is the zero-order distribution function for electrons, $\nu(c)$ is the collision frequency of electrons with all scattering species, given by

$$\nu(c) = c \sum_{s \neq e} n_s Q_{es}(c) \tag{4-3}$$

and Q_{es} is the scattering cross section of electrons for momentum transfer:

$$Q_{es}(c) = 2\pi \int_0^\infty (1 - \cos \chi) b \, db \tag{4-4}$$

where b is the impact parameter and χ is the scattering angle, which depends upon b and c. It is often convenient to evaluate the collision frequency at the average thermal speed, given by

$$\langle c \rangle_s = \sqrt{\frac{8kT_e}{\pi m_e}} \tag{4-5}$$

and to take f_0 as Maxwellian about the electron temperature, so that from Eq. (4-2), σ becomes

$$\sigma = \frac{n_e e^2}{m_e \nu_e} \tag{4-6}$$

where

$$\nu_e = \nu_e(\langle c \rangle_e) = \sum_{s \neq e} \nu_{es} \tag{4-7}$$

and

$$\nu_{es} = n_s \langle c \rangle_e Q_{es}(\langle c \rangle_e) \tag{4-8}$$

Some average values of various cross sections are shown in Fig. 4-2. Cross sections for other gases may be found in Refs. 7 and 8. If one defines a conductivity σ_{eI} based on collisions with ions only and a conductivity σ_{en} based upon collisions with neutral particles only as follows,

$$\sigma_{en} = \frac{n_e e^2}{m_e \sum_n \nu_{en}} \tag{4-9}$$

$$\sigma_{eI} = \frac{n_e e^2}{m_e \nu_{eI}} \tag{4-10}$$

then Eq. (4-6) can be approximated as[1]

$$\frac{1}{\sigma} = \frac{1}{\sigma_{en}} + \frac{1}{\sigma_{eI}} \tag{4-11}$$

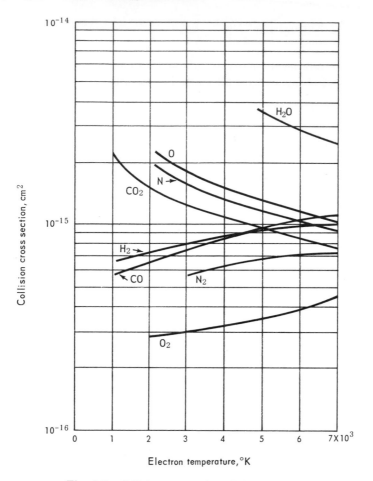

Fig. 4-2. *Collision cross sections of electrons with some atoms and molecules. (W. Chinitz, L. Eisen, and R. Gross, ARS Preprint 706-58.)*

In evaluating the collision cross section for electrons with ions, the integral in Eq. (4-4) diverges because of the long range of the coulombic force. However, if $n_e d^3 \gg 1$, the coulombic-force field is shielded for values of $b > d$; hence one usually takes the upper limit of the integral of Eq. (4-4) to be d. Then σ_{eI} becomes[9]

$$\sigma_{eI} = \frac{\gamma_E n_e (4\pi K_0)^2 (2kT_e)^{3/2}}{\pi^{3/2} m_e^{1/2} e^2 \left(\sum_{s \neq e} n_s Z_s^2 \right) \ln \Lambda_I} \tag{4-12}$$

where Λ_I is the ratio of the Debye shielding length to the average impact parameter,

$$\Lambda_I = \frac{3}{2e^2 Z_I} \left[\frac{2(4\pi K_0 kT)^3}{\pi \sum_s n_s Z_s^2} \right]^{1/2} \tag{4-13}$$

and γ_E is a correction factor which accounts for the effect of electron-electron collisions on the shape of the distribution function; for a singly ionized gas this factor is 0.582.[9] Since the temperature of the gas in an MHD generator will rarely be high enough to cause more than single ionization, Eqs. (4-12) and (4-13) reduce to

$$\sigma_{eI} = \frac{1.508 \times 10^{-2} T_e^{3/2}}{\ln \Lambda} \tag{4-14}$$

$$\Lambda = \frac{1.2389 \times 10^4 T_e^{3/2}}{n_e^{1/2}} \tag{4-15}$$

in MKSG units; that is, T_e is in degrees Kelvin, n_e is electrons per cubic meter, and σ_{eI} is ohms^{-1} per meter.

The mixing formula [Eq. (4-11)] has a maximum error of about 30 percent as compared with the complete formula [Eq. (4-2)].[8]

2-2. Tensor Electrical Conductivity

In the presence of a magnetic field, the electrons tend to drift at right angles to both the electric field and magnetic field. Under these conditions, the electrical conductivity becomes a tensor, and the term $(1/\nu)$ in Eq. (4-2) must be replaced by the tensor $\mathbf{\Omega}$, where

$$\mathbf{\Omega} = \begin{vmatrix} \dfrac{\nu}{\nu^2 + \omega_e^2} & -\dfrac{\omega_e}{\nu^2 + \omega_e^2} & 0 \\[2mm] \dfrac{\omega_e}{\nu^2 + \omega_e^2} & \dfrac{\nu}{\nu^2 + \omega_e^2} & 0 \\[2mm] 0 & 0 & \dfrac{1}{\nu} \end{vmatrix} \tag{4-16}$$

where the magnetic field is in the z direction and ω_e is the electron cyclotron frequency, eB/m_e.

Again, it is convenient to consider ν a constant, as given by Eq. (4-7), so that the tensor electron conductivity becomes

$$\sigma_{ij} = \sigma \begin{vmatrix} \dfrac{1}{1 + \omega_e^2 \tau_e^2} & -\dfrac{\omega_e \tau_e}{1 + \omega_e^2 \tau_e^2} & 0 \\[3mm] \dfrac{\omega_e \tau_e}{1 + \omega_e^2 \tau_e^2} & \dfrac{1}{1 + \omega_e^2 \tau_e^2} & 0 \\[3mm] 0 & 0 & 1 \end{vmatrix} \tag{4-17a}$$

where σ is given by Eq. (4-11), $\tau_e = (\nu_e)^{-1}$, and $\omega_e \tau_e$ is the Hall parameter, which can be written also as the ratio of the electron mean free path to the Larmor radius or in terms of the scalar electrical conductivity or in terms of the electron mobility, respectively, as follows:

$$\omega_e \tau_e = \frac{eB}{m_e} \frac{\lambda_e}{\langle c \rangle_e} = \frac{\lambda_e}{r_e} = \frac{\sigma B}{n_e e} = \mu_e B \tag{4-17b}$$

Equation (4-17a and b) shows that as the magnetic field is increased, the magnitude of the electron current is reduced and is rotated from the E^* vector.

2-3. Ion Slip

Because the ion mass is greater than the electron mass, the corresponding Hall parameter for ions $\omega_I \tau_{In}$ is always smaller than that for electrons and the ion current is not as greatly affected by the presence of the magnetic field. Thus, as the magnetic field is increased, the electron current is reduced to the point where it is comparable in magnitude to the ion current and Eq. (4-14) must be corrected for the ion contribution.[10] For a very slightly ionized gas, this correction is obtained by substitution of σ' for σ, and $(\omega_e \tau_e)'$ for $\omega_e \tau_e$, where[1]

$$\sigma' = \frac{\sigma}{1 + \omega_e \tau_e \omega_I \tau_{In}} \tag{4-18}$$

$$(\omega_e \tau_e)' = \frac{\omega_e \tau_e}{1 + \omega_e \tau_e \omega_I \tau_{In}} = \beta_e' \tag{4-19}$$

and the total conduction current is given by

$$\mathbf{j} = \sigma' \cdot \mathbf{E}^* \tag{4-20}$$

in the plane perpendicular to $\mathbf{B}$. Finally, it should be noted that a gradient in the electron pressure, number density, or temperature also causes an electron current, but these are not usually important for MHD generators.

3. Seeding and Ionization in Magnetohydrodynamic Generators

Two types of ionization are of present interest for MHD generators: thermal ionization and magnetically induced ionization. Although radio-frequency waves can be used to produce a low amount of ionization in a gas, the high degree of ionization which is required for MHD generators leads to a very small skin depth so that the r-f field cannot produce the required degree of ionization before the plasma becomes self-shielding. Radio-activity can also produce ionization, but a practical method has not yet been suggested for utilizing this in a generator. Photoionization, although relatively efficient, requires a very long light path in seeded gas for the ionizing light to be absorbed because of the small photoionization cross section of most atoms and molecules. Electron-beam ionization may prove effective if the recombination rate is sufficiently low. For example, Shair[11] has preionized a 1500°K stream of argon and cesium at atmospheric pressure and has measured a resulting conductivity of 6 mhos/m approximately 20 cm downstream of the electron beam; however, power generation has not yet been achieved. For flames, a certain amount of chemi-ionization has been observed, but the amount is usually insufficient. For these reasons, the first two methods of ionization have received the most attention. These are covered in more detail below.

3-1. Thermal Ionization

If the gas is in equilibrium (including radiation equilibrium), statistical mechanics can be used to determine the degree of ionization from Saha's equation, given by[12]

$$\frac{n_e n_I}{n_n} = \frac{2P_I}{P_n}\left(\frac{2\pi m_e kT}{h^2}\right)^{3/2} e^{-E_I/kT} \qquad (4\text{-}21a)$$

for the reaction $n \rightleftharpoons e + I$, where E_I is the ionization energy for this reaction and P_I and P_n are the internal-partition functions for the ion and neutral atom, respectively (see Table 4-2). From Table 4-1, it is obvious that sufficient thermal ionization cannot be achieved in air, combustion gases, or noble gases at the temperatures corresponding to ordinary combustion temperatures or heat exchangers. However, by the addition to the carrier gas of small amounts of an easily ionized compound such as the alkali metals, sufficient thermal ionization can be achieved.

Even then, only a small fraction of the ionizable material is ionized. Generally, the electron cross section of the seed material is much larger

Table 4-1.   *Molecular Weights and Ionization Potentials*†

Gas	Molecular weight	Ionization energy, electron volts	
		I	II
Noble gases			
Helium	4.03	24.46	54.14
Neon	21.83	21.47	40.9
Argon	39.4	15.68	27.76
Krypton	83.7	13.93	26.4
Xenon	130.2	12.08	21.1
Common gases			
H	1.008	13.53	
H_2	2.016	15.6	
N	14.008	14.48	29.47
N_2	28.016	15.51	
O	16.000	13.55	34.93
O_2	32.000	15.51	
CO	28.01	14.1	
CO_2	40.02	14.4	
NO	30.008	9.5	
Metal vapors (atoms)			
Lithium	6.940	5.363	75.26
Sodium	23.00	5.12	47.06
Aluminum	26.97	5.96	18.74
Potassium	39.10	4.318	31.66
Calcium	40.8	6.09	11.82
Rubidium	85.48	4.16	27.36
Cesium	132.91	3.87	14.8
Barium	137.36	5.19	9.95
Mercury	200.61	10.39	18.65

† From *Handbook of Chemistry and Physics*, 33d ed., Chemical Rubber Publishing Co.

than the gas cross section;[7] hence, as seed material is added to a gas, the corresponding conductivity at first increases, then decreases. It can be shown easily that the optimum seeding ratio is only a few percent. In addition to the ionization of the alkali metals, one must also take into account the production of negative ions by electron attachment to atoms, molecules, or radicals. This effect is important at the lower ranges of temperature.

Table 4-2. *Internal Partition Functions* P_{int} *of Various Neutral and Singly Ionized Seeding Elements†*

Element	Q^i at ground state, $T = 0°K$	2000°K	3000°K	4000°K	5000°K	6000°K	7000°K
Li	2	2.0000	2.0000	2.0579	2.0840	2.1716	2.2950
Li+	1	1	1	1	1	1	1
Na	2	2.0000	2.0018	2.0141	2.1468	2.1052	2.2134
Na+	1	1	1	1	1	1	1
K	2	2.0000	2.0000	2.0568	2.2421	2.3516	2.6074
K+	1	1	1	1	1	1	1
Rb	2	2.0000	2.0089	2.0630	2.1967	2.4043	2.6700
Rb+	1	1	1	1	1	1	1
Cs	2	2.0000	2.0245	2.1516	2.3950	2.7962	3.2898
Cs+	1	1	1	1	1	1	1
Ca	1	1.0000	1.0000	1.0340	1.1482	1.3272	1.5970
Ca+	2	2.0000	2.0087	2.0748	2.1992	2.3917	2.6439
Sr	1	1.0000	1.0000	1.0511	1.2411	1.5226	1.9371
Sr+	2	2	2	2	2	2	2
Ba	1	1.0000	1.1970	1.7008	2.4901	3.4752	4.5980
Ba+	2	2.2252	2.7920	3.4866	4.1732	4.8370	5.4324
Al	2	5.692	5.792	5.843	5.874	5.895	5.947
Al+	1	1	1	1	1	1	1

† From Robert S. Buchanan, "Study of a Seeded Plasma," University of Michigan Report, ARL 62-310, Contract 33(616)-8126, March, 1962.

The result of calculations of electrical conductivities for combustion gases[13] is shown in Fig. 4-3 for an assumed elastic cross section of 10^{-15} cm². This cross section may be too low by a factor of 2 or 3.[8]

For combustion cycles, the use of pure alkali metals is quite expensive, and a less expensive form must be used. Usually the alkali metal carbonate is used, either as a powder or in an aqueous solution. The hydroxide may also be used, dissolved in alcohol and mixed with the fuel oil with an emulsifier. In addition, pollucite, which is a natural ore containing 27 percent cesium, has been considered.

For application to closed Rankine cycles using liquid metals, in which the vapor in the generator may be "wet," that is, contain droplets of liquid, theories of ionization have recently been developed which take into account electron and ion capture and thermionic emission of the droplet as well as the gaseous atoms. Although the equilibrium ionization depends on the droplet size, for a droplet radius greater than 50 A, it is approximately given by [14,15]

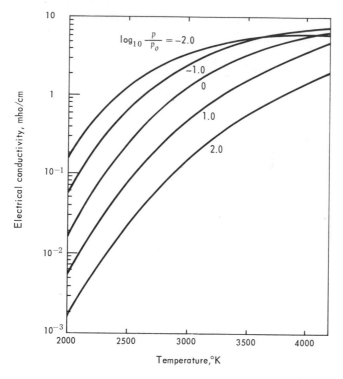

Fig. 4-3. *Electrical conductivity of combustion gases seeded with 1 percent potassium.*[13] $Q_{eg} = 10^{-15}$ *cm²;* $Q_{ek} = 40 \times 10^{-15}$ *cm²;* $P_o = 1.0$ *atm.*

$$n_e = 2 \left(\frac{2\pi m_e kT}{h^2} \right)^{3/2} e^{-\phi_s/kT} \qquad\qquad (4\text{-}21b)$$

where ϕ_s is the work function of the flat liquid surface.

3-2. Magnetically Induced Ionization

One of the simplest methods of nonequilibrium ionization is the application of a d-c voltage across a gas at reduced pressure. In this case, the electric field feeds energy to the electrons, which in turn transfer the energy to the heavy particles in the gas. But because of the small mass ratio, only a small fraction of the electron energy is transferred during an elastic collision with heavy particles. If the majority of the electron collisions are elastic, the effect is that the electron translational energy is much higher than that of the heavier gas particles. The initial concentration of electrons is due to cosmic radiation and other random processes; these are "heated" by the above process and, as they acquire energies greater than the ionization energy, cause additional ionization. This process is known as a glow discharge and was one of the first demonstrations of sustained electrical discharges in gases.

Only recently was it demonstrated that the same effect could be achieved in seeded noble gases if the gas temperature was elevated.[16] Equation (4-36) describes the electron heating; if one assumes that gradients in the gas may be neglected, this becomes

$$\mathbf{E^*} \cdot \mathbf{j}_e = 3kn_e m_e (T_e - T) \sum_{s \neq e} \frac{\delta_s \nu_{es}}{m.} \tag{4-22}$$

The electron current is given by Eq. (4-17a), and the degree of ionization may be obtained from Saha's equation, Eq. (4-21a), based on the electron temperature. Saha's equation may be used because the ionization cross section is much larger for electron impacts than for heavy-particle impacts. Thus, at high electron densities, electron impacts are mainly responsible for ionization. Deionization provides the detailed balance required from statistical mechanical considerations. Thus, the ionization and deionization processes depend on only the electron temperature and are insensitive to the temperature of the heavy particles. Therefore, the degree of ionization should be predicted by Saha's equation, based on electron temperature. The agreement between theory and experiment[17] is shown in Fig. 4-4. Note that the discrepancy decreases with increasing electron density. The discrepancy can be explained on the basis of the effect of radiation losses. In general the resonant radiation from the first excited level of the seed atoms is trapped within the gas because of the high population of seed atoms in the ground state; but the population of upper states is insufficient to trap radiation from the transitions of upper states. The next effect is a loss of electron energy, so that the electron temperature is not so high as that predicted by the assumption of only elastic collisions. Work currently in progress has shown that in argon and potassium mixtures this effect also exists in the presence of a magnetic field but with a slight reduction in the measured conductivity.[18]

In applying this technique to MHD generators, it is obvious that the carrier gas must be an inert gas because the values of δ_s for diatomic and polyatomic gases are too great to allow for appreciable electron heating.

The above theory has been extended to include the effect of small alkali-metal droplets on alkali-metal vapors as may exist in a closed Rankine cycle.[14,15] The results indicate that for droplet sizes greater than about 50 A, considerable electron heating should still be possible. Smaller

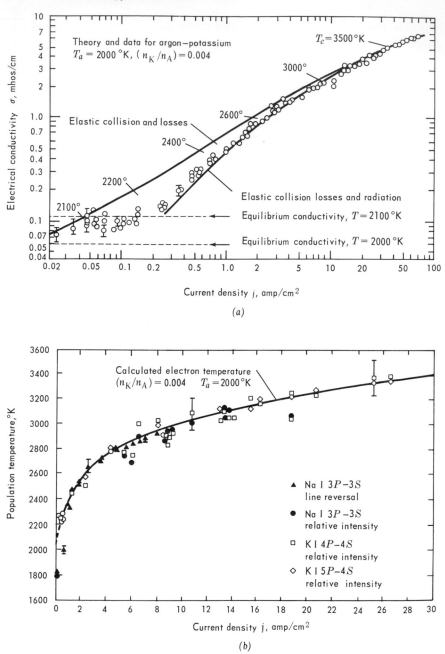

Fig. 4-4. *Nonequilibrium ionization in noble gases seeded with potassium.*[17]   *(a) Electrical conductivity in argon; (b) electron temperature in argon.*

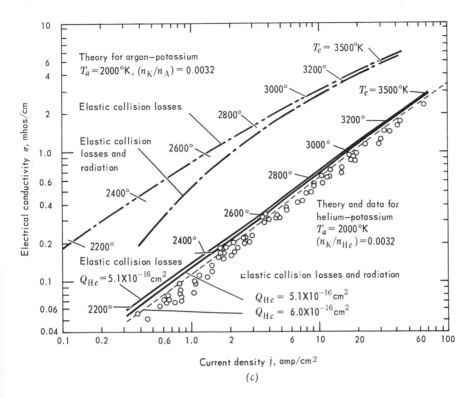

Fig. 4-4 *(Continued).* *(c) Electrical conductivity in helium.*

droplet sizes generally depress the electron temperature. For example, measurements in potassium with 2 percent moisture at 0.005 atm have shown that the resulting conductivity is depressed by an order of magnitude.[14] This corresponds for a value of δ for the droplets of about 100, which indicates a droplet size of about 10 A. However, for an MHD generator, this would correspond to a small increase in required magnetic field.[15] In an MHD generator the induced Faraday and Hall fields may be used for electron heating. With the use of Eq. (4-17a), the left side of Eq. (4-22) becomes

$$\mathbf{E}^* \cdot \mathbf{j}_e = \frac{\sigma}{1 + \beta_e^2} |\mathbf{E}^*|^2 \qquad (4\text{-}23)$$

To proceed further, the geometry of the generator must be specified since the value of $\mathbf{E}^*$ depends on the electrode configuration. Magnetically induced ionization is presently being investigated mainly in segmented-electrode generators; hence this case is given below.

Segmented electrodes.[19]   In the segmented-electrode generator, the total Hall current is zero so that the electric field from Eq. (5-44) is given by

$$E_y^* = -(1 - K)UB$$

$$E_x^* = -\frac{(1 - K)\beta_e UB}{1 + \beta_e \beta_I} \tag{4-24}$$

Substitution of Eq. (4-24) into Eq. (4-23) yields

$$|E^{*2}| = \frac{\sigma(1 - K)^2 U^2 B^2}{1 + \beta_e^2} \left[\frac{1 + \beta_e^2 + 2\beta_e \beta_I + \beta_e^2 \beta_I^2}{(1 + \beta_e \beta_I)^2} \right] \tag{4-25}$$

In the numerator of the bracket, β_I may be neglected in comparison with β_e; substitution of Eq. (4-25) into Eq. (4-22) yields

$$\frac{T_e}{T} = 1 + \frac{\nu(1 - K)^2 \beta_e^2 M^2}{3\delta(1 + \beta_e \beta_I)^2} \tag{4-26}$$

for the asymptotic electron temperature where M is the gas-dynamic Mach number U/a and a is the frozen sound speed given by

$$a^2 = \frac{\gamma p}{\rho} = \frac{\gamma \sum_s n_s k T_s}{\sum n_s m_s}$$

Because of the small number density and mass of electrons, the sound speed can be approximated by

$$a^2 = \frac{\gamma k T}{\sum_{s \neq e} X_s m_s} \tag{4-27}$$

where X_s is the number fraction of the s species, n_s/n.   In Eq. (4-26), δ is the average correction factor for inelastic collisions, given by

$$\delta = \frac{\left(\sum_{s \neq e} X_s m_s \right)\left(\sum_{s \neq e} X_s Q_{es} \delta_s / m_s \right)}{\sum_{s \neq e} X_s Q_{es}} \tag{4-28}$$

From Eq. (4-28), it can be seen that if the species with the largest cross section also has a large mass, it is possible to obtain values of δ less than unity.[19]

As the magnetic field, i.e., β_e, is increased, the factor $\beta_e^2/(1 + \beta_e\beta_I)^2$ has a maximum when $\beta_e = (\mu_e/\mu_I)^{1/2}$, which can be of the order of 10 to 20. The maximum value of the factor is therefore

$$\left.\frac{\beta_e^2}{(1 + \beta_e\beta_I)^2}\right|_{max} = \frac{\beta_{e_{max}}^2}{4} = \frac{1}{4}\frac{\mu_e}{\mu_I} \qquad (4\text{-}29)$$

which is of the order of 25 to 250. Thus, considerable electron heating should be possible in a segmented-electrode generator.[20]

Present status. An extensive review of the theory and status of magnetically induced ionization as of 1964 may be found in Ref. 21. As of that time, the results of a few experiments aimed at achieving magnetically induced ionization had been disappointing. The possible mechanisms responsible for the poor results are nonuniformities in the gas, which tend to short out the Hall currents and decrease the electron heating; fluctuations in the gas properties (see Sec. 7); or possibly nonuniform current flow in the vicinity of segmented electrodes (see Sec. 7). This last effect may be particularly deleterious because, coupled with electron heating, the nonuniformities may lead to shorting of the Hall current between adjacent electrodes through the gas. This is caused by the Joule heating in the gas adjacent to the insulator between two adjacent electrodes, which varies as $(\omega_e\tau_e)^4$, while from Eq. (4-26) the Joule heating in the body of the gas varies as $(\omega_e\tau_e)^2$. The local Joule heating may increase the local electron temperature and therefore the degree of ionization near the electrodes, thus leading to shorting. Detailed theoretical calculations by Kerrebrock[22] have indicated that this effect can lead to reductions of overall performance. It was also found that cooling of the insulator (and possibly electrodes) should reduce the shorting by reducing the local electron temperature. In addition, coarser segmentation, by increasing the path length for the shorting current, should reduce the shorting. It was also concluded that operation at low values of $\omega_e\tau_e$ (compensated by a high Mach number) would lead to better performance than operation at high values of $\omega_e\tau_e$. This is consistent with the dependence of the shorting current on $(\omega_e\tau_e)^4$. By combining all these effects, Kerrebrock calculated a stability boundary for which shorting could be avoided and concludes that the available experimental data are consistent with his theoretical results.[22]

The shorting effect has recently been verified by Zauderer[23] in a shock-tube-driven generator. He found that at high values of $\omega_e\tau_e$, if the rates of electrode width to electrode pitch are greater than 0.75, the segmented electrodes act as one continuous electrode.

Experiments have also been performed recently which were designed to investigate the possibility of a stability boundary as suggested above by Klepeis and Rosa.[24]   A mixture of helium and cesium was used, heated to temperatures of 1900 to 2000°K and at a Mach number of 0.8.   However, the segmentation was reduced ($h/d = 4$; see Sec. 7) as suggested. For a magnetic field corresponding to a theoretical value of $\omega_e \tau_e$ of 2.5, at short circuit, a slight increase in conductivity was measured.   However, at a higher value of $\omega_e \tau_e$ equal to 4, there was a notable decrease in measured electrical current.   This lends some support to the theory of local electron heating.   On the other hand, considerable electrical noise was measured, so that it is possible that fluctuations played a role.

Other experiments in heated helium and cesium have been run by McNab and Brown[25] at a gas temperature of about 1500 to 1650°K and at a Mach number of about 0.1 and 0.9 atm pressure.   Only a single pair of electrodes was used in a magnetic field of 10,000 gauss corresponding to $\omega_e \tau_e = 2.9$.   Power was produced, and increases in the conductivity of a factor of 6 above the equilibrium value of 1 mho/m were measured.   When correlated in a manner similar to that shown in Fig. 4-4, the data correspond to a value of δ equal to 4.   This increase in conductivity corresponds to an increase in the electron temperature of 200°K, while on the basis of Eq. (4-26), an increase of only 80°K is expected even for $\delta = 1$.

The results of both of these more recent experiments indicate that a modest amount of magnetically induced ionization has in fact been realized, but additional experimental work is necessary to determine the maximum ionization that can be achieved.

4.   Magnetohydrodynamic Equations

In this section, the equations of fluid mechanics both for species and overall are presented.   The overall equations will be used in Sec. 8 for analysis of compressible flow in generators.   The electron energy equation has already been used in Sec. 3.2 for electron heating; and the electron momentum equation may be regarded as equivalent to a generalized Ohm's law for electron conduction.

The global equation of continuity is as follows:

Global continuity

$$\frac{\partial \rho}{\partial t} + \boldsymbol{\nabla} \cdot (\rho \mathbf{v}) = 0 \tag{4-30}$$

In addition to the global equation of continuity, it is sometimes necessary to consider the equation of continuity for each species.   This is as follows:

Species continuity

$$\frac{\partial \rho_s}{\partial t} + \mathbf{\nabla} \cdot (\rho_s \mathbf{v}_s) = \dot{\rho}_s \tag{4-31}$$

When each of the species-continuity equations is multiplied by the ratio of charge to mass q_s/m_s and summed, there results the equation of charge conservation:

Charge conservation

$$\frac{\partial \rho_e}{\partial t} + \mathbf{\nabla} \cdot \mathbf{J} = 0 \tag{4-32}$$

where $\mathbf{J} = \displaystyle\sum_s n_s e Z_s \mathbf{v}_s = \mathbf{v}\rho_e + \mathbf{j}$ and $\mathbf{j}$ is the total conduction current, $\mathbf{j} = \displaystyle\sum_s n_s e Z_s \mathbf{v}_s.$

For the momentum equation, the Lorentz force $\mathbf{J} \times \mathbf{B}$ and the electrostatic force $\rho_e \mathbf{E}$ must be added to the ordinary equations of fluid mechanics.

Momentum

$$\frac{D\mathbf{v}}{Dt} + \mathbf{\nabla} p + \mathbf{\nabla} \cdot \boldsymbol{\tau} = \mathbf{J} \times \mathbf{B} + \rho_e \mathbf{E}$$
$$= \mathbf{j} \times \mathbf{B} + \rho_e \mathbf{E}^* \tag{4-33}$$

where $\boldsymbol{\tau}$ is shear-stress tensor and $D/Dt = \partial/\partial t + \mathbf{v} \cdot \mathbf{\nabla}$.

Since in MHD generators the gas is close to electrical neutrality, the only additional term is the Lorentz force due to the conduction current. It should be noted that the steady-steady momentum equation for electrons leads to the Ohm's law for electrons.

The overall energy equation is given by

Energy

$$\rho \frac{DH}{Dt} - \frac{\partial p}{\partial t} = -\mathbf{\nabla} \cdot \mathbf{q} - \mathbf{\nabla} \cdot (\mathbf{v} \cdot \boldsymbol{\tau}) + \mathbf{E} \cdot \mathbf{J} \tag{4-34}$$

where H is the total enthalpy,

$$H = h + \frac{1}{2} v^2 = \sum_s \left(\int C_{p_s} \, dT + h_s{}^0 \right) + \frac{1}{2} v^2 \tag{4-35}$$

Since the ionized gas is essentially neutral, the total current $\mathbf{J}$ in Eq. (4-35) can be replaced by the conduction current. It should be noted that the heavy particles in the gas equilibrate their translational energy within a few collisions; hence they have a common temperature T. However, because of the small electron mass, the electrons equilibrate with the heavy particles very slowly through elastic collisions; they may have a different temperature. This is described by the energy equation for electrons,

$$n_e \frac{D_e}{Dt}\left(\frac{3}{2} kT_e + \frac{1}{2} v_e^2\right) + \nabla \cdot q_e + p_e \nabla \cdot \mathbf{v}_e$$

$$= \mathbf{E}^* \cdot \mathbf{j}_e + 3kn_e m_e(T - T_e) \sum_{s \neq e} \frac{\delta_s \nu_{es}}{m_s} \quad (4\text{-}36)$$

where δ_s is a correction factor to account for inelastic collisions with each species and additional ionization has been neglected. The value of δ_s may be obtained from Ref. 26.

5. *Local Inviscid Analyses of Linear MHD Generators*

In the local analysis of an MHD generator, one usually assumes that the properties, such as conductivity, density, gas velocity, and Hall parameter, are all constant. The advantage of such an analysis is that the gross operating characteristics can be determined. In the following analysis, viscosity and thermal conductivity will also be neglected. The velocity U is taken constant in the x direction, and the magnetic field is taken constant in the z direction (see Fig. 4-5). The induced electric field $\mathbf{v} \times \mathbf{B}$ is then UB in the negative y direction. Then from Eq. (4-20), the components of the current become

$$j_x = \frac{\sigma}{(1 + \beta_I \beta_e)^2 + \beta_e^2} [(1 + \beta_I \beta_e)E_x - \beta_e(E_y - UB)] \quad (4\text{-}37)$$

$$j_y = \frac{\sigma}{(1 + \beta_I \beta_e)^2 + \beta_e^2} [(1 + \beta_I \beta_e)(E_y - UB) + \beta_e E_x]$$

where $\beta_I = \omega_I \tau_{In}$ and $\beta_e = \omega_e \tau_e$.

In the absence of velocity or thermal boundary layers both E_x and E_y may be considered constant (although more generally they may be a func-

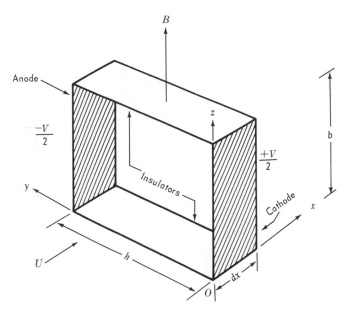

Fig. 4-5. *Schematic diagram for "local analysis" of linear MHD generators.*

tion of x).   Then all variables are constant across a cross section, so that the electric field and current in the direction of the magnetic field are zero.†

We will next use this simple model to analyze the three most common types of linear generators: the continuous-electrode generator, the segmented-electrode generator, and the Hall generator (see Fig. 4-6).

5-1. *Continuous-electrode Generator*

With the electrodes continuous along each side of the generator with a different constant potential on each, no axial electric field can develop and therefore $E_x = 0$.   Then from Eq. (4-37), the transverse component of the current is

$$j_y = \frac{\sigma}{(1 + \beta_e\beta_I)^2 + \beta_e^2} [(1 + \beta_e\beta_I)(E_y - UB)] \qquad (4\text{-}38)$$

† Velocity boundary layers on the insulators cause the induced field $\mathbf{v} \times \mathbf{B}$ within the boundary layer to be less than that at the center line.   Under these conditions the current in the boundary layer may be in the opposite direction from that in the main flow and thus constitute a "leakage" current.   However, if the electrical conductivity is constant, the average axial velocity across a cross section may be used instead of U.

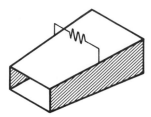

Continuous electrodes

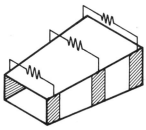

Segmented electrodes

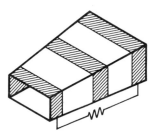

Fig. 4-6. Linear-generator geometries having rectangular cross sections.

Hall generator

The open-circuit condition implies that $j_y = 0$; thus, from Eq. (4-38), the open-circuit electric field is UB. Under short-circuit conditions, $E_y = 0$ (except for the finite electrical resistance of the electrodes and external connection). Thus, in general, $0 < E_y < UB$. It is common to express the electric field under load as a fraction K of the open-circuit electric field; thus, for the continuous electrode geometry,

$$K = \frac{E_y}{UB} \tag{4-39}$$

where for generation of electrical power $0 < K < 1$. Note that j_y is then negative and the Lorentz force $\mathbf{j} \times \mathbf{B}$ is in the negative x direction, that is, *opposite* to the flow direction. Thus, in the generator, the Lorentz force tends to *retard* the flow.

In addition to the transverse component of the electric current, there is also a component in the downstream direction given by

$$j_x = \frac{\sigma \beta_e (1 - K) UB}{(1 + \beta_I \beta_e)^2 + \beta_e^2} \qquad (4\text{-}40)$$

where use has been made of Eq. (4-39). Thus, the current, as it flows across the generator, also tends to flow downstream. Actually, it is the current in the downstream direction which is responsible for the Lorentz force on the gas through collision between the electrons and heavy particles.

The power generated per unit volume is $P = -\mathbf{E} \cdot \mathbf{j}$, which becomes $j_y E_y$ since $E_x = 0$. From Eqs. (4-38) and (4-39) this becomes

$$P = \frac{\sigma K (1 - K) U^2 B^2 (1 + \beta_e \beta_I)}{(1 + \beta_e \beta_I)^2 \beta_e^2} \qquad (4\text{-}41)$$

Equation (4-41) can also be written as

$$P = \frac{n_e m_e U^2 K (1 - K)}{\tau_e} \frac{\beta_e^2 (1 + \beta_e^2 \mu_I / \mu_e)}{(1 + \beta_e^2 \mu_I / \mu_e)^2 + \beta_e^2} \qquad (4\text{-}42)$$

where μ_I and μ_e are the ion and electron mobilities $e\tau_{In}/m_I$ and $e\tau_e/m_e$, respectively. The factor on the right side of Eq. (4-42) represents the effects of the Hall reduction in electrical conductivity and ion slip for this geometry and has two asymptotes. The first asymptote corresponds to extraction of the electron kinetic energy, which is replenished by collisions with the heavy particles. The second asymptote corresponds to extraction of the ion kinetic energy, but this requires values of the magnetic field which are beyond present capabilities. For a value of $\omega_e \tau_e$ of about 2, the power density is approximately 80 percent of the first asymptote; hence, increases in the magnetic field above that required to achieve this value are not warranted.

From Eq. (4-41), it is obvious that the power-generation density is a maximum when $K = \frac{1}{2}$, which corresponds to matched impedance, that is, when the load resistance is equal to the generator internal resistance. However, for some applications, it may not be desirable to operate at maximum power density but, instead, closer to maximum efficiency. For the purpose of a local analysis, a local conversion efficiency may be defined as the ratio of the generated power to the flow work which is required to overcome the Lorentz force, or

$$\eta_L = \frac{P}{\mathbf{v} \cdot \mathbf{j} \times \mathbf{B}} \qquad (4\text{-}43)$$

In the present geometry, the denominator of Eq. (4-43) is Uj_yB, while the numerator is E_yj_y; thus, the local efficiency for this geometry is $E_y/UB = K$, from (4-39). The polytropic efficiency, however, is less than K (see Sec. 6).

5-2. *Segmented-electrode Generator*

In the previous section, it was shown that with increasing magnetic field, the generated power density has a low first asymptote, because of the Hall reduction in electrical conductivity in the direction of the electric field. To increase the power density, the segmented-electrode generator has been devised,[27,28] in which each opposite pair of electrodes is connected to a single load (see Fig. 4-6). In this arrangement, the current flow is essentially transverse to the gas flow and no net Hall current exists in the downstream direction.

With the Hall current j_x equal to zero, Eq. (4-37) predicts that an electric field will develop in the axial direction given by

$$E_x = \frac{\beta_e}{1 + \beta_e\beta_I} (E_y - UB) \tag{4-44}$$

so that the current in the y direction becomes

$$j_y = \frac{\sigma}{1 + \beta_e\beta_I} (E_y - UB) \tag{4-45}$$

As in the previous section, the open-circuit voltage corresponding to $j_y = 0$ is UB; we therefore take the electric field under load as KUB. The Lorentz force $\mathbf{j} \times \mathbf{B}$ now acts only in the negative x direction so that it acts only to retard the flow. This force is caused mainly by the ion slip.

The power density is $-\mathbf{E} \cdot \mathbf{j} = -E_yj_y$, or

$$\begin{aligned}
P &= \frac{K(1 - K)\sigma U^2B^2}{1 + \beta_e\beta_I} \\
&= \frac{n_em_eU^2K(1 - K)}{\tau_e} \frac{\beta_e^2}{1 + \beta_e^2\mu_I/\mu_e}
\end{aligned} \tag{4-46}$$

As in the case of continuous electrodes, the power density initially increases quadratically with increasing magnetic field (since $\beta_e = e\tau_eB/m_e$, and the last factor of Eq. (4-46) becomes asymptotic to μ_e/μ_I (see Fig. 4-7). However, for intermediate values of β_e, no first asymptote appears in the power density as was the case for continuous electrodes. Thus, for $1 < \beta_e < \mu_e/\mu_I$, the generated power of the segmented-electrode geometry greatly exceeds that for the continuous-electrode geometry.

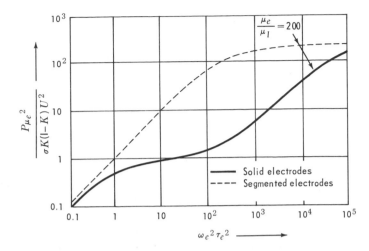

Fig. 4-7. *Power density for continuous (solid) and segmented electrodes.*

The local efficiency is still equal to K, since $\eta_L = E_y j_y / UB j_y$. Thus, the increase in power density has been obtained with no sacrifice in efficiency. The power density is still a maximum when $K = \frac{1}{2}$.

The segmented-electrode generator has the disadvantage, as compared with the continuous-electrode or Hall generator, of requiring a multiplicity of loads, each at a different potential. This can be corrected by providing external connections between electrode segments on opposite sides of the generator which are at the same potential. In this way, the number of loads can be reduced to a few or even one.

5-3. Hall Generator[29]

It was shown in the previous section that when the electrodes are segmented, an electric field develops in the flow direction. This electric field is maximum when the opposite electrodes are short-circuited, that is, when $E_y = 0$. If the electrode pair at the inlet is connected through a load to the pair at the exit, a current should flow through the load. With $E_y = 0$, the current density in the $+x$ direction is obtained from Eq. (4-37):

$$j_x = \frac{\sigma}{(1 + \beta_e \beta_I)^2 + \beta_e^2} [(1 + \beta_e \beta_I) E_x + \beta_e UB] \qquad (4\text{-}47)$$

When open-circuited, the axial electric field is $-\beta_e UB / (1 + \beta_e \beta_I)$; under load the axial electric field will be some fraction K_H of this value, $E_x = -\beta_e K_H UB / (1 + \beta_e \beta_I)$, so that

$$j_x = \frac{\sigma \beta_e (1 - K_H) UB}{(1 + \beta_e \beta_I)^2 + \beta_e^2} \tag{4-48}$$

Note that the definition of K_H is different from K for the continuous- and segmented-electrode geometries. The generated power density is

$$P = -E_x j_x$$

$$= \frac{K_H(1 - K_H)\sigma \beta_e^2 U^2 B^2}{(1 + \beta_e \beta_I)[(1 + \beta_e \beta_I)^2 + \beta_e^2]}$$

$$= \frac{n_e m_e U^2 K_H (1 - K_H)}{\tau_e} \frac{\beta_e^4}{(1 + \beta_e^2 \mu_I/\mu_e)[(1 + \beta_e^2 \mu_I/\mu_e)^2 + \beta_e^2]} \tag{4-49}$$

In this geometry, as the magnetic field is increased from zero, the power increases as the fourth power of the magnetic field, in contrast to the quadratic dependence of the continuous- and segmented-electrode geometries. An asymptote is reached when $\beta_e > \mu_e/\mu_I$, equal to $(\mu_e/\mu_I)^3 \beta_e^{-2}$, which is considerably smaller than the asymptote of μ_e/μ_I obtained in the continuous- and segmented-electrode generators. However, for $2 < \beta_e < (\mu_e/\mu_I)^{1/2}$, the power density approaches that of the segmented-electrode geometry.

The retarding Lorentz force $j_y B$ becomes

$$F_x = \frac{-\sigma U B^2}{1 + \beta_e \beta_I} \frac{1 + \beta_e'^2 K_H}{1 + \beta_e'^2} \tag{4-50}$$

where β_e' is the effective Hall parameter for electrons defined in Eq. (4-19). Note that the retarding Lorentz force is a minimum when the load is short-circuited, that is, when $K_H = 0$. This is in sharp contrast to the previous geometry, where the retarding force is a maximum when short-circuited.

The local efficiency of the Hall generator is the ratio of the power, Eq. (4-49), to the flow work UF_x when F_x is given by Eq. (4-50). Thus,

$$\eta_L = \frac{\beta_e'^2 K_H (1 - K_H)}{1 + \beta_e'^2 K_H} \tag{4-51}$$

Values of the local efficiency are shown in Fig. 4-8, where it is seen that β_e' must be large in order for the local efficiency to be close to unity. For large values of $\beta_e'^2$, the efficiency becomes

$$\lim_{\beta_e' \to \infty} \eta_L \to (1 - K_H) \tag{4-52}$$

Thus, maximum efficiency is achieved when the Hall generator is operated at close to short circuit, which is opposite to that of the Faraday generators previously discussed.

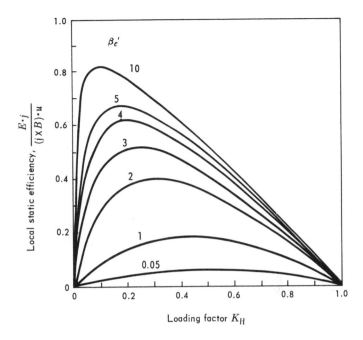

Fig. 4-8. *Local static efficiencies of a Hall MHD generator for various values of β_e'.*

Experiments in seeded combustion gases have essentially verified the power relations given above for the continuous-electrode, segmented-electrode, and Hall generators.[30]   In those experiments, however, the electrical conductivity and generator dimensions were relatively small, so that the Lorentz force was small in comparison with the friction pressure drop; hence, it was not possible to verify the efficiency relations.

5-4. A-C Power Generation

At the present time, various proposed methods for the generation of a-c power do not appear promising.   The primary difficulty lies with the low magnetic Reynolds number, defined as $\sigma u \mu_0 L$ where L is a typical length, which is a measure of the displacement of the magnetic field by a flowing, electrically conducting fluid and, for an a-c MHD generator, is related to the power factor.   For example, one may conceive of generating a-c power by alternating the magnetic field in a linear MHD generator of the type previously described.   Now, the energy associated with the magnetic field is $B^2/2\mu_0$ per unit volume.   If the magnetic field is operated a-c with a frequency f, the average rate of power flow to the magnetic field, which may be regarded as the reactive power, is $Bf/2\mu_0$. On the other hand, the maximum average power, from Eq. (4-41), is of the order of $-\frac{1}{8}\sigma U^2 B^2$, which is the load power. Thus, the ratio of the reactive power to load power is

$$\frac{4f}{\sigma u^2 \mu_0} = \frac{4}{\sigma u \mu_0 L} \tag{4-53}$$

where L is the length that the gas moves during one cycle. Thus the power factor is inversely proportional to the magnetic Reynolds number. As an example, consider a generator in which the conductivity is 30 mhos/m and the gas velocity is 10^3 m/sec. Then for the reactive power to be equal or less than the load power, the frequency must be 0.1 cycle per second or less, which is not very useful. For 60 cycles, this ratio is 600. Not only is this impractical because of the large number of capacitors which must be used to reduce the overall reactive load, but the circuits must be extremely nonlossy.

The situation is not very different for induction MHD generators. The ratio of reactive power to real power is still equal to the reciprocal of the magnetic Reynolds number, which is now defined as

$$R_m = \frac{\mu_0 \sigma u \lambda (1 - S)}{2\pi} \tag{4-54}$$

where λ is the wavelength of the generator windings, in the direction of the flow, and S is the slip velocity of the traveling magnetic field with respect to the gas.[1] The load power is given by

$$P = \frac{1}{2} \frac{S(1 - S)\sigma u^2 B_0^2}{1 + R_m^2} \tag{4-55}$$

Thus, the slip velocity S replaces the load factor K. The factor of $\frac{1}{2}$ is caused by the sinusoidal variation of power output, as is usually associated with a-c power. Equation (4-55) clearly shows that increasing the magnetic Reynolds number will decrease the power density. However, it is unlikely that magnetic Reynolds numbers in excess of unity can be achieved as previously explained.

Another problem is the high frequency of the current; the frequency is given by $u_B/\lambda = u/S\lambda$. The gas velocity must be high in order to have a high power density. Thus, the frequency will be quite high, unless the wavelength is made exceptionally long, which will cause the generator length also to be long.

6. Conversion Efficiency of MHD Generators

The local efficiency which was defined in the previous section must be converted to be useful for thermodynamic cycles, the reason being that the previous definition was based on local conditions instead of stagnation conditions. The local efficiency was defined by Eq. (4-43) and can also be represented on a Mollier diagram along the static line AB (see Fig. 4-9). Consider two axial stations 1 and 2 along an MHD generator which are a distance Δx apart. As the gas passes between these two stations, the total enthalpy per unit mass is changed by ΔH, which is also equal to the change in static enthalpy if the change in gas velocity is negligible, while the static pressure change is $p_1\text{-}p_2$. The ideal change in static enthalpy between these two pressures is Δh_i. The *local* efficiency may therefore also be defined as

$$\eta_L = \frac{\Delta H}{\Delta h_i} \tag{4-56}$$

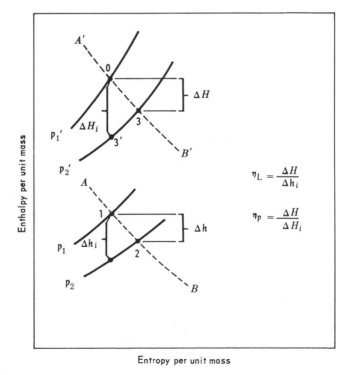

Fig. 4-9. *Relation between local and polytropic efficiencies.*

However, the thermodynamicist is usually interested in the *stagnation* behavior of the gas, as along the line $A'B'$. The reason for this is that the gas usually starts at a small Mach number in a combustor or heat exchanger and, after being accelerated in a nozzle and passing through the generator, is again brought almost to rest to recover the pressure or to pass the gas through a heat exchanger or some other low-speed device. The local efficiency calculated on the basis of stagnation conditions is called the *polytropic* efficiency η_p, sometimes called the *stage* or *local adiabatic* efficiency. From Fig. 4-9, $\eta_p = \Delta H/\Delta H_i$. Now, because of the spreading of the constant-pressure lines with increasing enthalpy, $\Delta H_i > \Delta h_i$; hence, $\eta_p < \eta_L$.

It can be shown that the relation between the polytropic efficiency and the local efficiency is given by[1]

$$\eta_p = (T_s/\eta_L b_e T + 1 - T_s/T)^{-1} \tag{4-57}$$

where T_s/T is the ratio of the local stagnation temperature to static temperature, which for a perfect gas is given by

$$\frac{T_s}{T} = 1 + \frac{\gamma - 1}{2} M^2 \tag{4-58}$$

where M is the local Mach number and b_e is the fraction of the pressure drop due to the Lorentz force. For example, consider a frictionless generator; for this case $b_e = 1$, and use of Eq. (4-58) in Eq. (4-57) yields

$$\eta_p = \frac{\eta_L}{1 + [(\gamma - 1)/2]M^2(1 - \eta_L)} \tag{4-59}$$

Thus, for the polytropic efficiency to be close to the local efficiency η_L, either η_L must be close to unity or else $\frac{1}{2}(\gamma - 1)M^2$ must be small. Thus, the local efficiency η_L is identically equal to the polytropic efficiency of a subsonic, zero-heat-transfer, zero-friction flow. For combustion gases where $\gamma \approx 1.2$, $M \approx 1$, and $\eta_L = 0.8$, the polytropic efficiency is only 2 percent less than η_L. But for gases in which $\gamma = 5/3$, $M = 2$, and $\eta_L = 0.8$, the polytropic efficiency is almost 25 percent less than the local efficiency η_L.

The overall generator efficiency is defined as

$$\eta_g = \frac{a_e(H_0 - H_3)}{H_0 - H_{3'}} \tag{4-60}$$

where a_e is the fraction of $(H_0 - H_3)$ converted into electrical energy. The generator efficiency can also be written as

$$\eta_g = a_e \frac{\left[1 - (p_{s_3}/p_{s_0})^{\langle \eta_p^{(\gamma-1)}/a_e\gamma \rangle}\right]}{\left[1 - (p_{s_3}/p_{s_0})^{\langle (\gamma-1)/\gamma \rangle}\right]} \qquad (4\text{-}61)$$

where the brackets $\langle \ \rangle$ indicate average values. For small pressure ratios across the generator, that is, for $p_{s_3}/p_{s_0} \approx 1$, the generator efficiency given by Eq. (4-61) becomes just η_p. But for large pressure ratios, the pressure-ratio terms in Eq. (4-61) become small and the generator efficiency approaches a_e; if the pressure ratio is sufficiently large, the generator efficiency becomes independent of the polytropic efficiency. This effect is well known in the design of steam turbines and is the reason for designing them for very large pressure ratios. The reason for the high efficiency is as follows: The dissipation in each stage, or at each section of the generator, appears as heat energy which is passed onto the next stage or section; the main effect of the dissipation is a loss of total pressure, which is small because of the flattening of the constant-pressure lines at low pressure on the Mollier diagram. From Eq. (4-61), it is seen that the generator efficiency is larger, the larger the pressure ratio. Note that large pressure ratios imply large temperature ratios. However, in an MHD generator, in which combustion gases are used at pressures greater than 1 atm, the lowest total temperature at which the gas still has sufficient electrical conductivity is about 2300°K; the highest possible flame temperature is about 4500°K. For these conditions, it is important that the polytropic efficiency be as high as possible because the generator efficiency, as calculated from Eq. (4-61), will be only slightly larger than η_p. The generator efficiency will be improved appreciably over the polytropic efficiency only if the pressure ratio is very large, which requires some method for improving the electrical conductivity at low temperatures.

7. Electrical Losses in MHD Generators

In addition to the friction losses described in Sec. 6, there may be electrical losses in the MHD generator, caused by inhomogeneous current flow in the generator. Generally, there are four such losses:

1. End losses, associated with eddy currents at the inlet and exit of the generator
2. Effects in the vicinity of segmented electrodes, especially when the conductivity is tensor
3. Instabilities associated with the Lorentz force

4.   Inhomogeneities and fluctuations in the electrical properties of the gas, which tend to short out the Hall current

Each of these losses will be discussed below.

7-1. End Losses

End losses are caused by the flow of current from the positive electrode to the negative electrode in the ionized gas upstream and downstream of the magnetic field.   For the mathematical analysis of such problems, it is usually assumed that the gas properties, velocity, and magnetic field are constant, that the boundary layer is negligible, and that the sides of the generator are straight and parallel.   With these assumptions, there is no variation in the direction of the magnetic field, so that the problem becomes two-dimensional in the plane normal to **B**.   Also, because of the assumption of constant properties, both the electric-field gradient and electric-current-stream function obey Laplace's equation.   Thus, the problem can generally be solved by conformal mapping.   The results show that for a rectangular channel, the losses at the inlet and outlet cause the net conversion efficiency to be decreased.[31,32]   The expression is

$$\eta = K \left[1 - \frac{Ka^*}{1 - K} \right] \tag{4-62}$$

where K is the generator loading factor and a^* is proportional to the generator aspect ratio,

$$a^* = \frac{2}{\pi} \frac{h}{L} \ln 2 \tag{4-63}$$

Note that as the generator becomes very long, that is, as $a^* \to 0$, the expression for the efficiency becomes identical with the "local" efficiency K.   Also, $K = 0$ still corresponds to short circuit, but open-circuit conditions correspond to the bracket in Eq. (4-62) equal to zero, e.g., when

$$K_{o.c.} = \frac{1}{1 + a^*} \tag{4-64}$$

Thus, the larger the value of a^*, the smaller the open-circuit voltage.   However, when the voltage is equal to the open-circuit voltage, the efficiency is equal to zero, rather than equal to K as for the ideal generator.   A typical efficiency curve is shown in Fig. 4-10 for an aspect ratio $L/h = 1$.   Note that the maximum efficiency is only 0.29, corresponding to a loading factor of 0.45.   As the aspect ratio L/h increases, a^* decreases and both the maximum efficiency and loading factor at maximum efficiency increase.   For any given aspect ratio, the maximum efficiency is obtained by equating

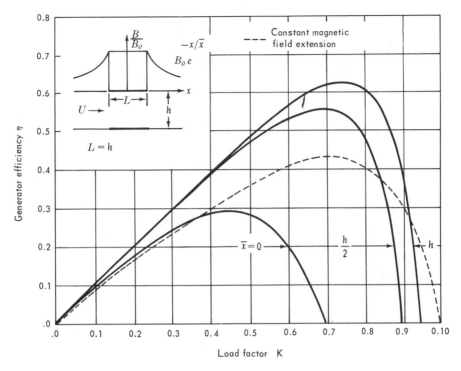

Fig. 4-10. *Generator efficiency for channel length equal to channel width.*

to zero the derivative of Eq. (4-62).   The maximum efficiency is then given by

$$\eta_m = \frac{\sqrt{1/a^* + 1} - 1}{\sqrt{1/a^* + 1} + 1} \tag{4-65}$$

This maximum efficiency is shown in Fig. 4-11.   It is seen that large aspect ratios are required to obtain efficiencies greater than 0.6.

For a given aspect ratio, the efficiency can be improved by the insertion of insulating vanes at the inlet and exit parallel to the flow but external to the magnetic-field region.   For example, a single inlet vane and exit vane placed in midstream will double the apparent aspect ratio; two equally spaced vanes will triple the apparent aspect ratio, etc.

Another method of improving the efficiency is to extend the magnetic field.   Actually, most magnetic fields decrease exponentially away from the pole faces so that this case was also investigated.[31]   The resulting efficiencies are shown in Fig. 4-10 for two different e-folding lengths of the magnetic field, $\frac{1}{2}h$ and h.   It is seen that considerable improvement in the

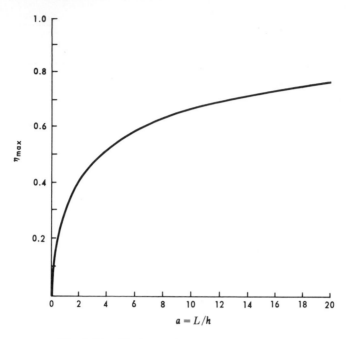

Fig. 4-11. *Maximum efficiency considering end losses — zero extension to the magnetic field.*

efficiency is obtained by slight shading of the magnetic field. This theory has been extended to account for boundary-layer losses; and experimental measurements in a liquid-metal generator have essentially verified the theory, except the theoretical predicted efficiencies were approximately 10 percent higher than the measured efficiencies.[33]

7-2. Losses due to Segmented Electrodes

In Sec. 5, it was shown that segmentation of electrodes should stop the axial Hall currents. In this section, we will examine in detail the current flow in the vicinity of such electrodes, with the same assumptions as made above. The components of current, due to the Faraday and electrical potential fields, respectively, are given by

$$j_{B_x} = \frac{\sigma \beta'_e U B}{1 + \beta'^2_e} \qquad j_{B_y} = -\frac{\sigma U B}{1 + \beta'^2_e} \tag{4-66}$$

$$j_{\phi_x} = \frac{\sigma}{1 + \beta'^2_e}\left[-\frac{\partial \phi}{\partial X} + \beta'_e \frac{\partial \phi}{\partial Y}\right]$$

$$j_{\phi_y} = \frac{\sigma}{1 + \beta'^2_e}\left[-\frac{\partial \phi}{\partial Y} - \beta'_e \frac{\partial \phi}{\partial X}\right] \tag{4-67}$$

where j_B is the induced current $\mathbf{\delta} \cdot (\mathbf{v} \times \mathbf{B})$ and $j_\phi = -\mathbf{\delta} \cdot \nabla \phi$. Thus, if j_{ϕ_y} is specified as zero on a boundary, $\partial \phi / \partial Y = -\beta_e \partial \phi / \partial X$. Thus, the equipotential lines have a slope of β_e^{-1} with respect to the axis.

To solve this type of problem, one may conformally map the original region such that the equipotential lines are straight and equally spaced in the transformed plane. The boundaries along which the potential lines are sloped are then mapped at the appropriate angle to the equipotential lines. Using this technique, the potential map for the continuous electrodes has been calculated[28] when the electrical conductivity upstream of the electrode region is zero.

Using this same technique, the potential field and current have been obtained when the magnetic field and electrical conductivity are extended infinitely upstream of the electrodes[34] and when the electrodes are skewed with respect to one another.[35] Recent experiments in seeded argon and nitrogen indicate less current concentration than predicted for the first case,[36] which is probably caused by voltage drops near the electrodes. The mapping technique has also been used to determine the current flow in the vicinity of segmented electrodes.[28] The calculated current distributions are shown in Fig. 4-12. It is seen that there is a concentration of current in the downstream portion of the cathode; and also, the distortion of the current lines extends into the stream only a distance equal to the electrode length. This distortion of the current distribution along a flat electrode has been observed in combustion gases,[37] but in nitrogen or argon, considerable smoothing has been observed.[36]

If the electrode-pitch distance were infinitely small, the effective transverse conductivity would be equal to the scalar electron conductivity σ'. However, the current concentration (for constant electrical conductivity) causes an additional impedance, which causes the effective transverse conductivity to be reduced. Since the Hall electric field is directly proportional to the transverse current density, any decrease in transverse current immediately reduces the axial electric field. This relationship is given below, for $(\omega_e \tau_e)' > 1$.

$$\frac{\sigma_{eff}}{\sigma'} = \frac{E_x}{\beta_{,} U B (1 - K)} = \left[1 + \frac{d}{h} (\omega_e \tau_e' - 0.441) \right]^{-1} \tag{4-68}$$

where d is the electrode pitch. Equation (4-68) shows that for large values of $(\omega_e \tau_e)'$, very small electrode pitches are required in order that the transverse conductivity σ_{eff} be close to the theoretical value σ'.

The effect of end losses with segmented electrodes has also been investigated theoretically.[38,39] It has been found that as $(\omega_e \tau_e)'$ increases, the end losses decrease because the eddy currents become skewed and

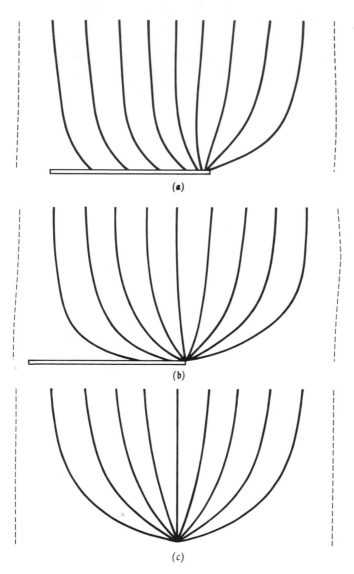

Fig. 4-12.   *Current flow lines.   (a) Segmented electrodes with ωτ = 1.
(b) Segmented electrodes with ωτ = 3; note that most of the current flows
into the right-hand corner of the electrode.   (c) Infinitely thin electrode; this
case is independent of ωτ.   The dashed lines in the figure represent current
dividing lines between adjacent electrodes.*

thereby decreased. The effect of segmented electrodes on magnetically induced ionization was discussed in Sec. 3-2.

7-3. Instabilities in MHD Generators

Because the Lorentz force in an MHD generator is in the direction such as to retard the flow, it is possible that small disturbances may amplify. For example, in a Faraday generator, if the conductivity of the gas at a given place in a generator increases, the transverse electric current will also increase. This will cause an increase in the local ohmic heating and an increase in the local Lorentz force, which will also cause further compressional heating. The local heating will cause a further increase in the electrical conductivity, and therefore there exists the possibility of amplification and growth of fluctuations. Actually, for the case described above, the rate of amplification is believed to be small.[40] On the other hand, in a segmented-electrode generator, transverse waves are amplified by the Hall effect.[41] In general, it was found that these waves would amplify when the product of the Hall parameter and Mach number was greater than unity. When the boundary conditions were included, it was calculated that the self-excited oscillations would be insufficient to generate appreciable a-c power.[42]

7-4. Losses Due to Fluctuations

The flow in gaseous MHD generators is known to be turbulent, which is caused by the high Reynolds number associated with high velocity. Thus, the gas can be expected to have fluctuations in velocity, density, temperature, and degree of ionization. Such fluctuations can decrease the overall electrical conductivity. This decrease can be illustrated in a simple manner for the following simplified example. Consider a gas across which there is an applied voltage, and assume the electrical conductivity fluctuates by a fraction α. These fluctuations cause the local electric field to vary by an amount E'. The instantaneous Ohm's law may be written as

$$
\begin{aligned}
j = \sigma E &= \sigma_0 (1 + \alpha)(E_0 + E') \\
&= \sigma_0 (E_0 + E' + \alpha E_0 + \alpha E')
\end{aligned}
\tag{4-69}
$$

Assuming that α is a known quantity, we wish to determine the fluctuating part of the electric field E'. To do this, we may assume that α varies as follows:

$$
\alpha = \alpha_0 \exp i(\omega t - \mathbf{K} \cdot \mathbf{x})
\tag{4-70}
$$

and

$$E' = \mathcal{E}_0 \exp i(\omega t - \mathbf{K} \cdot \mathbf{x}) \tag{4-71}$$

We may neglect electromagnetic waves and therefore the displacement current. Then,

$$\nabla \cdot \mathbf{j} = 0 \tag{4-72}$$

Substitution of Eqs. (4-69 to 4-71) into (4-72) and neglecting $\alpha E'$ gives the following expression for the amplitude of the fluctuating part of the electric field:

$$\mathcal{E}_0 = -\alpha_0 E_0 \tag{4-73}$$

When $\mathcal{E}_0$ is substituted into Eq. (4-69) and the time average is taken, we obtain

$$\langle j \rangle = \sigma_0 (1 - \tfrac{1}{2}\alpha_0^2) E_0 \tag{4-74}$$

Thus, the current is reduced by the fluctuations. For an MHD generator, fluctuations in density can cause fluctuations in temperature and hence in the degree of ionization. In addition, the Hall effect amplifies the magnitude of the fluctuations. Thus, for a generator when fluctuations are included, the equation corresponding to Eq. (4-45) is[43]

$$\langle j_y \rangle = \sigma_0 (E_y - uB) \left[1 - \left(\frac{\Delta\rho}{\rho}\right)^2 \omega_e^2 \tau_e^2 (\gamma - 1)^2 \left(\frac{E_I}{2kT}\right)^2 \right] \tag{4-75}$$

where $\Delta\rho/\rho$ is the fluctuation in density. For example, if $\omega_e \tau_e = 5$, $\gamma = 1.3$, $E_I = 4.32$ electron volts (for potassium seed), and $T = 3000°\mathrm{K}$, 1 percent fluctuations in the density will produce a 1.7 percent reduction in electrical conductivity. Thus, from the foregoing analysis, it does not appear that a large reduction in the equivalent d-c conductivity can be expected. However, the above analysis uses the assumption of perfect mixing of the temperature and seeding. In experiments, fluctuations of about 10 percent in the load current have been observed. It is possible that these are caused by incomplete mixing of the gases or seed material. In either event, further investigations are warranted.

8. *Compressible Flow in Faraday-current MHD Generators*

In this section, expressions are derived for the change in properties in an MHD generator, the compressibility of the gas being taken into account, and will concentrate on linear flows with variable cross section. Friction and heat transfer will be neglected. The quasi one-dimensional-flow equations will be used, together with the perfect gas law, since the degree of ionization is generally low so that the compressibility factor is unity. The conservation of mass is given by

$$\rho u A = \dot{m} = \text{const} \tag{4-76}$$

and the magnetic field is specified, usually constant. With these equations, there are always two more unknowns than equations; hence, no general solution is possible. Two additional relations are required. In the following, the generator load factor K, which is the ratio of E_y to uB, will be specified, since this ratio is related to polytropic efficiency and one would normally wish to design the generator with η_p nearly constant. In addition, one of the flow variables, such as u, M, T, p, ρ, or A, can be specified. The path of the gas on a temperature-entropy diagram is shown in Fig. 4-13 for several generators. The initial stagnation conditions are shown as subscript zero. The gas is then isentropically accelerated to some velocity (1) in a nozzle; this velocity may be either subsonic or supersonic. The gas then enters the generator and, as a result of ohmic heating of the gas in the generator, the entropy at the exit (2) is increased. The effect of the entropy change is that the exit stagnation pressure p_3 is always less than the inlet stagnation pressure p_0.

For Faraday generators, the transverse electrical current density from Eq. (4-45) may be written (assuming $\beta_e \beta_I \ll 1$) as:

$$j_y = -\sigma(1 - K)uB \tag{4-77}$$

With the assumption of quasi one-dimensional flow, the momentum equation (4-33) becomes

Momentum

$$\rho u \frac{du}{dx} + \frac{dp}{dx} = -\sigma(1 - K)uB^2 \tag{4-78}$$

For either the segmented- or continuous-electrode generator, $E_x j_x = 0$, so that the only contribution to the energy equation (4-34) is $E_y j_y$. Thus the energy equation becomes

Energy

$$\rho u \frac{d}{dx}\left(C_p T + \frac{1}{2} u^2\right) = -\sigma K(1 - K)u^2 B^2 \tag{4-79}$$

The effect of any transverse pressure gradients due to Hall currents is generally neglected. In the remainder of this section, only the solution

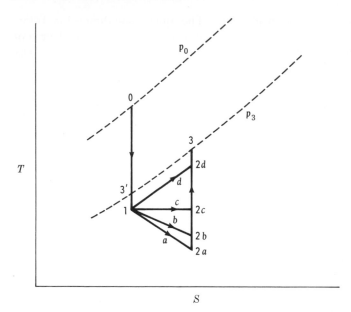

Fig. 4-13. *Paths on a Mollier diagram for various linear MHD generators. Point (0) stagnation conditions upstream of generator; (1) generator inlet; (2) generator exhaust; (3) stagnation conditions corresponding to generator exhaust. (a) Constant velocity; (b) constant Mach number; (c) constant temperature; (d) constant pressure.*

for constant-velocity flow will be given, since it is of major interest to the design of MHD generators.

Constant-velocity generator. In the constant-velocity generator, u is taken constant. The first integral is then obtained by division of the momentum equation by the energy equation and integration, to obtain

$$\frac{T(x)}{T_1} = \left(\frac{p(x)}{p_1}\right)^{K(\gamma-1)/\gamma} \tag{4-80}$$

The usually isentropic expression corresponds to $K = 1$, so that Eq. (4-80) shows that for the same pressure ratio, the temperature decrease in an MHD generator is *always* less than isentropic.

The entropy change may be calculated from

$$\Delta S = C_p \ln\left(\frac{T}{T_1}\right) - R \ln\frac{p}{p_1}$$

$$= C_p \frac{1-K}{K} \ln\frac{T_1}{T} \tag{4-81}$$

which shows the rapid increase in entropy with decreasing K. The variation with x is given directly by integration of Eq. (4-78), which for σ constant becomes

$$p_1 - p = \sigma(1 - K)uB^2 \tag{4-82}$$

so that the generator length is given by

$$L = \frac{p_1 - p_2}{(1 - K)\sigma u B^2} \tag{4-83}$$

The pressure drop may also be expressed in terms of the magnetic interaction parameter I,

$$\frac{p_1 - p_2}{p_1} = M^2\gamma(1 - K)I \tag{4-84}$$

where $I = \sigma B^2 L/\rho u$. Now, in order for an appreciable fraction of the energy to be extracted, the temperature ratio T_2/T_1 should be small, which means from Eq. (4-80) that $p_2/p_1 \ll 1$. Thus, Eq. (4-84) shows that I must be of the order of unity.

From Eq. (4-83) one may also observe that the length is minimized when the product $\sigma u/\rho_1$ is a maximum. For thermal ionization, however, as u is increased, the static temperature decreases [see Eq. (4-79)] and the degree of ionization also decreases. One therefore finds that there is an optimum inlet temperature ratio, given by

$$\frac{T_1}{T_0} = \frac{\xi + \zeta \pm \sqrt{\xi^2 - 2\xi\zeta + \zeta^2 + \frac{4}{3}\zeta}}{2\xi - \frac{2}{3}} \tag{4-85}$$

where

$$\xi = \frac{\gamma}{\gamma - 1} - \frac{1}{2}$$

$$\zeta = \frac{E_I}{3kT_0}$$

From Eq. (4-85) one may show that for combustion gases the optimum inlet Mach number is slightly supersonic.

The above results were obtained by assuming the conductivity was constant; however, the equations may also be integrated for thermal ionization, neglecting the Hall effect.[44] The variation of conductivity for slight ionization is given by

$$\frac{\sigma}{\sigma_1} = \left(\frac{T}{T_1}\right)^{3/4}\left(\frac{p_1}{p}\right)^{1/2}\exp\left(-\frac{E_I}{2kT_1}\right)\left(1 - \frac{T_1}{T}\right) \tag{4-86}$$

which may be approximated by

$$\frac{\sigma}{\sigma_1} = \left(\frac{T}{T_1}\right)^{\Gamma} \left(\frac{p_1}{p}\right)^{\epsilon} \tag{4-87}$$

where

$$\Gamma = \tfrac{3}{4} + \frac{E_I/2kT_1(1 - T_1/T)}{\ln(T/T_1)}$$

$$\epsilon = \tfrac{1}{2}$$

The variation of Γ with temperature is small, and Γ may be evaluated at some average temperature. With Eqs. (4-87) and (4-80), the energy equation can be integrated to obtain

$$\frac{T}{T_1}(x) = \left(1 + \frac{\Xi x}{x^*}\right)^{-1/\Xi} \tag{4-88}$$

where

$$\Xi = \Gamma - \frac{\gamma}{\gamma - 1}\frac{\epsilon + 1}{K}$$

$$x^* = \frac{\gamma}{\gamma - 1}\frac{1}{K}\frac{p_1}{(1 - K)\sigma_1 u B^2}$$

With $p(x)$ or $T(x)$ determined by Eq. (4-82) or (4-88) and $T(x)$ or $p(x)$ obtained from Eq. (4-80), the density may be obtained from the perfect gas law, and the area variation $A(x)$ is obtained from Eq. (4-76). Assuming that Ξ is approximately constant, the generator length is minimized by minimizing x^*, that is, $p_1/\sigma_1 u$, yielding the same results as given by Eq. (4-85).

For constant specific heat C_p, the generator efficiency, as defined by Eq. (4-60), becomes

$$\eta_g = \frac{T_0 - T_3}{T_0 - T_{3'}} = \frac{1 - (T_3/T_0)}{1 - (T_{3'}/T_0)} \tag{4-89}$$

where $T_{3'}$ is the temperature corresponding to an isentropic expansion from (T_0, p_0) to pressure p_3:

$$\frac{T_{3'}}{T_0} = \left(\frac{p_3}{p_0}\right)^{(\gamma-1)/\gamma} \tag{4-90}$$

For low subsonic Mach numbers, the generator efficiency is always greater than the polytropic efficiency, that is, greater than the loading factor due to the reheat factor; but for supersonic Mach numbers, the generator efficiency can be considerably less than K due to the Mach-number effect given in Eq. (4-59).

9. MHD-power-generation Systems

There are three general types of MHD-generator systems.   In the simplest system, liquid or solid fuel and liquid oxidizer are burned, seed is added, and the resulting gas mixture is passed through the generator with no further recovery of the remaining thermal energy or seed material in the exhaust gases.   Such a system is practical only for small or short-duration generators.   Since the amount of energy required to pump the liquid (or solid) fuel and oxidizer is small, all the generated electrical power is available for the load except that required to energize the magnet, if it is an electromagnet.   This system will be discussed further in Sec. 9-1.

For the generation of bulk power, fossil fuel must be used for economic reasons, and the oxidizer must be air, although some enrichment with additional oxygen may be possible.   In order for the combustion temperature to be high enough for thermal ionization, preheating of the incoming air is necessary.   The exhaust temperature of the gas from the generator is determined by the decrease in the ionization of the gas; but because combustion gases must be thermally ionized, the exhaust temperature is still very high.   For economic operation further extraction of this energy is necessary, which may be accomplished by using the exhaust gases to generate steam power.   These systems are described further in Sec. 9-2.

Finally, the gas which passes through the generator may be in a completely closed cycle; that is, the gas (or vapor) is heated in a heat exchanger, expanded through a nozzle, passed through the generator, cooled, and recompressed (or pumped) back through the heat exchanger.   For such a cycle, the maximum temperature of the gas is set by the allowable working temperature of the materials in the heat exchanger.   At the present state of development of refractory materials, it is highly unlikely that sufficiently high temperatures can be sustained over long periods of time to permit thermal ionization; thus, some form of nonthermal ionization is necessary.

9-1. Simple Open Cycle

In the simple open cycle, fuel and oxidizer are burned and "seed" material is added without preheating.   The combustion products are accelerated by a nozzle, passed into the generator, and exhausted into the atmosphere. Since seeded combustion gases are not sufficiently conducting below about

4000°F at a pressure of 1 atm, the flame temperature must exceed 4000°F in order to extract any electrical power. Because the temperature of most flames with air is below 4000°F, it is necessary to use either pure oxygen or a chemical oxidizer. Even if pure oxygen is used, the flame temperature with ordinary hydrocarbons is not especially high because of dissociation of the products of combustion (see Table 4-3). The overall efficiency for this type open-cycle generator can be expressed in terms of the enthalpy difference between the flame temperature and ambient:

$$\eta_t = \frac{\text{net electrical energy/unit mass of gas}}{H_0 - h_a}$$

where H_0 is the total enthalpy of the products of combustion at the combustor pressure and h_a is the sensible enthalpy of the same gas if cooled to ambient pressure and temperature. The net work is the difference between the generator inlet total enthalpy and the exit total enthalpy, less any heat transfer and power for auxiliary equipment. Thus,

$$\eta_t = \frac{H_0 - h_2 - \frac{1}{2}u_2^2 - Q - P_{aux}}{H_0 - h_a}$$

The thermal efficiency is therefore limited by the minimum temperature $T_{\min}$ at which there is sufficient ionization and by the exhaust velocity. If the exhaust velocity is reduced by adjusting the cross-sectional area, additional energy can be extracted from the gas before $T_{\min}$ is reached; however, decreasing the gas velocity generally increases the generator length. For this reason, it is desirable to use the higher flame temperatures.

Table 4-3.   *Flame Temperatures of Fuels Burned with Liquid Oxygen at 20 Atm Pressure*

Fuel	Flame temperature, °F
Ethyl alcohol†	5250
Kerosene†	5570
Hydrogen†	~5400
Methane†	5040
Cyanogen	~8200

† From G. P. Sutton, *Rocket Propulsion Elements*, 2d ed., John Wiley & Sons, Inc., New York 1956.

As of the present time, all combustion MHD-generator experiments have been open-cycle, utilizing alcohol, fuel oil, or hydrogen as the fuel with various mixtures of oxygen and nitrogen. The first such experiments were performed by Halasz and Karlovitz[45] at Westinghouse from about 1936 to 1946, using electron-beam ionization. Due to rapid recombination and formation of negative ions, the generated power density was far below theoretical. No further experiments were performed until about 1958, when experiments were initiated using thermal ionization of seeded gases. The earliest of these experiments utilized plasma jets as the method for thermal heating of the gas, since gas temperatures could easily be obtained which are much higher than those available from combustion flames. In these experiments, the measured electrical conductivity and generated power agreed within a factor of 2 of the theoretically predicted performance, although the total power was small (less than 12 kw) and the run times were less than 10 sec.[50] These experiments mainly verified the validity of the physical principle of MHD power generation.

The first successful combustion experiment was performed at Westinghouse Electric[46] by Way et al., in which over 10 kw was generated, followed rapidly by similar experiments.[47,48] The largest combustion experiment at the present time is AVCO Mark 6,[49] which has generated 20 mw (see Fig. 4-14). A Hall generator has also been successfully operated on an air-hydrogen flame.[30]

For the plasma jet and combustion experiments, some initial experiments were performed using stabilized zirconia for the insulator; however, at high temperatures the zirconia generally becomes electrically conducting and most experimenters have changed to magnesia for the insulator. One unexpected effect is that the resistivity of the ceramic decreases during an experiment;[30] it is not yet known whether this is because of the presence of potassium, which could change the chemical composition of the surface of the insulator. The presence of molten ash will probably intensify this problem.

For very large MHD generators, wall cooling may be possible without adversely affecting the performance, and experiments have been performed in which water-cooled tubes were used as the insulator.[49] These same tubes can also serve as the electrodes if the tubes follow equipotential lines as in the series-segmented geometry and if an insulation is placed between the tubes. Since the temperature of the tubes is low, presumably the temperature of the insulation between them will also be low, and hence alumina may be satisfactory.

The most commonly used electrode material has been graphite, although silicon carbide has also been utilized.[30] However, zircon compounds have also been utilized because of their relatively high electrical conductivity, both with and without embedded tungsten.[47] In general, if the electrodes are sufficiently hot to emit electrons thermionically, there has been almost zero cathode voltage drop;[37] otherwise voltage drops up to 100 volts have been observed.[50] The graphite and carbide electrodes have been observed to erode very rapidly when used with products of combustion.

Fig. 4-14.   *The AVCO Mark 6 linear combustion MHD generator.*   (*AVCO Corp.*)

The seed has generally been injected as a salt, carbonate, or hydroxide. The salt dissolves readily in water, which provides a convenient method for injection, but powdered potassium carbonate has also been used. The hydroxide dissolves easily in alcohol, which then can be mixed directly with the fuel,[46] eliminating the necessity for a separate injection system and also allowing for more precise control of the seed-injection rate.

Also listed in Table 4-3 is the flame temperature with cyanogen, C_2N_2. The high flame temperature results not so much from a larger heat of combustion as from the fact that the products of combustion CO and N_2 do not dissociate. Detailed calculations of the performance of an oxycyanogen generator indicate that over 36 percent of the input chemical energy can be converted into terminal power.[51] This is to be compared with about 15 percent for hydrocarbon fuels. However, no generator experiments with cyanogen have been conducted.

An interesting application of open-cycle generation is the use of an explosive to generate the combustion gases. In recent experiments by Jones et al.,[52] a 1-lb charge of explosive seeded with cesium picrate generated a power pulse with a peak of 280 Mw for a duration of about 200 μsec, for a total output of 36 kilojoules in a generator which is 1.5 m in length.

9-2. Open Cycle with Recovery

The previous open cycle is clearly unsuited for economic operation for three reasons: the seed material is not recovered; chemical oxidizers are expensive; and finally, the thermal energy of the exhaust gases is not recovered. For the economic generation of bulk power these three problems must be considered.

The cheapest available oxidizer is obviously air, although power is required to compress it to the required combustion pressure. In addition, common fossil fuels must be used if the fuel cost is to be minimized. Since it is impossible to burn fossil fuels with air and achieve sufficiently high combustion temperatures to ionize the seed material, preheating of the inlet air with possible oxygen enrichment is required to increase the combustion temperature; that is, a regenerative cycle is required[53] (see Figs. 4-15 and 4-16).

Now, because the specific heat of combustion gas is larger than that for air, the regenerator hot-side exit temperature T_4 will normally be considerably higher than the regenerator cold-side inlet temperature, and additional energy can be recovered from the exhaust gases by producing steam and using a steam turbine. It is possible to couple the turbine directly to the air compressor and use any remaining shaft power to generate electrical power. The net power output is then the direct current gen-

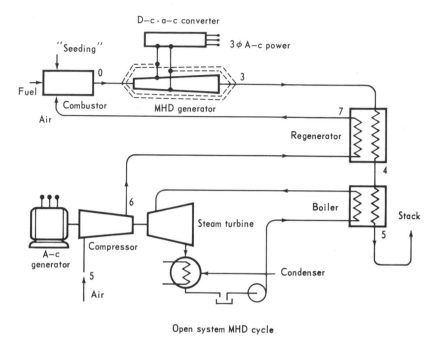

Fig. 4-15. *Regenerative cycle, flow schematic.* (*After S. Way.*)

erated in the MHD generator, plus any remaining steam power, less the magnet and auxiliary power. With these types of calculations, overall thermal efficiencies as high as 56 percent have been calculated.[53]

Several problems in the cycle are evident. First, for combustion products and about 1 percent molar potassium seeding, T_2 is about 4000°F, and the regenerator walls will then be close to this temperature. At the present time, economic materials which will withstand this temperature for long periods of time are not known.

On the basis of fuel cost and preheat, coal seems to be the best fuel for economic operation of an MHD generator. On the other hand, the high ash content of coal causes additional difficulties. Although it is possible to remove as much as 90 percent of the ash in a "cyclone" burner, the remaining ash becomes mixed with the seed material, which may be a potassium compound or pollucite. Since economic operation requires recovery of the seed material, the 10 percent ash must be recovered as well, and recirculated. To keep the "seed" makeup at a minimum, scrubbers and electrostatic precipitators are required; but a more important problem is the large weight of ash that must be recirculated through the system in

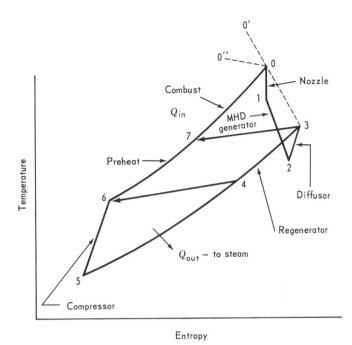

Fig. 4-16. *Regenerative cycle, temperature-entropy diagram.*

order to make use of the seed trapped in it.   In addition, the molten ash will coat out on the inside of the generator and quite likely short out the electrodes and will coat out on the regenerator.   Thus, the problems of burning coal are quite difficult.

In addition to the problems caused by ash, two other important problems are associated with continuously operated generators.   First, the potassium attacks insulating materials and makes them conducting. Second, the electrode materials—tungsten, carbon, or silicon carbide—are chemically eroded by combustion gases.   This last problem might be solved by using consumable electrodes, that is, feeding the electrodes continuously into the generator in a manner similar to that used in electric-arc furnaces.

The largest problem that is faced by large-scale, continuous generation of power by fossil-fuel MHD generators is economics.   Although this system shows promise of increasing the overall thermal efficiency to as much as 56 percent as compared with 40 percent for conventional steam plants, the additional investment in the magnet, generator duct, compressors, regenerator, scrubbers, precipitators, and d-c to a-c inverters if the a-c is required causes the plant cost of the generated electrical power to be essentially the same as that for present-day steam plants.[54]

The economics have recently been reexamined by Rosner and Dzung.[55] They concluded that if the fuel cost is $.30/million Btu, MHD generation is competitive with boiling-water nuclear reactors, but if $.20/million Btu, the power cost is 15 percent less, between 4 and 5 mils/kwh.   Put a different way, for MHD power generation to be competitive, the total plant investment must be less than about $125/kw for $.30/million Btu, or less than about $117/kw for $.20/million Btu.   It should be noted that precise calculations of the required plant costs are presently not possible.

9-3. Closed Nuclear-MHD Cycle

A third possible application for MHD power generation is a closed cycle with a nuclear heat source.   This appears to be especially attractive for the generation of electrical power in space, where the heat rejection must be by radiation, because the heat rejection per unit area varies as the fourth power of the radiator surface temperature thereby favoring high-tempera- ture cycles.   High-temperature nuclear reactors are under development, but the corresponding development of turbogenerators is difficult because of the combination of high operating temperatures, turbine blade stresses, and the corrosive properties of some high-temperature working fluids, notably liquid metals.   The advantage of the MHD generator is that the stress level is reduced drastically.   On the other hand, it is not likely that the reactor temperature will be sufficiently high that thermal ioniza- tion of the working fluid in the MHD generator will be possible; thus, some form of nonthermal ionization will be required.

The Rankine (vapor) cycle is especially attractive for space applica- tions because the heat rejection is at constant temperature and the pumping power is small.   For such cycles, the optimum condensor temperature is 75 to 80 percent of the boiling temperature.[56]   At the present state of development of refractory materials, it appears that the upper temperature for Rankine cycles may be about 2500°R with a corresponding reject temperature of 1900°R.   These temperatures require the use of a liquid metal, such as potassium or sodium, for the working fluid but are too low for thermal ionization even with the addition to cesium.   Calculations for magnetically induced ionization, however, indicate that this may be possible in potassium for relatively high field strengths.[15]

The Rankine cycle has one main disadvantage: at the high tempera- tures necessary to minimize the radiator size, liquid metals are quite corro- sive.   On the other hand, an inert gas such as helium, which could be used in a gas cycle, is not corrosive.   The gas cycle has two disadvantages for space applications: a large compressor is required, and the heat rejection is at a continuously varying temperature which causes the radiator area to be 6 to 10 times that of a Rankine cycle with the same T_0.   However, since a corrosionless noble gas can be used, the reactor can be operated at a higher temperature.   Also, regeneration may be used; thus the radiator areas can be equalized.   This temperature is possibly too high for the use of gas turbines but not for MHD generators.

Of course, a magnetic field must be incorporated into a nuclear-MHD space-power system, which raises two additional problems: the weight of the magnet and the rejection of heat from the magnet.   These problems may be solved by the use of high-field superconducting materials.   The high electric current densities of superconductors reduce the weight of the windings, while the only required heat rejection is that which is conducted into the magnet dewar, which tends to boil off the liquid helium in which superconductors are kept.   The liquid helium can either be recooled by a cryostat, which requires additional weight, power, and radiators, or sufficient liquid helium can be stored to allow boil-off of the helium during the required mission time.

MHD-nuclear closed gas cycles for terrestrial applications differ from those for space applications in one very important aspect: the heat rejection can be at low temperatures, corresponding to ambient cooling water.   This allows the use of the waste heat for the generator of steam power to drive a steam turbine which is directly coupled to a compressor.   Calculations[1] have indicated that the resulting thermal efficiency varies from 42 percent for a reactor outlet temperature of 2000°F to 54 percent for a reactor outlet temperature of 3000°F.   With the use of regeneration in addition to the steam turbocompressor, the efficiency for the lower reactor outlet temperature can be improved even further.[1]   More recently, efficiencies as high as 53.5 percent have been calculated for the latter cycle using a reactor outlet temperature of 3590°F.[57]

Instead of regeneration, one could use the thermal energy in the MHD-generator exhaust to generate steam electric power.   However, since the efficiency of the steam portion of the cycle is 40 percent, such a use of the steam will decrease the overall plant efficiency.   Because of this effect, it is claimed that it is just as efficient to omit the steam part of the cycle completely and use part of the MHD-generated electrical power to drive electric motors to operate the compressors.[57]

Of course, it is not necessary for the working fluid of an MHD generator to be an ionized gas; it could, for example, be a liquid metal or a mixture of gas or vapor and liquid metal.   Such a generator has the advantage of the very high electrical conductivity of liquid metals at all temperatures. The main problem is the conversion of the thermal energy from the nuclear reactor into kinetic energy of motion of the liquid metal of high vapor pressure.   One concept for such a liquid-metal generator for space applica-

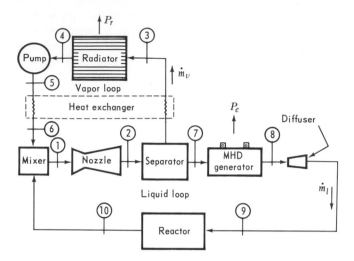

Fig. 4-17.   *Two-fluid MHD-power-conversion cycle.*[58]

tions is shown in Fig. 4-17.[58]   A liquid metal of low vapor pressure is heated by the nuclear reactor, then mixed with a second liquid metal which has a lower boiling point.   The hot liquid metal causes the lower-temperature liquid metal to vaporize.   The mixture is passed into a nozzle which allows the vapor to expand and accelerate the droplets of liquid metal.   The mixture is then separated, without appreciable loss of kinetic energy or head of the liquid metal, and this head then forces the liquid metal through the generator against the Lorentz force.   Although progress has been made in the development of the components for such a system,[33] the reported generator efficiency is only 48 percent.   This leads to overall thermal efficiencies of 6 to 7 percent and a total power-supply weight of 40 lb/kw.   At the present time, these values are less favorable than calculated weights for space Rankine cycles using turboalternators.

10.   Summary

In this chapter, the fundamental relations for MHD generators have been presented.   These relations have been well verified in experimental generators.   Most of the present effort is devoted to solving engineering problems to increase efficiency, power density, and material lifetimes.   It appears that small open-cycle generators generating up to tens of megawatts for short periods of time will be available soon.

For application of combustion MHD generators to bulk power, many additional problems need solution, such as seed recovery, very long material lifetimes, superconducting magnets, high-temperature recuperators, ash-handling systems, d-c to a-c conversion, etc. It will be necessary to solve each of these problems in order to determine the economic feasibility of these power plants.

For closed-cycle applications, rapid progress is being made toward liquid-metal generators in a two-fluid cycle. This may have its first application for space power. Progress toward achieving nonequilibrium ionization (so that a vapor or gas may be used in the generator) is presently in its infancy. While the results are promising, much more work needs to be accomplished before its potential can be fully evaluated.

References

1. Sutton, G. W., and A. Sherman: *Engineering Magnetohydrodynamics*, McGraw-Hill Book Company, New York, 1965.
2. Coombe, R. A. (ed.): *Magneto-hydrodynamic Generation of Electrical Power*, Chapman & Hall, Ltd., London, 1964.
3. *Symposia on Engineering Aspects of Magnetohydrodynamics:*
    First, 1960, University of Pennsylvania.
    Second, 1961, University of Pennsylvania, C. Mannal and N. Mather (eds.), Columbia University Press, New York, 1962.
    Third, 1962, University of Rochester, N. Mather and G. W. Sutton (eds.), Gordon and Breach, Science Publishers, Inc., New York, 1964.
    Fourth, 1963, University of California.
    Fifth, 1964, Massachusetts Institute of Technology.
    Sixth, 1965, University of Pittsburgh and Carnegie Institute of Technology.
4. *International Symposia on Magnetoplasmadynamic Electrical Power Generation:*
    First, 1962, Newcastle-upon-Tyne, The Institution of Electrical Engineers, London, 1963.
    Second, 1964, Paris, European Nuclear Energy Agency and Organization for Economic Cooperation, Paris, 1964.
5. Spencer, Barbara A: "Magnetohydrodynamic Power Generation: A Bibliography," *AVCO-Everett AMP* 110, June, 1963.
6. Chapman, S., and T. Cowling: *Mathematical Theory of Non-uniform Gases*, Cambridge University Press, London, 1952.
7. Brown, S.: *Basic Data of Plasma Physics*, John Wiley & Sons, Inc., New York, 1959.
8. Frost, L. S.: "Electrical Conductivity of Atmospheric Gases," *J. Appl. Phys.*, **32:** 2029 (1961).

9. Spitzer, L.: *Physics of Fully Ionized Gases*, p. 84, Interscience Publishers (Division of John Wiley & Sons, Inc.), New York, 1957.

10. Cowling, T.: *Magnetohydrodynamics*, pp. 105–108, Interscience Publishers (Division of John Wiley & Sons, Inc.,) New York, 1958.

11. Shair, F. H., and A. Sherman: "Electron Beam Preionization in an MHD Generator," Ref. 3, Sixth Symposium, 1965.

12. Saha, M.: *Phil. Mag*, **40**: 472 (1920).

13. Moffatt, W. C.: "Thermodynamics and Electrical Properties of Dissociated Combustion Gases," *Magnetogasdynamic Laboratory Rept.* 5, M.I.T., 1961.

14. Rowe, A. W., and J. L. Kerrebrock: "Nonequilibrium Electric Conductivity of Two-phase Metal Vapors," *AIAA J.*, **3**: 361–362 (1965).

15. Smith, J. M.: "Nonequilibrium Ionization in Wet Alkali Metal Vapors," *AIAA J.*, **3**: 648–651 (1965).

16. Kerrebrock, J.: "Conduction in Gases with Elevated Electron Temperatures," Ref. 3, Second Symposium, 1961, pp. 327–346.

17. Cool, T. A., and E. Zukoski: "Recombination Rates and Nonequilibrium Electrical Conductivity in a Seeded Plasma," Ref. 3, Sixth Symposium, 1965.

18. Brederlow, G., R. Hodgson, and W. Riedmuller: "Nonequilibrium Electrical Conductivity and Electron Temperature Measurements in Electric Fields and Crossed Electrical Fields and Cross Electric and Magnetic Fields," Ref. 3, Sixth Symposium, 1965.

19. Byron, S., P. Bortz, and G. Russell: "Electron-Ion Reaction Rate Theory," Ref. 3, Fourth Symposium, 1963.

20. Hurwitz, H., Jr., G. W. Sutton, and S. Tamor: "Electron Heating in Magnetohydrodynamic Power Generators," *ARS J.*, **32**: 1237–1243 (1962).

21. Kerrebrock, J. L.: "Magnetohydrodynamic Generators with Nonequilibrium Ionization," *AIAA J.*, **3**: 591–601 (1965).

22. Kerrebrock, J. L.: "Segmented Electrode Losses in MHD Generators with Nonequilibrium Ionization," Ref. 3, Sixth Symposium, 1965.

23. Zauderer, B.: "Shock Tube Studies of Magnetically Induced Ionization," Ref. 3, Sixth Symposium, 1965.

24. Klepeis, J., and R. Rosa: "Experimental Studies of Strong Hall Effects and U X B Induced Ionization; II," Ref. 3, Sixth Symposium, 1965.

25. McNab, I. R., and R. Brown: "Electrical Conductivity Experiments in an MPD Generator," Ref. 3, Sixth Symposium, 1965.

26. Massey, H., and J. D. Craggs: *Handbuch der Physik*, vol. 37/1, pp. 314–415, Springer-Verlag OHG, Berlin.

27. Steg, L., and G. W. Sutton: "The Prospects of MHD Power Generation," *Astronautics*, August, 1960, pp. 22–25, 82, 84–86.

28. Hurwitz, H., Jr., R. Kilb, and G. W. Sutton: "Influence of Tensor Conductivity on Current Distribution in a MHD Generator," *J. Appl. Phys.*, **32**: 205–216 (1961).

29. Harris, L. P., and J. D. Cobine: "The Significance of the Hall Effect for Three MHD Generator Configurations," *Trans. ASME, ser. A*, **83A**: 392–396 (1961).

30. Harris, L. P., and G. E. Moore: "Some Electrical Measurements on MHD Channels," Ref. 3, Third Symposium, 1962.

31. Sutton, G. W., H. Hurwitz, Jr., and H. Poritsky, Jr.: "Electrical and Pressure Losses in a Magnetohydrodynamic Channel due to End Current Loops," *Trans. AIEE Communications and Electronics,* **801:** 687–696 (1962).

32. Fishman, F.: "End Effects in Magnetohydrodynamic Channel Flow," *AVCO-Everett Res. Lab. Rept.* 78, June, 1959.

33. Elliott, D. G.. "DC Liquid-Metal Magnetohydrodynamic Power Generator," Ref. 3, Sixth Symposium, 1965.

34. Podolsky, B., and A. Sherman: "Some Aspects of the Hall Effect in Crossed Field MHD Accelerators," ARS Preprint 1531–60 (1960).

35. Podolsky, B., and A. Sherman: "The Influence of Tensor Conductivity on End Currents in Crossed Field MHD Channels with Skewed Electrodes," *J. Appl. Phys.,* **33:** 1414–1418 (1962).

36. Hoffman, M. A., and G. C. Oates: Electrode Current Distribution in Linear MHD Channel Flows," Ref. 3, Sixth Symposium, 1965.

37. Louis, J. F., J. Lothrop, and T. R. Brogan: Fluid Dynamic Studies with a Magnetohydrodynamic Generator," *Phys. Fluids,* **7:** 362–374 (1964).

38. Sutton, G. W.: "End Losses in Magnetohydrodynamic Channels with Tensor Electrical Conductivity and Segmented Electrodes," *J. Appl. Phys.,* **34:** 396–403 (1963).

39. Dzung, L. S.: "Hall Effect and End Loop Losses of MHD Generators," Ref. 4, First Symposium, 1962.

40. Sutton, G. W., and E. Witalis: "Linearized Analysis of MHD Generator Flow Stability," Ref. 4, Second Symposium, 1964.

41. Velikhov, E. P.: "Hall Instability of Current-carrying Slightly-ionized Plasmas," Ref. 4, First Symposium, 1962.

42. McCune, J. E.: "Linear Theory of an MHD Oscillator," *AVCO-Everett Res. Lab. Rept.* 198, December, 1964.

43. McCune, J. E.: "Non-linear Effects of Fluctuations on MHD Performance," Ref. 3, Sixth Symposium, 1965.

44. Brocher, E. F.: "The Constant Velocity MHD Generator with Variable Electrical Conductivity," *J. Aerospace Sci.,* **29:** 626–627 (1962).

45. Karlovitz, Bela, and D. Halasz: "History of the K&H Generator and Conclusions Drawn from the Experimental Results," Ref. 3, Third Symposium, 1962.

46. Way, S., S. M. DeCorso, R. L. Hundstad, G. A. Kemeney, W. Stewart, and W. E. Young: "Experiments with MHD Power Generation," *Trans. ASME,* **83A** (*J. Eng. Power*): 397 (1961).

47. Blackman, V. H., M. S. Jones, Jr., and A. Demetriades: "MHD Power Generation Studies in Rectangular Channels," Ref. 3, Second Symposium, 1961.

48. Mullaney, G. J., and N. R. Dibelius: "Small MHD Power Generator Using Combustion Gases as an Energy Source," *ARS J.,* **31:** 555–557 (1961).

49. Louis, J. F., G. Gal, and P. R. Blackburn: "Detailed Theoretical and Experimental Study on a Large MHD Generator," Ref. 3, Fifth Symposium, 1964.

50. Sutton, G. W., and F. Robben: "Preliminary Experiments on MHD Channel Flow with Slightly Ionized Gases," *Proc. Symp. on Electromagnetics and Fluid Dynamics of Gaseous Plasma*, Polytechnic Press, Brooklyn, 1962, pp. 307–321.

51. Sherman, A.: "A High Performance Short Time Duration, MHD Generator System," *ARS Space Power Conf.*, September, 1962, Preprint 2558–62.

52. Jones, M. S., Jr., P. W. Webster, F. H. Webb, Jr., C. D. Bangerter, A. H. Peterson, and L. Davis: "Large Scale Explosively Driven MHD Generator Experiments," Ref. 3, Sixth Symposium, 1965.

53. Sporn, P., and A. Kantrowitz: "Magnetohydrodynamics—Future Power Process?" *Power*, *103*(11): 62–65 (1959).

54. Brown, J. W. W.: "Some Aspects of MHD Power Plant Economics," Ref. 3, Third Symposium, 1962.

55. Rosner, M., and L. S. Dzung: "Efficiency of Large-scale Open-loop MHD-power Generation," Ref. 3, Sixth Symposium, 1965.

56. Pitkin, E. T.: "Optimum Radiator Temperature for Space Power Systems," *ARS J.*, *29*: 596–597 (1959).

57. Booth, L. A.: "Prospects for a 1000 Mw(e) Nuclear Reactor/MHD Power-plant," Ref. 3, Sixth Symposium, 1965.

58. Elliott, D. G.: "Two-fluid Magnetohydrodynamic Cycle for Nuclear-Electric Power Conversion," *ARS J.*, *32*: 924–928 (1962).

Symbols

a acoustic sound speed

a_e fraction of total enthalpy converted to electrical energy

A cross-sectional area of generator

b_e fraction of pressure drop due to Lorentz force

b generator height in direction of magnetic field

$\mathbf{B}$ magnetic field

c thermal speed

C_p specific heat at constant pressure

d Debye shielding length

e electron charge

$\mathbf{E}$ stationary electric field

$\mathbf{E}^*$ moving electric field, $\mathbf{E} + \mathbf{v} \times \mathbf{B}$

E_s ionization energy, s species

f velocity distribution function

$\mathbf{F}$ Lorentz force density

h generator width

h static enthalpy

h° chemical enthalpy

H total enthalpy, $h + \frac{1}{2}v^2$

I magnetic interaction parameter

$\mathbf{j}$ conduction current
$\mathbf{J}$ total electric current, $\mathbf{j} + \rho_e \mathbf{v}$
k Boltzmann's constant
K_0 permittivity of vacuum
K Faraday-generator loading factor
K_H Hall-generator loading factor
L characteristic length
m_s mass of s particle
M Mach number
n_s number density of s species
n total number density, $\Sigma_s n_s$
p pressure
P electrical power density
$\mathbf{q}$ heat-flux vector
Q_{rs} collision cross section between r and s particles
r_e electron Larmor radius
R_m magnetic Reynolds number
R gas constant
R_L external resistance
S slip-speed ratio
t time
T temperature
$\mathbf{v}$ gas velocity (u, v, w)
$\mathbf{V}$ diffusion velocity
$\mathbf{x}$ spatial coordinates (x, y, z)
y complex coordinates
Z_s number of charges on s particle

Greek

ν collision frequency
ρ total mass density, $\Sigma_s \rho_s$
ρ_s mass density of s species
ρ_e charge density
σ electrical conductivity
τ_s collision time, s species, $\left(\langle c \rangle_s \sum_r n_r Q_{sr}\right)^{-1}$
$\boldsymbol{\tau}$ shear-stress tensor
ϕ electric-field potential
χ scattering cross section
ψ current-stream function
ω_s cyclotron frequency, s species, $eZ_s B / m_s$
α degree of ionization

β_s Hall parameter, s species, $\omega_s \tau_s = \mu_s B$
γ ratio of specific heats
δ_s elastic loss constant, s species
η_g generator adiabatic efficiency
η_L generator local efficiency
η_p generator polytropic efficiency
η_t generator thermal efficiency
λ wavelength
λ_s mean free path, s species
μ_s mobility, s species
μ_0 permeability of vacuum

Subscripts

e electron, electrical
i isentropic
I ion
s stagnation, species

5

THERMIONIC ENERGY CONVERSION

E. Blue and J. H. Ingold

1. INTRODUCTION

Thermionic energy conversion is a method of converting heat energy into electrical energy by thermionic emission. In this process, electrons are thermionically emitted from the surface of a metal by heating the metal and imparting sufficient energy to some of the electrons so that they overcome retarding forces at the surface of the metal and escape. As Fig. 5-1 shows, the typical thermionic energy converter has three main components: the thermionic emitter, the collector, and the "working fluid" shown in the interelectrode region. The working fluid in the so-called "vacuum converter" is an electron gas; in the vapor-filled converter it is a mixture of atoms and almost equal numbers of electrons and positive ions, i.e., a partially ionized plasma.

Qualitatively, the operation of a thermionic converter is as follows: Electrons are liberated from the emitter by adding heat Q_{in}. Some of these electrons, which become part of the working fluid, overcome retarding forces and migrate to a cold electrode, the collector, where part of their energy is lost in the form of heat and the remainder drives the electrons through an external load back to the emitter. The collector, of course, must be cooled by removing heat Q_{out} to compensate for heating by the working fluid and radiation from the emitter.

In order to obtain a quantitative understanding of the thermionic converter, it is necessary to consider surface phenomena such as thermionic emission and surface ionization and recombination. In addition, to understand how the charged particles migrate in the interelectrode region,

General Electric Vallecitos Atomic Laboratory, Pleasanton, California.

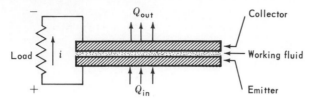

Fig. 5-1.   *Schematic of a thermionic energy converter.*

knowledge of space-charge fields and transport properties of a plasma is required. Some of these surface and volume phenomena will be reviewed briefly below.

1-1. Surface Phenomena

The interior of a metal and the boundary between the metal and vacuum may be characterized by the energy diagram shown in Fig. 5-2. It is known from quantum theory that there are discrete energy levels allowed for the bound electrons while the free or conduction electrons fill in the "continuum" of energies. At 0°K, the highest occupied level of energy $\mathcal{E}_F$ is referred to as the Fermi level.

Because of the presence of the ions in the metal, the conduction electrons move in an essentially equipotential region. However, at the "surface" of the metal there is a potential energy barrier since there is no ion to the right of the outermost ion and an "image force" retards the electron. Although the exact position of the surface cannot be specified, it is a short distance to the right of the last ion. For an electron to escape from the

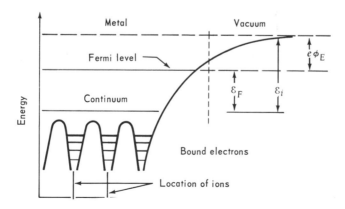

Fig. 5-2.   *Energy diagram for a metal.*

metal, it must have kinetic energy equivalent to the work required to remove it from the Fermi level to a point at rest "outside" the metal. This energy $e\phi_E = \mathcal{E}_i - \mathcal{E}_F$ is referred to as the *work function* of the metal emitter where $\mathcal{E}_i$ is the internal potential energy and e is the charge on the electron. If outside the metal is defined as the distance over which the electrostatic image force becomes negligible, then outside is of the order of 10^{-7} m. It is for this reason that the surface of the metal is often characterized by a step change in a potential-energy diagram.

As already mentioned, at absolute zero the highest occupied level of energy is the Fermi level $\mathcal{E}_F$ and none of the electrons can escape. At higher temperatures, however, some of the electrons have energy sufficient to overcome the work-function barrier. These thermionically emitted electrons cool the metal, and the cooling is important in determining the efficiency of a thermionic converter. To compute the thermionic emission from a metal and obtain an expression for the electron cooling, it is necessary to know how the conduction electrons in the metal are distributed in energy. Fermi, and independently Dirac, derived the most probable energy distribution for an electron gas.[1] In their derivation, the quantum nature of the electron and the Pauli exclusion principle were taken into account. The Fermi-Dirac law of distribution of energy, for temperatures not too large, i.e., $T_E \leq 3000°$K, is given by

$$f(\mathcal{E}) \, d\mathcal{E} = \frac{4\pi/h^3 (2em_e)^{3/2} \sqrt{\mathcal{E}} \, d\mathcal{E}}{1 + \exp\left[(\mathcal{E} - \mathcal{E}_F)/e\theta_E\right]} \qquad \text{electrons/m}^3 \qquad (5\text{-}1)$$

where $f(\mathcal{E}) \, d\mathcal{E}$ is the number of electrons per unit volume in the energy range $d\mathcal{E}$, m_e is the mass of the electron, $\theta_E = kT_E/e$ is the volt equivalent of temperature, k is the Boltzmann constant, and T_E is the absolute temperature of the metal emitter. The shape of the distribution given by Eq. (5-1) is shown in Fig. 5-3 for absolute zero and 2000°K. It is interesting to note that at a temperature of 2000°K only the high-energy portion of the distribution is changed significantly from the zero-temperature distribution.

Those electrons possessing energies in excess of $\mathcal{E}_i$, that is, with x-directed velocities in excess of $(2\mathcal{E}_i/m_e)^{1/2}$, will escape from the metal. If $\mathcal{E}$ is replaced by $\frac{1}{2} m_e c^2$ and $4\pi c^2 \, dc$ by $du \, dv \, dw$, the number of electrons striking unit area per unit time with velocity components in du is

$$uf(u) \, du = \frac{2m_e{}^3}{h^3} \exp\left(\frac{\mathcal{E}_F}{e\theta_E}\right) \int_{-\infty}^{\infty} dv \int_{-\infty}^{\infty} dw$$

$$\exp\left[-\frac{m_e}{2e\theta_E}(u^2 + v^2 + w^2)\right] u \, du \qquad \text{m}^{-2} \text{ sec}^{-1} \quad (5\text{-}2)$$

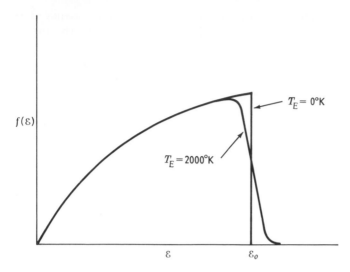

Fig. 5-3. *Energy distribution in metal at 0 and 2000° K.*

where c is the magnitude of the velocity with components u, v, and w and where the 1 in the denominator has been neglected since $\exp\left[(\varepsilon - \varepsilon_F)/e\theta_E\right] \gg 1$ for $\varepsilon \geq \varepsilon_i$. The emission current density is obtained by integrating $uf(u)\,du$ over all u greater than $(2\varepsilon_i/m)^{1/2}$:

$$J_S = -e \int_{\sqrt{2\varepsilon_i/m_e}}^{\infty} uf(u)\,du = -\frac{4\pi e m_e}{h^3}(kT_E)^2 \exp -\frac{\phi_E}{\theta_E} \qquad \text{A/m}^2$$

$$(5\text{-}3)$$

This is the well-known Richardson-Dushman equation for the saturated current density of electrons from a solid. It should be noted that the above derivation does not include reflection at the surface, quantum mechanical tunneling, or the effect of an electric field at the surface.

An average electron which is thermionically emitted from the metal will carry off an energy given by the gain in potential energy acquired in escaping the metal $e\phi_F$ plus the kinetic energy associated with its translational motion. The kinetic energy associated with the translational motion is found by averaging $\frac{1}{2}m_e u^2$ over the forward part of the distribution given by Eq. (5-2):

$$\frac{\int_0^{\infty} \frac{1}{2}m_e u^2 uf(u)\,du}{\int_0^{\infty} uf(u)\,du} = 2kT_E$$

Thus, at saturation, the emitter will be cooled by an amount equal to

$$-J_S(\phi_E + 2\theta_E)$$

To compute the saturation electron emission and the electron cooling, it is necessary to know the work function of the metal. A common experimental method used to determine the work function of a solid is to measure the saturated electron emission for different emitter temperatures and plot the results in the form of a Richardson curve of $\ln(-J_S/T_E^2)$ versus $(1/T_E)$. According to Eq. (5-3), such a plot should have an intercept equal to the Richardson constant A_R where

$$A_R = \frac{4\pi emk^2}{h^3} = 1.2 \times 10^6 \qquad A/\text{m}^2$$

and a slope equal to $-(e\phi_E/k)$. Figure 5-4 shows some Richardson plots from a study of some refractory metal carbides, which were considered as possible emitters for nuclear applications.[2] It can be seen that the curves are linear as predicted by theory. Measured Richardson constants very often depart considerably from the theoretical value, and this fact may be attributed to a work function with a linear temperature dependence. The temperature dependence of the measured work function may be attributed to nonuniformities in the surface work function, changes in the surface which depend on temperature, or adsorbed gases on the surface.

Vacuum work functions for some polycrystalline metals which might be used as electrodes in thermionic converters are:

Metal	Work function, volts
Nb	4.0
Mo	4.2
Ta	4.2
Cu	4.5
W	4.6
Re	5.0
Ni	5.0
Os	5.5

It is to be understood that the work functions listed are for illustrative purposes only, because the work function will generally depend on how the material is prepared, heat-treated, etc.

The work function of a metal surface can be changed significantly by adsorbed gases. Some of the first measurements of this effect were made by Taylor and Langmuir,[3] who measured the saturated current density from a tungsten wire immersed in cesium vapor. If the measured current density is plotted versus reciprocal cathode temperature for various cesium

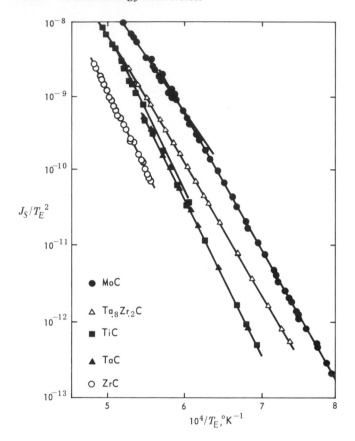

Fig. 5-4. *Richardson curves for some refractory carbides.* [*After J. H. Ingold, J. Appl. Phys.,* **34**: *2033 (1963).*]

pressures, a set of so-called "S" curves is obtained, one for each arrival rate μ_a. Figure 5-5 shows the results of some recent measurements[4] and an extrapolation of some of the early low-pressure measurements to higher pressures. At very high temperatures there is no adsorbed cesium on the surface and the curve looks like a Richardson curve; i.e., the work function is constant (4.6 volts), and the current decreases with decreasing temperature. As the temperature is lowered further, cesium begins to adsorb on the surface and the work function is lowered. Eventually, the enhancement of current caused by the lowering of the work function is greater than the attenuation of current caused by the lowering of temperature. Then the current increases with decreasing temperature until the surface is practically covered and the work function is again constant (1.69 volts). A theory for the adsorption of vapor on a metal was devel-

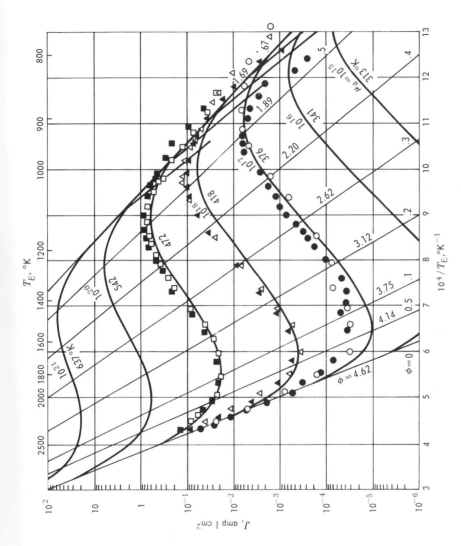

Fig. 5-5.   *Electron emission of cesiated tungsten.   (Reprinted by permission from "Thermionic Energy Conversion," J. M. Houston and H. F. Webster, Advances in Electronics, vol. XVII, Academic Press Inc., New York, 1962.)*

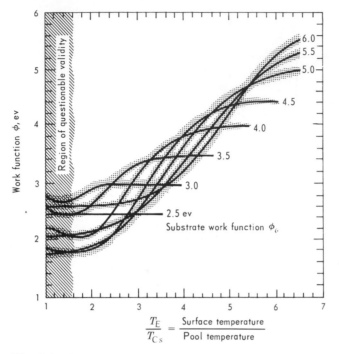

Fig. 5-6. *Computed work function of surfaces in cesium vapor at pressures between 0.1 and 10 torr (481 $<$ T_{Cs} $<$ 647°K). [After N. S. Rasor and C. Warner, J. Appl. Phys., 35: 2589 (1964).]*

oped by Taylor and Langmuir[3] and has been extended recently by other workers.[5]   Figure 5-6 shows theoretical results in the form of a plot of cesiated work function versus the ratio of surface temperature T_E to cesium-pool temperature T_{Cs} for different bare work functions.

Another surface phenomenon which plays an important role in the behavior of a thermionic converter is surface ionization, because the ions help to reduce space-charge in the interelectrode space.   To compute the outgoing current of ions from the surface of a metal, it is necessary to know the probability β that an atom or ion will leave the surface as an ion.   If it is assumed that the average incident particle remains on the surface long enough to "thermalize," the ion emission rate Γ_{p+} will be related to the incident fluxes of neutrals and ions by the equation

$$\Gamma_{p+} = \beta(\Gamma_{p-} + \Gamma_{a-}) \qquad (5\text{-}4)$$

where Γ_{p-} and Γ_{a-} are the incident fluxes of ions and neutrals, respectively. An expression for β can be developed by considering an equilibrium mix-

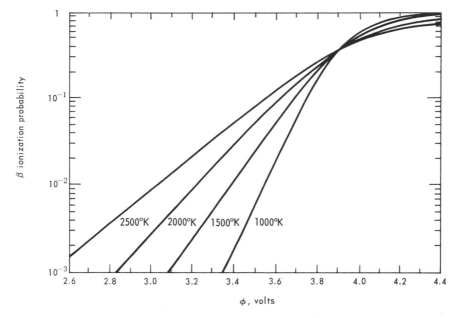

Fig. 5-7. *Surface-ionization probability for cesium. (Reprinted by permission from "Thermionic Energy Conversion," J. M. Houston and H. F. Webster, Advances in Electronics, vol. XVII, Academic Press Inc., New York, 1962.)*

ture of ideal atomic, ionic, and electronic gases on the surface of a metal and by assuming that the equilibrium concentration of electrons is determined by thermionic emission from the metal. The result is

$$\beta = \left[1 + 2 \exp \frac{I - \phi_E}{\theta_E}\right]^{-1}$$

which is the so-called "Langmuir-Saha ionization probability" where I is the first ionization potential of the gas. Figure 5-7 shows how the ionization probability β for cesium ($I = 3.89$ volts) depends on the work function.

The atoms and ions which strike the surface thermalize and eventually evaporate and carry off heat energy, just as the electrons do. For an atom current density Γ_a, the heat transfer is given by

$$\Gamma_a(h_a + 2kT_E)$$

and for an ion current density Γ_p, by

$$\Gamma_p(h_p + 2kT_E)$$

where h_a and h_p are the atomic and ionic heats of vaporization, respectively. These expressions do not take into account radiation, excited atoms, or an elevated plasma temperature.

1-2. Volume Phenomena

After the charged particles leave the electrode surfaces, their migration will be influenced by forces caused by gradients in the electric potential, particle densities, and particle temperatures. To carry out a macroscopic analysis of the charged-particle migration, it is necessary to obtain a simultaneous solution to a set of equations composed of Maxwell's equations for the electromagnetic field and the Boltzmann transport equations of kinetic theory. With the exception of some special cases, it is not possible to obtain exact analytic solutions to this set of equations. However, techniques have been developed which give approximate solutions. The analysis is greatly simplified when collisions can be ignored, as is usually done when considering the vacuum converter or the low-pressure vapor converter. By definition low-pressure operation occurs when the pressure is low enough that the average electron makes no collisions in transit from emitter to collector. For electrons undergoing elastic collisions in cesium vapor, there are three mean free paths to be considered: electron-electron (λ_{ee}), electron-ion (λ_{ep}), and electron-atom (λ_{ea}). In terms of these individual mean free paths, the average mean free path is given approximately by the equation

$$\lambda^{-1} = \lambda_{ee}{}^{-1} + \lambda_{ep}{}^{-1} + \lambda_{ea}{}^{-1}$$

An estimate of λ_{ee} is given by the relation

$$\lambda_{ee} = \left(\frac{3kT_e}{m_e}\right)^{1/2} t_c \tag{5-5}$$

where t_c is the time between collisions. Spitzer defines the self-collision time t_c for a group of particles interacting with each other as the time required for any anisotropy in the velocity distribution to disappear.[6] The expression which Spitzer gives for this time is

$$t_c = \frac{45.8 m_e{}^{1/2}(kT_e)^{3/2}\epsilon_0{}^2}{n_e e^4 \ln \Lambda}$$

where n_e is the electron density, Λ is the ratio of the Debye length $(kT_e\epsilon_0/e^2 n_e)^{1/2}$ to the average radius of interaction $e^2/12\pi\epsilon_0 kT_e$ of the electron, and ϵ_0 is the permittivity of free space. According to this equation, the self-collision time of electrons for a density of 10^{18} m^{-3} and a temperature of 1160°K is of the order of 10^{-9} sec. When this expression for t_c is used in Eq. (5-5), the following expression for λ_{ee} is obtained:

$$\lambda_{ee} = \frac{79.2(\epsilon_0\theta/e)^2}{n_e \ln \Lambda}$$

The electron-atom mean free path is given by simple kinetic theory as

$$\lambda_{ea} = \frac{1}{n_a\sigma_a}$$

where n_a is the atom density and σ_a is the electron-atom scattering cross section. A variety of experiments directed toward evaluating σ_a for electrons in cesium vapor have been performed. The results of these experiments have been summarized,[7] and a simple averaging of these results gives σ_a approximately equal to 1.76×10^{-18} m² for 0.1 to 0.3 ev electrons. This is about eight times larger than the geometric cross section of the cesium atom.

If it is assumed that λ_{ep} is on the same order as λ_{ee}, λ is given approximately by the expression

$$\lambda^{-1} = \frac{(e/\epsilon_0\theta)^2 n_e \ln \Lambda}{39.6} + n_a\sigma_a \qquad \text{m}^{-1} \tag{5-6}$$

For a cesium plasma in the absence of an electric field, expressions for n_e and n_a in terms of the cesium pressure p_{Cs} and the plasma temperature T can be obtained from the relations

$$n_a + n_p = \frac{p_{Cs}}{kT} \tag{5-7}$$

$$n_e n_p = K n_a \tag{5-8}$$

$$n_e = n_p \tag{5-9}$$

where n_p is the ion density and K is the Saha equilibrium constant. The ideal gas law embodied in Eq. (5-7) holds only when the atom-atom–collision mean free path is small compared with the electrode spacing. Otherwise T in Eq. (5-7) should be replaced by $(TT_{Cs})^{1/2}$ according to Knudsen's law. However, this is a small error which does not significantly alter the results of the present discussion, so that Eq. (5-7) will be used for all pressures. Equations (5-7) to (5-9) can be solved for n_e and n_a in terms of p_{Cs} and T and give

$$n_e = K \frac{\sqrt{1 + 4p_{Cs}/kTK} - 1}{2}$$

$$n_a = K \frac{(\sqrt{1 + 4p_{Cs}/kTK} - 1)^2}{4}$$

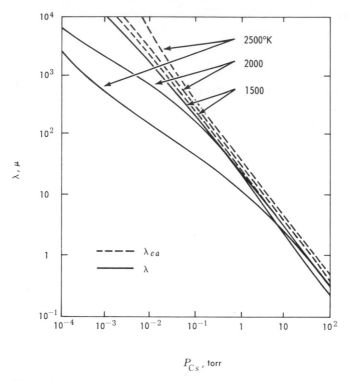

P_{Cs}, torr

Fig. 5-8. *Electron mean free path (microns) for elastic collisions with atoms λ_{ea} and with all particles λ versus pressure for various gas temperatures.*

The elimination of n_e and n_a from Eq. (5-6) by use of these equations gives

$$\lambda^{-1} = K \left(\sqrt{1 + 4p_{Cs}/kTK} - 1\right)$$
$$\left[\left(\frac{e}{\epsilon_0 \theta}\right)^2 \frac{\ln \Lambda}{79.2} + \frac{\sigma_a}{4} \left(\sqrt{\frac{1 + 4p_{Cs}}{kTK}} - 1\right)\right]$$

which is the desired relation for λ in terms of T and p_{Cs}.   Figure 5-8 shows the variation of λ (solid curves) and λ_{ea} (dashed curves) with temperature and cesium-vapor pressure.   The actual mean free path λ deviates from the electron-atom mean free path λ_{ea} for low pressures and high temperatures where the fractional ionization becomes appreciable.   The relative importance of electron-electron and electron-ion interactions versus electron-neutral interactions is illustrated in Fig. 5-9, which shows the variation of $\lambda_{ea}/\lambda_{ee}$ with temperature and cesium-vapor pressure.   These curves show that electron-neutral interactions dominate the transport of electrons at high pressure and low temperature. Thus in a typical cesium converter with an emitter temperature of 2000°K, a cesium-vapor pressure of 10 torr, and an electrode spacing l of 254 μ (.010 in.), the ratio l/λ is approximately 85. Hence the converter operation falls into the high-pressure regime. On the other hand, for a cesium-vapor pressure of 10^{-3} torr, the ratio l/λ is approximately 0.13; hence, the converter operation falls into the low-pressure regime. It should be remembered that the above discussion is based on equilibrium considerations. When the electron temperature is considerably higher than the emitter temperature, the electron temperature should be used to estimate the fractional ionization. This might result in the dominant scattering mechanism in the high-pressure regime being coulombic in nature.

The remainder of this chapter will be devoted to a more detailed theoretical discussion of the effects of volume phenomena on thermionic-converter operation and a presentation of some recent experimental results.

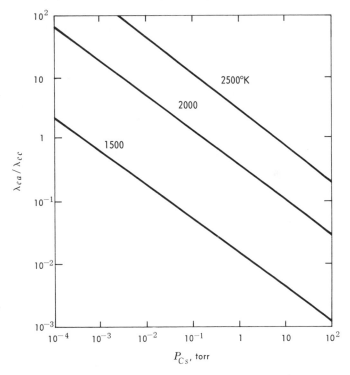

Fig. 5-9. *Variation of the ratio of electron-atom to electron-electron mean free path $\lambda_{ea}/\lambda_{ee}$ with pressure for various gas temperatures.*

The emphasis is placed on volume phenomena because the state of understanding of converter-surface physics is much better than that of converter-transport physics.

2. Background Theory

The primary objective of a theoretical analysis of the operation of a thermionic converter is to calculate the electric-potential distribution in the interelectrode space. Once the potential distribution is known, it is a simple matter to obtain current-voltage characteristics for different electrode temperatures and electrode spacings. The current-voltage characteristic automatically gives the power-voltage characteristic which is of primary interest to the engineer. Finally, the efficiency-voltage characteristic is obtained from the power-voltage characteristic, if the total heat power input to the emitter is known.

To calculate the electric-potential distribution in the interelectrode space of a thermionic converter, it is necessary to follow the motions of charged particles as they migrate from emitter to collector under the influence of forces caused by gradients in the electric potential, particle densities, and particle temperatures. To do this, the simultaneous solution to a set of equations composed of Maxwell's equations for the electromagnetic field in free space and the Boltzmann transport equations of kinetic theory is needed. In the discussion that follows, attention will be focused on the steady-state cases where the magnetic field is negligible. Therefore, the only electromagnetic-field equation required is Poisson's equation.

The transport equations which describe the migration of charged particles in a thermionic converter are based on kinetic theory. In turn, kinetic theory is based on the concept of the velocity distribution function $f_i(\mathbf{r}, \mathbf{c}, t)$, which is defined as the probability of finding a particle of the ith kind at position $\mathbf{r}$ with velocity $\mathbf{c}$ at time t. (The velocity vector $\mathbf{c}$ has components u, v, and w, which correspond to the x, y, and z coordinates.) Gas properties are defined by integrals over the velocity distribution. These gas properties are the particle densities

$$n_i = \int f_i d\mathbf{c}_i$$

where the integration extends over all values of $\mathbf{c}_i$, the average velocities of the particles

$$\langle \mathbf{c}_i \rangle = n_i^{-1} \int \mathbf{c}_i f_i d\mathbf{c}_i$$

and the average kinetic energies of the particles

$$\langle \tfrac{1}{2} m_i c_i^2 \rangle = n_i^{-1} \int \tfrac{1}{2} m_i c_i^2 f_i d\mathbf{c}_i$$

where m_i is the mass of the ith kind of particle.

Additional relations defining current, temperature, pressure, and heat flow in terms of these averages are required. The particle flux density $\mathbf{\Gamma}_i$ is defined by

$$\mathbf{\Gamma}_i = n_i \langle \mathbf{c}_i \rangle$$

Following Chapman and Cowling,[8] the particle temperature T_i is defined in terms of the peculiar velocity $\mathbf{C}_i$ by

$$\tfrac{3}{2} k T_i = \langle \tfrac{1}{2} m_i C_i^2 \rangle \tag{5-10}$$

where $\mathbf{C}_i \equiv \mathbf{c}_i - \mathbf{c}_0$, with $\mathbf{c}_0$ being the center-of-mass velocity defined by

$$\sum_i n_i m_i \mathbf{c}_0 = \sum_i m_i \mathbf{\Gamma}_i \tag{5-11}$$

The corresponding pressure tensor $\mathbf{P}$ is defined by

$$\mathbf{P} = \sum_i n_i m_i \langle \mathbf{C}_i \mathbf{C}_i \rangle \tag{5-12}$$

Finally, the heat-flux vector $\mathbf{Q}$ is defined by

$$\mathbf{Q} \equiv \sum_i \tfrac{1}{2} n_i m_i \langle C_i^2 \mathbf{C}_i \rangle \tag{5-13}$$

The velocity distribution functions obey the well-known Boltzmann equation

$$\frac{df_i}{dt} = \frac{\partial f_i}{\partial t} + \mathbf{c}_i \cdot \nabla f_i + \mathbf{F}_i \cdot \nabla_c f_i = \sum_j \left(\frac{\partial_c f_i}{\partial t} \right)_j$$

where

$$\nabla_c = \mathbf{i} \frac{\partial}{\partial u} + \mathbf{j} \frac{\partial}{\partial v} + \mathbf{k} \frac{\partial}{\partial w}$$

$\mathbf{F}_i$ is the external force per unit mass on the ith kind of particle, and the quantity

$$\sum_j \left(\frac{\partial_c f_i}{\partial t} \right)_j$$

is the rate of change of f_i caused by collisions between the ith kind of particle and all other kinds of particles, including $j = i$. In most cases of practical interest, it is impossible to obtain an analytic solution for f_i because of the complexity of the quantity $(\partial_c f_i / \partial t)$, the so-called "collision integral." However, some information which relates the gas properties can be obtained from Boltzmann's equation without knowing the actual form of the velocity distribution function. For example, if $g_i(\mathbf{c}_i)$ is a function of the velocity associated with the ith kind of particle, multiplying Boltzmann's equation by $g_i d\mathbf{c}_i$ and integrating over all velocities gives

$$\int g_i \frac{df_i}{dt} d\mathbf{c}_i = n_i \Delta\langle g_i \rangle = \sum_j \int g_i \left(\frac{\partial_c f_i}{\partial t}\right)_j d\mathbf{c}_i$$

The quantity $n_i \Delta\langle g_i \rangle$ represents the change in $\langle g_i \rangle$ caused by collisions. If $g_i = m_i \mathbf{c}_i$, $n_i \Delta\langle m_i \mathbf{c}_i \rangle$ represents the gain (or loss) of momentum of the ith kind of particle caused by collisions with all other kinds of particles.

The evaluation of

$$\int g_i \frac{df_i}{dt} d\mathbf{c}_i = \int g_i \left(\frac{\partial f_i}{\partial t} + \mathbf{c}_i \cdot \nabla f_i + \mathbf{F}_i \cdot \nabla_c f_i\right) d\mathbf{c}_i$$

proceeds as follows:

$$\int g_i \frac{\partial f_i}{\partial t} d\mathbf{c}_i = \frac{\partial}{\partial t} \int g_i f_i d\mathbf{c}_i = \frac{\partial}{\partial t} n_i \langle g_i \rangle$$

$$\int g_i \mathbf{c}_i \cdot \nabla f_i d\mathbf{c}_i = \nabla \cdot \int g_i f_i \mathbf{c}_i d\mathbf{c}_i = \nabla \cdot n_i \langle g_i \mathbf{c}_i \rangle$$

$$\int g_i \mathbf{F}_i \cdot \nabla_c f_i d\mathbf{c}_i = -\mathbf{F}_i \cdot \int f_i \nabla_c g_i d\mathbf{c}_i = -n_i \mathbf{F}_i \cdot \langle \nabla_c g_i \rangle$$

where it has been assumed that g_i is a function of $\mathbf{c}_i$ only, that the quantity $g_i f_i$ tends to zero as $\mathbf{c}_i$ approaches infinity, and that $\mathbf{F}_i$ does not depend on $\mathbf{c}_i$. (The latter assumption restricts the following discussion to those cases in which the effects of magnetic fields are unimportant.) Therefore, the change in g_i due to collisions is given by the equation

$$n_i \Delta g_i = \int g_i \frac{df_i}{dt} d\mathbf{c}_i = \frac{\partial}{\partial t} n_i \langle g_i \rangle + \nabla \cdot n_i \langle g_i \mathbf{c}_i \rangle - n_i \mathbf{F}_i \cdot \langle \nabla_c g_i \rangle \qquad (5\text{-}14)$$

If the usual conservation laws are invoked, some important equations relating particle mass density, particle flux density, particle temperature, etc., can be derived from Eq. (5-14). The unique feature of these relations is that they are independent of the forms of the collision integrals. First, let $g_i = m_i$; then Eq. (5-14) becomes

$$n_i \, \Delta m_i = \frac{\partial}{\partial t} (n_i m_i) + \boldsymbol{\nabla} \cdot n_i m_i \langle \mathbf{c}_i \rangle$$

The quantity $n_i \, \Delta m_i$ is equal to the net rate at which particles of mass m_i are being generated per unit volume per unit time as a result of ionization and recombination. Second, let $g_i = m_i \mathbf{c}_i$; then Eq. (5-14) becomes

$$n_i \, \Delta m_i \langle \mathbf{c}_i \rangle = \frac{\partial}{\partial t} (n_i m_i \langle \mathbf{c}_i \rangle) + \boldsymbol{\nabla} \cdot n_i m_i \langle \mathbf{c}_i \mathbf{c}_i \rangle - n_i m_i \mathbf{F}_i \tag{5-15}$$

Since the gas temperature, pressure, and heat flux are defined in terms of the peculiar velocity $\mathbf{C}_i$, it is more appropriate to express Eq. (5-15) in terms of $\mathbf{C}_i$. By definition,

$$\langle \mathbf{c}_i \mathbf{c}_i \rangle = \langle (\mathbf{C}_i + \mathbf{c}_0)(\mathbf{C}_i + \mathbf{c}_0) \rangle = \langle \mathbf{C}_i \mathbf{C}_i \rangle + \mathbf{c}_0 \mathbf{c}_0 + 2 \mathbf{c}_0 \langle \mathbf{C}_i \rangle$$

Therefore, Eq. (5-15) can be written

$$n_i \, \Delta m_i \langle \mathbf{C}_i \rangle = \frac{\partial}{\partial t} (m_i \boldsymbol{\Gamma}_i) + \boldsymbol{\nabla} \cdot (\mathbf{P}_i + n_i m_i \mathbf{c}_0 \mathbf{c}_0 + 2 n_i m_i \langle \mathbf{C}_i \rangle \mathbf{c}_0) - n_i m_i \mathbf{F}_i$$

Since momentum is conserved in all collisions, it is necessary that

$$\sum_i n_i \, \Delta m_i \langle \mathbf{c}_i \rangle = 0$$

The resultant equation of motion for the system is

$$0 = \frac{\partial}{\partial t} \left(\sum_i m_i \boldsymbol{\Gamma}_i \right) + \boldsymbol{\nabla} \cdot \left(\mathbf{P} + \sum_i n_i m_i \mathbf{c}_0 \mathbf{c}_0 \right) - \sum_i n_i m_i \mathbf{F}_i$$

Finally, let $g_i = \tfrac{1}{2} m_i c_i^2$; then Eq. (5-14) becomes

$$n_i \, \Delta \frac{1}{2} m_i \langle c_i^2 \rangle = \frac{\partial}{\partial t} \left(\frac{1}{2} n_i m_i \langle c_i^2 \rangle \right) + \boldsymbol{\nabla} \cdot \frac{1}{2} n_i m_i \langle c_i^2 \mathbf{c}_i \rangle - n_i \mathbf{F}_i \cdot m_i \langle \mathbf{c}_i \rangle \tag{5-16}$$

By definition,

$$\tfrac{1}{2} m_i \langle c_i^2 \rangle = \tfrac{1}{2} m_i \langle C_i^2 \rangle + m_i \langle \mathbf{C}_i \rangle \cdot \mathbf{c}_0 + \tfrac{1}{2} m_i c_0^2 = \tfrac{3}{2} k T_i + m_i \langle \mathbf{C}_i \rangle \cdot \mathbf{c}_0 \\ + \tfrac{1}{2} m_i c_0^2$$

and

$$\tfrac{1}{2} n_i m_i \langle c_i^2 \mathbf{c}_i \rangle = \tfrac{1}{2} n_i m_i \langle C_i^2 \mathbf{C}_i \rangle + n_i m_i \mathbf{c}_0 \cdot \langle \mathbf{C}_i \mathbf{C}_i \rangle + \tfrac{1}{2} n_i m_i \mathbf{c}_0 \langle C_i^2 \rangle \\ + \tfrac{1}{2} n_i m_i c_0^2 \mathbf{c}_0 + \tfrac{1}{2} n_i m_i \langle \mathbf{C}_i \rangle c_0^2 + n_i m_i \langle \mathbf{C}_i \rangle \cdot \mathbf{c}_0 \mathbf{c}_0 = \mathbf{Q}_i + \mathbf{c}_0 \cdot \mathbf{P}_i \\ + (\tfrac{3}{2} k T_i + \tfrac{1}{2} m_i c_0^2) n_i \mathbf{c}_0 + \tfrac{1}{2} n_i m_i \langle \mathbf{C}_i \rangle c_0^2 + n_i m_i \langle \mathbf{C}_i \rangle \cdot \mathbf{c}_0 \mathbf{c}_0$$

Therefore, by summing over i, the following energy-conservation equation is developed:

$$\sum_i n_i \Delta \frac{1}{2} m_i \langle c_i{}^2 \rangle = \frac{\partial}{\partial t} \sum_i n_i \left(\frac{3}{2} kT_i + \frac{1}{2} m_i c_0{}^2 \right)$$

$$+ \, \boldsymbol{\nabla} \cdot \left[\mathbf{Q} + \mathbf{c}_0 \cdot \mathbf{P} + \sum_i n_i \mathbf{c}_0 \left(\frac{3}{2} kT_i + \frac{1}{2} m_i c_0{}^2 \right) \right] - \sum_i m_i \boldsymbol{\Gamma}_i \cdot \mathbf{F}_i$$

For a gas composed of more than one kind of particle, the conservation equations must be supplemented by additional equations relating the gas properties, n_i, $\boldsymbol{\Gamma}_i$, T_i, $\mathbf{P}_i$, and $\mathbf{Q}_i$. The form of the additional equations depends on whether or not the situation being investigated can be adequately described by assuming local thermodynamic equilibrium among the various particles.

For local thermodynamic equilibrium to exist in a gas in which there are gradients in the gas properties (n_i, $\mathbf{c}_i$, and T_i), collisions between the various particles must be numerous enough to maintain the velocity distribution functions f_i nearly isotropic. In other words, the gradient of the temperature must be small enough that the temperature does not vary appreciably over a distance equal to the mean free path. In this case, the temperatures T_i are approximately equal to each other; the pressure is approximately a scalar function of position; i.e.,

$$\mathbf{P} = \sum_i n_i kT \mathbf{I}$$

where $\mathbf{I} = (\mathbf{ii} + \mathbf{jj} + \mathbf{kk})$ is the identity tensor; and the heat-flux vector is given approximately by

$$\mathbf{Q} = -\kappa \, \boldsymbol{\nabla} T + \tfrac{5}{2} kT \sum_i n_i \langle \mathbf{C}_i \rangle$$

where κ is the thermal conductivity of the ensemble.

The required number of equations is completed by the addition of multicomponent diffusion equations such as those developed by Hirschfelder, Curtiss, and Bird.[9] These equations are developed by assuming that the distribution functions are approximately Maxwellian in the center-of-mass coordinate system. When thermal diffusion is neglected, these equations are

$$\frac{\sum_j kT(n_i \boldsymbol{\Gamma}_j - n_j \boldsymbol{\Gamma}_i)}{D_{ij} \sum_i n_i} = \boldsymbol{\nabla}(n_i kT) - n_i m_i \left[\mathbf{F}_i - \left(\frac{\partial \mathbf{c}_0}{\partial t} + \mathbf{c}_0 \cdot \boldsymbol{\nabla} \mathbf{c}_0 \right) \right]$$

$$(5\text{-}17)$$

where the D_{ij} are the binary diffusion coefficients for particles of type i diffusing relative to those of type j. Thus, for a j-component gas with flows in one direction, there are $2j + 2$ unknown dependent variables and the same number of differential equations to be solved simultaneously for these variables. The $2j + 2$ variables are the j-particle densities and the j current densities, plus the temperature and the electric potential. The $2j + 2$ equations are the j continuity equations, the $j - 1$ diffusion equations, the equation of total momentum conservation, the equation of total energy conservation, and Poisson's equation.

On the other hand, if the differences in the average energies of the various kinds of particles are large, the assumption of local thermodynamic equilibrium is not valid. In this case, it is necessary either to solve the Boltzmann equations or to assume the form of the velocity distribution functions and then to compute the collision integrals directly. Then for a j-component gas, there are $3j + 1$ unknown variables with the corresponding number of equations. The $3j + 1$ variables are the j-particle densities, the j-particle currents, the j-particle temperatures, and the electric potential. The $3j + 1$ equations are the j continuity equations, the j momentum equations, the j energy equations, and Poisson's equation.

The simplest case is one in which the effects of collisions on the f_i are negligible compared with those of electric fields so that $\partial_c f_i / \partial t$ can be dropped from Boltzmann's equation. The resulting equation is sometimes called the Vlasov equation or the collisionless Boltzmann equation. This approach was used in the first complete analysis of the vacuum thermionic converter. More will be said about this problem later.

In cases where the effects of collisions on the f_i are not negligible but where the time between collisions is large compared with the time any two particles are under the direct influence of each other, the form of $\partial_c f_i / \partial t$ is that which describes the effect of binary collisions:

$$\left(\frac{\partial_c f_i}{\partial t} \right)_j = \int \int \int [f_i(\mathbf{c}_i')f_j(\mathbf{c}_j') - f_i(\mathbf{c}_i)f_j(\mathbf{c}_j)]|\mathbf{c}_i - \mathbf{c}_j|b \, db \, d\chi \, d\mathbf{c}_j \quad (5\text{-}18)$$

where $\mathbf{c}_i'$ and $\mathbf{c}_j'$ are the velocities after the collision and $|\mathbf{c}_i - \mathbf{c}_j|$ denotes the magnitude of the relative velocity. The geometry of the collision is represented by the impact parameter b and scattering angle χ. A detailed derivation of Eq. (5-18) is given by Chapman and Cowling.[8] Thus, even for a one-component gas, the Boltzmann equation is a nonlinear integro-differential equation which, in general, can be solved only approximately.

When approximate results suffice, it is customary to assume a velocity distribution of the form

$$f_i(\mathbf{r}, \mathbf{c}_i) = n_i \left(\frac{m_i}{2\pi k T_i} \right)^{3/2} \exp \left[\frac{-m_i}{2k T_i} (\mathbf{c}_i - \langle \mathbf{c}_i \rangle)^2 \right] \quad (5\text{-}19)$$

where n_i, $\langle \mathbf{c}_i \rangle$, and T_i are functions of $\mathbf{r}$. This form of f is particularly suitable when the following conditions prevail: (1) The differences in the $\langle \mathbf{c}_i \rangle$ and the T_i are large; (2) the particle motions are approximately adiabatic; that is, $\mathbf{Q} \approx 0$; and (3) the anisotropy of $\mathbf{P}$ is unimportant, in which case the nondiagonal elements of $\mathbf{P}$ are taken to be zero and the diagonal elements may or may not be equal according to whether or not the situation is one in which collisions are numerous enough to maintain f nearly isotropic. In this case, the moment equations for the individual particles become

$$n_i \, \Delta m_i = \frac{\partial}{\partial t} (n_i m_i) + \mathbf{\nabla} \cdot m_i \mathbf{\Gamma}_i \tag{5-20}$$

$$n_i \, \Delta m_i \langle \mathbf{c}_i \rangle = \frac{\partial}{\partial t} (m_i \mathbf{\Gamma}_i) + \mathbf{\nabla} \cdot (n_i k T_i + n_i m_i \langle \mathbf{c}_i \rangle \langle \mathbf{c}_i \rangle) - n_i m_i \mathbf{F}_i \tag{5-21}$$

$$n_i \, \Delta \frac{1}{2} m_i \langle c_i{}^2 \rangle = \frac{\partial}{\partial t} \left(\frac{3}{2} n_i k T_i + \frac{1}{2} n_i m_i \langle c_i \rangle^2 \right)$$
$$+ \mathbf{\nabla} \cdot \left(\frac{5}{2} k T_i + \frac{1}{2} m_i \langle c_i \rangle^2 \right) \mathbf{\Gamma}_i - m_i \mathbf{\Gamma}_i \cdot \mathbf{F}_i \tag{5-22}$$

where

$$\tfrac{3}{2} k T_i \equiv \tfrac{1}{2} m_i \langle |\mathbf{c}_i - \langle \mathbf{c}_i \rangle|^2 \rangle$$

Computations of the second and third moments of the Boltzmann collision integral for various types of particle interactions have been made for distributions like that given by Eq. (5-19).† For a j-component gas in which the kinetic energy of the directed motion of each component is small compared with the corresponding mean thermal energy (kinetic energy of random motion), the moments of the collision integral have the forms

$$n_i \, \Delta m_i \langle \mathbf{c}_i \rangle = \sum_j \frac{n_i \mathbf{\Gamma}_j - n_j \mathbf{\Gamma}_i}{\alpha_{ij}}$$

$$n_i \, \Delta \frac{1}{2} m_i \langle c_i{}^2 \rangle = \sum_j \left[\frac{2 n_i n_j}{(m_i + m_j) \alpha_{ij}} \right] \left[\frac{3}{2} e(\theta_i - \theta_j) - \frac{1}{2} m_j \left| \frac{\mathbf{\Gamma}_i}{n_i} - \frac{\mathbf{\Gamma}_j}{n_j} \right|^2 \right]$$
$$\tag{5-23}$$

where α_{ij} depends on the type of particle interaction. For example, an interaction between hard spheres of radii r_i and r_j gives

$$\alpha_{ij} = \frac{3(m_i + m_j)}{8(2\pi k)^{1/2}(m_i m_j)^{1/2}(r_i + r_j)^2(m_i T_j + m_j T_i)}$$

† For example, see T. F. Morse, *Phys. Fluids*, **6**: 1420 (1963) and "Statistical Plasma Mechanics," in F. H. Clauser (ed.), *Plasma Dynamics*, Addison-Wesley Publishing Company, Inc., Reading, Mass., 1960.

whereas a coulombic interaction gives

$$\alpha_{ij} = \frac{3\epsilon_0^2 (2\pi k)^{3/2} (m_i T_j - m_j T_i)^{3/2}}{(m_i m_j)^{1/2} (m_i + m_j) e^4 \ln \Lambda}$$

The quantity $n_j(m_i + m_j)\alpha_{ij}$ has the dimensions of frequency and can be thought of as the frequency of collisions between the ith and jth kinds of particles. The particle diffusion equations are obtained by substituting Eq. (5-23) in Eq. (5-21). The result is similar to Eq. (5-17).

3. Vacuum Converter

3-1. Collisionless Theory

One of the first complete theoretical analyses of the operation of the vacuum converter was based on the space-charge theory developed by Langmuir.[10] His theory will be briefly reviewed here, and the results will be compared later with the results of transport theory as applied to the same problem. Langmuir assumed that the electrons in a plane diode are emitted with a Maxwellian velocity distribution and that after emission the electrons travel in the electric field that develops as a result of the applied potential and their own charge. This is tantamount to assuming that the steady-state velocity distribution function of the electrons in a plane diode satisfies the Vlasov equation, i.e., Boltzmann's equation with $\partial_c f/\partial t = 0$:

$$\mathbf{c} \cdot \nabla f + \frac{e}{m} \nabla V \cdot \nabla_c f = 0 \tag{5-24}$$

where m is the mass of the electron and V is the electric potential. In the case of infinite planar electrodes with uniform work functions, the electric potential is a function of x alone and f does not vary in the y and z directions. In this case, Eq. (5-24) reduces to

$$u \left(\frac{\partial f}{\partial x} \right) + \frac{e}{m} \left(\frac{dV}{dx} \right) \left(\frac{\partial f}{\partial u} \right) = 0$$

This equation is separable in x and u. The general solution is of the form

$$f(x, u) = \sum_{k=0}^{\infty} A_k \exp \left\{ B_k \left[\frac{eV(x)}{m} - \frac{1}{2} u^2 \right] \right\}$$

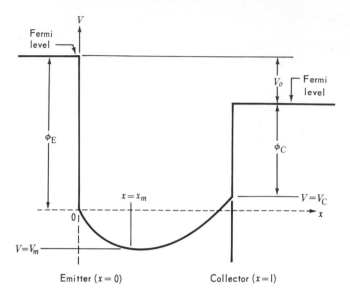

Fig. 5-10. *Electric potential diagram for vacuum thermionic converter.*

where the A_k and B_k are constants which must be determined by the boundary conditions on f. This form of the solution is such that the current density, defined by the equation

$$\Gamma = \int u f(x, u)\, du$$

is zero when u ranges from $-\infty$ to $+\infty$. This implies that the distribution must be truncated in velocity whenever there is a net current.

Langmuir assumed that the velocity distribution of the emitted electrons is Maxwellian and that the distribution in the backward direction at the emitter is a truncated Maxwellian. He based the latter assumption on the reasoning that when the net current is less than the saturation current, there must be a potential minimum in the gap which prevents the less energetic electrons from reaching the collector. It is these electrons which partially fill in the backward part of the distribution. These assumptions lead to the distribution

$$f(x, u) = \begin{cases} A_0 \exp \left\{ B_0 \left[\dfrac{eV(x)}{m} - \dfrac{1}{2} u^2 \right] \right\} & u \geq \pm u_l,\ x \gtrless x_m \\ 0 & u < \pm u_l,\ x \gtrless x_m \end{cases}$$

with

$$A_0 = 2n_m \left(\frac{m}{2\pi k T_E}\right)^{1/2} \exp\left(-\frac{eV_m}{kT_E}\right)$$

$$B_0 = \frac{m}{kT_E}$$

$$u_l = \left\{\frac{2e}{m}[V(x) - V_m]\right\}^{1/2}$$

where T_E is the emitter temperature, u_l is the velocity required for an electron to overcome a retarding potential of magnitude $V(x) - V_m$, n_m is the density at the minimum, x_m is the location of the minimum, and $V_m = V(x_m)$ is the depth of the minimum. The relationship between x_m and V_m is shown in the electric potential diagram of Fig. 5-10. Figure 5-11 shows the variation of $f(0, u)$ with u for different values of u_l.

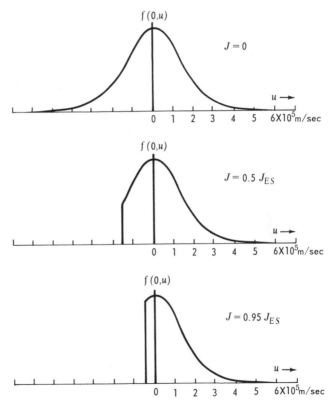

Fig. 5-11. *Variation of Langmuir distribution function $f(o,u)$ with u for $-J_{ES} = 2$ A/cm^2 and $T_E = 1160°K$.*

The constant n_m, which is the electron density at x_m, is found in terms of the emitter saturation current density J_{ES} and the depth V_m of the potential minimum by equating the outgoing current density at the emitter to J_{ES}:

$$J_{ES} = -e \int_0^\infty uf(0, u) \, du = -en_m \left(\frac{2kT_E}{\pi m}\right)^{1/2} \exp\left(\frac{-eV_m}{kT_E}\right) \qquad (5\text{-}25)$$

The net current density is given by

$$J = -e \int_{-u_l}^\infty uf(x, u) \, du = -en_m \left(\frac{2kT_E}{\pi m}\right)^{1/2} = J_{ES} \exp\frac{eV_m}{kT_E} \qquad (5\text{-}26)$$

where Eq. (5-25) has been used to relate J to J_{ES}. The electron density in the interelectrode space is given by

$$n(x) = \int_{-u_l}^\infty f(x, u) \, du = n_m e^\psi (1 \pm \text{erf } \sqrt{\psi}) \qquad x \lessgtr x_m$$

where

$$\psi = \frac{e[V(x) - V_m]}{kT_E}$$

and erf $\sqrt{\psi}$ is the error function defined by

$$\text{erf } \sqrt{\psi} = \frac{2}{\sqrt{\pi}} \int_0^{\sqrt{\psi}} e^{-t^2} \, dt$$

The potential distribution is found from Poisson's equation, which in dimensionless variables becomes

$$2\frac{d^2\psi}{d\xi^2} = e^\psi (1 \pm \text{erf } \sqrt{\psi}) \qquad \xi \lessgtr 0$$

where

$$\xi = \left(\frac{2e^2 n_m}{kT_E \epsilon_0}\right)^{1/2} (x - x_m) = (2\pi m)^{1/4}(kT_E)^{-3/4}\left(\frac{-eJ}{\epsilon_0}\right)^{1/2} (x - x_m)$$

$$(5\text{-}27)$$

The first integral of Poisson's equation is

$$\left(\frac{d\psi}{d\xi}\right)^2 = e^\psi - 1 \pm e^\psi \text{ erf } \sqrt{\psi} \pm 2\left(\frac{\psi}{\pi}\right)^{1/2} \qquad \xi \lessgtr 0$$

so that ξ is given by

$$\xi = \int_0^\psi \frac{dt}{[e^t - 1 \pm e^t \text{ erf } \sqrt{t} \pm 2(t/\pi)^{1/2}]^{1/2}}$$

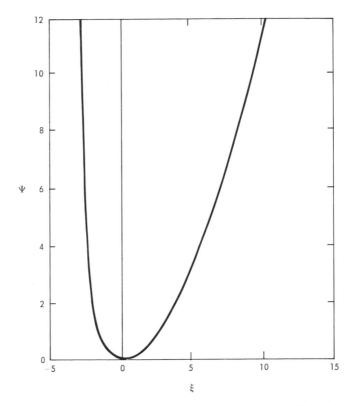

Fig. 5-12. *Reduced potential versus reduced distance for Langmuir distribution.*

A numerical integration gives the $\psi - \xi$ curve shown in Fig. 5-12. The current-voltage characteristic for a converter with given emitter temperature, emitter and collector work functions ϕ_E and ϕ_C, and electrode spacing l is found from this curve by choosing J, computing V_m by means of Eq. (5-26), computing $\psi_E = -eV_m/kT_E$, finding ξ_e from the $\psi - \xi$ curve, computing $-x_m$ from Eq. (5-27), computing $l + x_m$, computing ξ_C from Eq. (5-27), and finding ψ_C from the $\psi - \xi$ curve. This procedure gives a curve of current density J versus output voltage $V_o = \phi_C + V_C - \phi_E$ where output voltage has been defined as the potential of the collector Fermi level with respect to that of the emitter (cf. Fig. 5-10). The spacing dependence of the current-voltage characteristic of a vacuum converter found by this procedure is shown in Fig. 5-13. Note that the current does not approach saturation asymptotically.

The power-voltage characteristics corresponding to the current-voltage characteristics shown in Fig. 5-13 are shown in Fig. 5-14. The importance

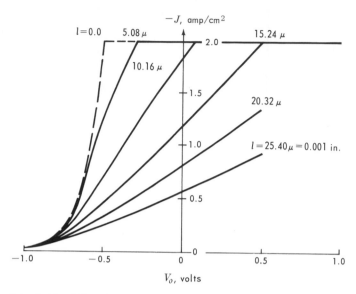

Fig. 5-13.   *Effect of spacing on current-voltage characteristic for Langmuir distribution. ϕ_E, 1.82 volts; ϕ_C, 1.32 volts; T_E, 1160° K; $-J_{ES}$, 2 amp/cm².*

of having a very small electrode spacing is apparent. The reason the output power density increases strongly with decreasing spacing is that the retarding potential V_m approaches zero as the electrode spacing tends to zero. Since this retarding potential, or space-charge barrier, limits the current density reaching the collector to a fraction exp (eV_m/kT_E) of the emitter saturation current density, it is important to have V_m as small as possible. The curves labeled $l = 0$ in Figs. 5-13 and 5-14 represent the upper limit obtainable when $V_m = 0$, i.e., for zero electrode spacing. Electrode spacings on the order of 0.0001 in. are very difficult to achieve and even more difficult to maintain during operation, so that another method of reducing the space-charge barrier has been devised. This method, which involves introducing positive ions into the interelectrode space, is discussed in the following sections.

The efficiency is defined as the ratio of electrical power output density delivered to the load to the input density required to maintain the emitter temperature. The power output density P_o is simply $J(V_o - V_w)$ where V_w is the voltage drop in the electrical lead. The power input density is equal to the sum of all the heat losses from the emitter. The heat losses are: (1) the electron cooling P_1; (2) the radiation loss P_2; and (3) the thermal conduction loss P_3 in the emitter electrical lead. In practice, insulating mechanical spacers are used to maintain the electrode spacing in close-spaced vacuum converters, but since there is no theoretical lower limit to their size, thermal conduction losses in such spacers will be ignored.

The electron cooling is equal to the average energy required to lift the electrons from the Fermi level of the emitter over the work-function barrier into the interelectrode space. This energy is the sum of the potential energy $-J\phi_E$ of the escaping electrons and the average kinetic energy of the escaping electrons. The average kinetic energy associated with the x component of velocity is given by the integral

$$\int_{-u_l}^{\infty} \tfrac{1}{2} mu^3 f(0, u)\, du = -J(-V_m + \theta_E)$$

Since there is an average kinetic energy of $\tfrac{1}{2}kT_E$ associated with the y and z velocity components, the total electron cooling is

$$P_1 = -J(\phi_e - V_m + 2\theta_E) \tag{5-28}$$

The radiation loss is given by

$$P_2 = (\epsilon_E^{-1} + \epsilon_C^{-1} + 1)^{-1}\sigma(T_E^4 - T_C^4)$$

based on the assumption of infinite parallel plane geometry where ϵ_E and ϵ_C are the total thermal emissivities of the emitter and collector, respectively, σ is the Stefan-Boltzmann constant, and T_C is the collector temperature.

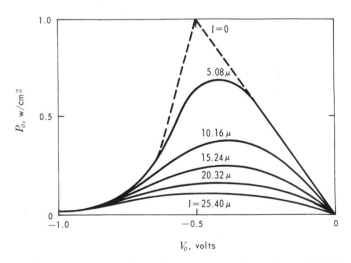

Fig. 5-14. *Effect of spacing on power-voltage characteristic for Langmuir distribution. ϕ_E, 1.82 volts; ϕ_C, 1.32 volts; T_E, 1160°K; $-J_{ES}$, 2 amp/cm².*

The thermal conduction loss in the emitter electrical lead is given by the first integral of the steady-state heat-flow equation

$$\frac{d}{dx}\frac{\kappa_w dT}{dx} = -J^2 \left(\frac{A_E}{A_w}\right)^2 \rho_w \tag{5-29}$$

where $T(x)$ is the temperature distribution in the lead, A_E is the emitter surface area, and A_w is the cross section of the lead. If the thermal conductivity κ_w and the electrical resistivity ρ_w are assumed to be related by the Wiedeman-Franz law[11]

$$\kappa_w \rho_w = \frac{\pi^2 k^2 T}{3e^2}$$

Eq. (5-29) can be written

$$\frac{\kappa_w dT}{dx}\frac{d}{dT}\frac{\kappa_w dT}{dx} = -J^2 \left(\frac{A_E}{A_w}\right)^2 \frac{\pi^2 k^2}{3e^2} T$$

This equation can be integrated to give

$$\left(\frac{\kappa_w dT}{dx}\right)^2_E - \left(\frac{\kappa_w dT}{dx}\right)^2_C = -J^2 \left(\frac{A_E}{A_w}\right)^2 \frac{\pi^2}{3}(\theta_E^2 - \theta_C^2)$$

if the temperature of the cooler end of the lead is taken to be the collector temperature and if radiation from the lead is neglected. Therefore, since $(\kappa_w dT/dx)_E - (\kappa_w dT/dx)_C = -JV_w$, the thermal conduction loss P_3 is given by the relation

$$P_3 = -\frac{A_w}{A_E}\left(\frac{\kappa_w dT}{dx}\right)_E = \frac{1}{2} J\left[\frac{\pi^2(\theta_E^2 - \theta_C^2)}{3V_w} - V_w\right]$$

Thus the efficiency η is given by

$$\eta = \frac{J(V_o - V_w)}{-J(\phi_E - V_m + 2\theta_E) + \epsilon\sigma(e/k)^4(\theta_E^4 - \theta_C^4)} \tag{5-30}$$
$$+ \tfrac{1}{2}J[\pi^2(\theta_E^2 - \theta_C^2)/3V_w - V_w]$$

where $\epsilon \equiv (\epsilon_E^{-1} + \epsilon_C^{-1} - 1)^{-1}$. This equation can be maximized with respect to V_w. The resulting optimum lead voltage drop is

$$V_w = -\left[\frac{\pi^2(\theta_E^2 - \theta_C^2)\eta}{3(2 - \eta)}\right]^{1/2} \tag{5-31}$$

Since $V_w = JA_E\rho_w l_w/A_w$, where l_w is the length of the lead, Eq. (5-31) gives the optimum lead geometry factor l_w/A_w for each current density J.

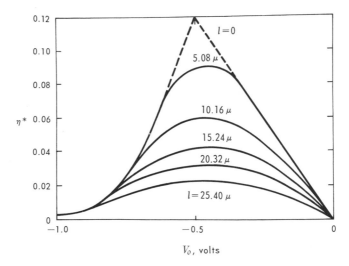

Fig. 5-15. *Effect of spacing on efficiency-voltage characteristic.*

Equation (5-31) can be substituted in Eq. (5-30) and the result solved for η to give

$$\eta = \eta^* \left\{ 1 - \left[\frac{(2 - \eta^*)\eta^* V_o^2}{\omega} + \eta^{*2} \right]^{1/2} \left(\frac{V_o^2}{\omega} + \eta^* \right)^{-1} \right\}$$

where $\omega = \pi^2(\theta_E^2 - \theta_C^2)/3$ and η^* is the efficiency obtained when lead losses are ignored; i.e.,

$$\eta^* = \frac{J V_o}{P_1 + P_2}$$

Figure 5-15 shows $\eta^* - V_o$ characteristics corresponding to the power-voltage characteristics shown in Fig. 5-14. Curves of η versus V_o are not given because each point on the $\eta - V_o$ characteristics requires a different lead geometry which is given by Eq. (5-31). The $\eta^* - V_o$ characteristics shown in Fig. 5-15 are based on electrode emissivities of 0.6 and on zero collector temperature in order to be consistent with the theory as outlined above.

3-2. Collisional Theory

In the preceding section, Langmuir's space-charge theory and its application to the vacuum converter were described. The basis of Langmuir's theory is the assumption that electron-electron collisions are unimportant

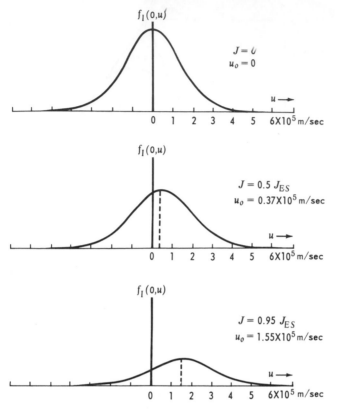

Fig. 5-16. *Variation of Case I distribution function $f_I(o,u)$ with u for $-J_{ES} = 2$ A/cm² and $T_E = 1160°K$.*

and that the velocity distribution in the emitting direction is Maxwell-Boltzmann. In this section, the same problem is treated by assuming that electron-electron collisions are important and that the velocity distribution is given by Eq. (5-19). The problem is worked out first for the case in which collisions are numerous enough to give a distribution which is isotropic in the center of mass (Case I)[12] and second for the case in which collisions are insufficient to maintain isotropy in the center of mass (Case II).

Case I. According to Eq. (5-19) the velocity distribution function is

$$f_I(x, \mathbf{c}) = n \left(\frac{m}{2\pi kT} \right)^{3/2} \exp \left\{ - \frac{m}{2kT} \left[(u - u_0)^2 + v^2 + w^2 \right] \right\}$$

where n, u_0, and T are functions of x. Integrating this distribution over v and w gives

$$f_I(x, u) = n \left(\frac{m}{2\pi kT} \right)^{1/2} \exp \frac{-m(u - u_0)^2}{2kT}$$

which is shown plotted versus u in Fig. 5-16 for $x = 0$ (cf. Fig. 5-11 for corresponding Langmuir distribution). The reason the amplitude decreases with increasing current is that the density decreases as the current increases [cf. Eq. (5-42)].

For planar geometry, Eqs. (5-20), (5-21), and (5-22) become, respectively,

$$\frac{d}{dx} (nu_0) = 0$$

$$\frac{d}{dx} (nkT + nmu_0^2) = en \frac{dV}{dx} \tag{5-32}$$

$$\frac{d}{dx} [nu_0(\tfrac{5}{2}kT + \tfrac{1}{2}mu_0^2)] = e(dV/dx)nu_0 \tag{5-33}$$

These three equations and Poisson's equation

$$\frac{d^2V}{dx^2} = \frac{en}{\epsilon_0} \tag{5-34}$$

form a complete set of equations to be solved simultaneously for $n(x)$, $u_0(x)$, $T(x)$, and $V(x)$. The continuity equation integrates to

$$nu_0 = \Gamma$$

where Γ is a constant. Equations (5-32) and (5-33) combine to give

$$\frac{n}{T^{3/2}} = \frac{n_E}{T_E^{3/2}} = \text{const} \tag{5-35}$$

which is the expected result for adiabatic ($Q = 0$) expansion. Substituting Poisson's equation for n in the right side of Eq. (5-32) gives an equation which integrates to

$$nkT + nmu_0^2 = \frac{\epsilon_0}{2} \left(\frac{dV}{dx} \right)^2 + C_1 \tag{5-36}$$

where C_1 is a constant. The energy equation integrates to

$$\frac{5}{2} kT + \frac{mu_0^2}{2} = eV + C_2 \tag{5-37}$$

where C_2 is a constant.   Equations (5-36) and (5-37) can be expressed in dimensionless form by using Eq. (5-35) and making the substitutions

$$\psi_I = \frac{e(V - V_m)}{kT_m}$$

$$\xi_I = \left(\frac{en_m}{kT_m\epsilon_0}\right)^{1/2}(x - x_m)$$

where n_m, V_m, and x_m have the same meaning as previously and T_m is the electron temperature at x_m.   In terms of these dimensionless variables, Eqs. (5-34), (5-36), and (5-37) become

$$\psi_I'' = \frac{n}{n_m}$$

$$\psi_I'^2 = 2\{[(\psi_I'')^{5/3} - 1] + a[(\psi_I'')^{-1} - 1]\} \tag{5-38}$$

$$\psi_I = \left(\frac{5}{2}\right)[(\psi_I'')^{2/3} - 1] + \frac{a}{2}[(\psi_I'')^{-2} - 1] \tag{5-39}$$

where the parameter a is defined as

$$a \equiv \frac{m\Gamma^2}{kT_m n_m{}^2} \tag{5-40}$$

the primes denote differentiation with respect to ξ_I, and the following boundary conditions have been used to evaluate C_1 and C_2:

$$\psi_I(0) = \psi_I'(0) = 0$$

Either Eq. (5-38) or Eq. (5-39) completely determines the potential distribution in terms of the parameter a.   These are not independent equations because T has been eliminated from them by means of Eq. (5-35).

Assuming that $n(x)$ is a monotonic decreasing function of position, which is reasonable when the collector saturation emission current is very small compared with the net current, it is necessary that $\psi_I'''(0) \neq 0$ by Eq. (5-38) [or Eq. (5-39)].

$$\psi_I'\psi_I'' = [\tfrac{5}{3}(\psi_I'')^{2/3} - a(\psi_I'')^{-2}]\psi_I'''$$

so that for $\psi'''(0)$ to be nonzero, it is required that $a = \tfrac{5}{3}$.   Therefore, by Eq. (5-40), the density at x_m is given by the equation

$$n_m = \left(\frac{3m}{5kT_m}\right)^{1/2}\frac{-J}{e}$$

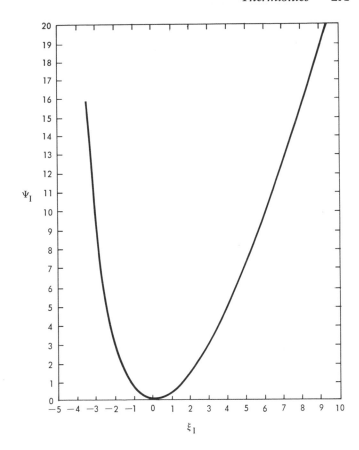

Fig. 5-17. *Reduced potential versus reduced distance for Case I distribution.*

which by Eq. (5-35) becomes

$$\frac{n_m}{n_E} = \left[\frac{3m}{5kT_E} \left(\frac{-J}{en_E} \right)^2 \right]^{3/8} \tag{5-41}$$

In order to compare the results of this theory with those of Langmuir's space-charge theory, Eq. (5-39) was integrated graphically by using Eq. (5-38) to eliminate ψ_I. The resulting $\psi_I - \xi_I$ curve is shown in Fig. 5-17. This curve is similar to Langmuir's curve in Fig. 5-12. The procedure by which current-voltage characteristics are obtained from this curve is similar to that used in the previous section on Langmuir's space-charge theory, except that the Boltzmann relation $J = J_S \exp{(-\psi_{IE})}$ cannot be used to evaluate ψ_{IE} in terms of J and J_{ES}. In the present case, ψ_{IE} is given in terms of $(\psi_I'')_E = n_E/n_m$ by Eq. (5-39). The density at the emitter is found in terms of J and J_{ES} by requiring that the outgoing current density at the emitter be equal to the saturation emission current density; i.e.,

$$J_{ES} = -e \int_0^\infty \int_{-\infty}^\infty \int_{-\infty}^\infty u f_I(0, \mathbf{c}) \, d\mathbf{c} = -\frac{1}{4} e n_E v_E \exp\left(\frac{-m u_{0E}^2}{2kT_E}\right)$$
$$+ \frac{1}{2} J \left\{ 1 + \operatorname{erf}\left[\left(\frac{m}{2kT_E}\right)^{1/2} u_{0E}\right] \right\} \quad (5\text{-}42)$$

where $v_e = (8kT_E/\pi m)^{1/2}$ is the mean thermal speed associated with a Maxwellian velocity distribution at the emitter temperature. Since $u_{0E} = \Gamma/n_E = -J/en_E$, this equation gives n_E in terms of J and J_{ES}. In particular, if the net current density J is zero, $J_{ES} = -\frac{1}{4}en_E v_e$, which is the well-known equilibrium relation, and as J approaches J_{ES}, n_E approaches zero (u_{0E} approaches infinity). It will be seen later that this boundary condition results in a current-voltage characteristic which approaches saturation current asymptotically.

The steps for obtaining a current-voltage characteristic from the $\psi_I - \xi_I$ curve are as follows:

1. Specify T_E, ϕ_E, ϕ_C, and l.
2. Specify J, compute J/J_{ES}.
3. Find n_E according to Eq. (5-42).
4. Compute n_E/n_m according to Eq. (5-41).
5. Compute ψ_{IE} according to Eq. (5-34) evaluated at the emitter. [Note that $(\psi_I'')_E = n_E/n_m$.]
6. Find ξ_{IE} from the $\psi_I - \xi_I$ curve (Fig. 5-17).
7. Compute T_m according to Eq. (5-35).
8. Compute $L_D = (kT_m\epsilon_0/e^2 n_m)^{1/2}$.
9. Compute $x_m = L_D \xi_{IE}$.
10. Compute $x_C = l - x_m$.
11. Compute $\xi_{IC} = x_C/L_D$.
12. Find ψ_{IC} from the $\psi_I - \xi$ curve (Fig. 5-17).
13. Compute $V_C = (\psi_{IC} - \psi_{IE})(kT_m/e)$.
14. Compute $V_o = -\phi_E + (\phi_C + V_C)$.
15. Plot J versus V_o.

Current-voltage characteristics obtained by this procedure are shown as solid curves labeled I in Fig. 5-18, and the corresponding curves resulting from Langmuir's space-charge theory are shown for comparison as broken curves. [The solid curves labeled II result from using a slightly different form for the velocity distribution (Case II), which will be discussed later.]

The electron cooling in this case is slightly different from Langmuir's.

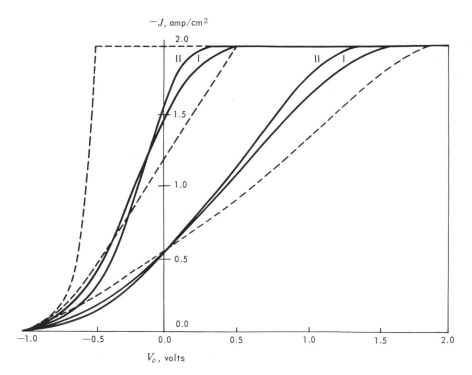

Fig. 5-18. *Current-voltage characteristics for Cases I and II. The dashed curves are Langmuir's results. From left to right, the electrode spacings are 15.2 μ and 25.4 μ. ϕ_E, 1.82 volts; ϕ_C, 1.32 volts; T_E, 1160°K; $-J_{ES}$, 2 amp/cm².*

The difference between the two theories lies in the kinetic-energy part of the electron-cooling term. The Langmuir theory results in a contribution of $(-V_m + 2\theta_E)$ volts per electron to the electron cooling. The present theory results in a contribution of $(5\theta_E/2 + mu_{0E}/2e)$ volts per electron, which can be verified by computing the value of the integral

$$\int_{-\infty}^{\infty} \int_{-\infty}^{\infty} \int_{-\infty}^{\infty} \tfrac{1}{2} mc^2 u f_I(0, \mathbf{c}) \, d\mathbf{c}$$

Case II. A distribution which is analogous to Langmuir's distribution in that the gas properties associated with the y and z components of velocity do not change with position is

$$f_{II}(x, \mathbf{c}) = n \left(\frac{m}{2\pi k T_{\parallel}}\right)^{1/2} \exp\left[\frac{-m(u - u_0)^2}{2k T_{\parallel}}\right] \frac{m}{2\pi k T_E} \exp\frac{-m(v^2 + w^2)}{2k T_E}$$

where

$$T_{||} \equiv \frac{m}{k} (u - u_0)^2$$

is the "temperature" associated with the x component of velocity.
The values of $\mathbf{P}$ and $\mathbf{Q}$ corresponding to this distribution are

$$\mathbf{P} = n_k T_{||} \mathbf{ii} + n_k T_E (\mathbf{jj} + \mathbf{kk})$$
$$\mathbf{Q} = 0$$

Using these values of $\mathbf{P}$ and $\mathbf{Q}$, the three moment equations reduce to

$$\frac{d}{dx} (nu_0) = 0 \tag{5-43}$$

$$\frac{d}{dx} (nkT_{||} + nmu_0^2) = en\frac{dV}{dx} \tag{5-44}$$

$$\frac{d}{dx} \{nu_0[(\tfrac{3}{2})kT_{||} + (\tfrac{1}{2})mu_0^2]\} = e\left(\frac{dV}{dx}\right) nu_0 \tag{5-45}$$

These equations and Poisson's equation form a complete set to be solved
simultaneously for $n(x)$, $u_0(x)$, $T_{||}(x)$, and $V(x)$.
Combining Eqs. (5-43) to (5-45) gives

$$\frac{d}{dx} \ln T_{||} = \frac{2d}{dx} \ln n$$

which can be integrated to give

$$\frac{T_{||}}{n^2} = \frac{T_E}{n_E^2} = \text{const} \tag{5-46}$$

As before, Eqs. (5-43) to (5-45) can each be integrated. The resulting
equations are

$$nu_0 = \Gamma$$

$$nkT_{||} + nmu_0^2 = \frac{\epsilon_0}{2}\left(\frac{dV}{dx}\right)^2 + C_1 \tag{5-47}$$

$$(3/2)kT_{||} + mu_0^2 = eV + C_2 \tag{5-48}$$

where Γ, C_1, and C_2 are constants of integration. By taking $T_{||} = T_{||m}n^2/n_m^2$ and $u_0 = \Gamma/n$ and introducing the reduced variables

$$\psi_{II} = \frac{e(V - V_m)}{kT_{||m}}$$

$$\xi_{II} = \left(\frac{e^2 n_m}{kT_{||m}\epsilon_0}\right)^{1/2} (x - x_m)$$

Eqs. (5-34), (5-47), and (5-48) can be written in dimensionless form. The result is

$$\psi_{II}'' = nn_m$$

$$\psi_{II}' = 2[(\psi_{II}'')^3 - 1 + b(\psi_{II}'')^{-1} - 1] \tag{5-49}$$

$$\psi_{II} = \tfrac{3}{2}[(\psi_{II}'')^2 - 1 + b(\psi_{II}'')^{-2} - 1] \tag{5-50}$$

where the primes denote differentiation with respect to ξ_{II}, the parameter b is defined as

$$b \equiv \frac{m\Gamma^2}{kT_{\|m}n_m{}^2} \tag{5-51}$$

and the conditions $\psi_{II}(0) = \psi_{II}'(0) = 0$ have been used to evaluate the constants C_1 and C_2. By Eq. (5-49) [or Eq. (5-50)],

$$\psi_{II}'\psi_{II}'' = [3(\psi_{II}'')^2 - b(\psi_{II}'')^{-2}]\psi_{II}'''$$

so that for $\psi_{II}'''(0)$ to be nonzero, as before, it is required that $b = 3$. Therefore, by Eq. (5-51) the density at x_m is now given by the equation

$$n_m = \left(\frac{m}{3kT_{\|m}}\right)^{1/2} \frac{-J}{e}$$

which by Eq. (5-46) becomes

$$\frac{n_m}{n_E} = \left[\frac{m}{3kT_E}\left(\frac{-J}{en_E}\right)^2\right]^{1/4} \tag{5-52}$$

Equation (5-50) was integrated graphically by using Eq. (5-49) to eliminate ψ_{II}''. The resulting $\psi_{II} - \xi_{II}$ curve is shown in Fig. 5-19. The procedure by which current-voltage characteristics are obtained from this curve is similar to that used for Case I, except that the density at the potential minimum is different and the computation of ψ_{IIE} is different. In the present case, ψ_{II} is given terms of $(\psi_{II})_E = n_E/n_m$ by Eq. (5-50). Therefore, the steps which are different from those listed for Case I are:

4. Compute n_E/n_m according to Eq. (5-52).
5. Compute ψ_{IIE} according to Eq. (5-50) evaluated at the emitter. (Note that $\psi_{IIE}'' = n_E/n_m$.)
6. Find ξ_{II} from the $\psi_{II} - \xi_{II}$ curve (Fig. 5-19).
7. Compute $T_{\|m}$ according to Eq. (5-46).
8. Compute $L_D = (kT_{\|m}\epsilon_0/e^2n_m)^{1/2}$.
12. Find ψ_{IIC} from the $\psi_{II} - \xi_{II}$ curve (Fig. 5-19).
13. Compute $V_C = (\psi_{IIC} - \psi_{IIE})(kT_{\|m}/e)$.

Current-voltage characteristics obtained by this procedure are shown as solid curves labeled II in Fig. 5-18.

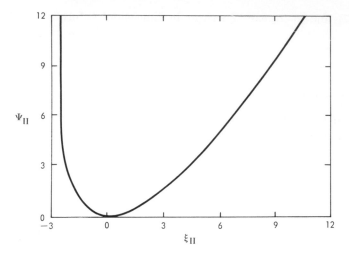

Fig. 5-19.   *Reduced potential versus reduced distance for Case II distribution.*

Several distinguishing features stand out when a comparison of the Langmuir analysis and the collisional approximation is made.   For example, the saturated current is approached asymptotically on the collisional model, whereas the collisionless treatment predicts an abrupt saturation at a finite voltage.   This difference between the two results is not surprising since, if electron-electron collisions are important, it might be expected that an infinite accelerating potential would be required to prevent any back current from reaching the emitter.   Another feature of the collisional model is that zero field occurs at the emitter at a current which is less than the saturated current, whereas the collisionless model predicts zero field at saturation.   This result may be attributed to back scattering by collisions.   In addition, for small currents, the voltage required to obtain a given current is greater for the collisional model than for the collisionless model.   Since the velocity distribution functions which are assumed at the emitter for both models are very similar for small currents, this difference might also be attributed to the effect of back scattering by collisions.   On the other hand, at large currents the voltage required for a given current is *less* for the collisional model than for the collisionless model.   This might be attributed to the form of the distribution functions at the emitter, which are quite different at currents near saturation.   In particular the density for the collisional model is lower than that of the collisionless model for a given current.

A major difference between this collisional treatment and Langmuir's collisionless treatment is the form of the velocity distribution function at the emitter. Langmuir assumed that the outgoing part of the distribution is Maxwellian, whereas in the present treatment, it was necessary to assume that the outgoing part of the distribution is Maxwellian in the center of mass in order to obtain a solution. (There is some theoretical justification for Langmuir's assumption in that the high-energy tail of the equilibrium distribution inside the metal, which is a Fermi-Dirac distribution, is approximated very closely by a Maxwell distribution.) In principle, however, it should be possible to match a solution to the Boltzmann equation to any distribution at the emitting plane. This might lead, for example, to a solution which is Maxwellian in the forward direction at the emitter and "relaxes" over a distance equal to a few mean free paths to a distribution which is Maxwellian in the center of mass.

3-3. *Experimental Results*

The Power Tube Department of the General Electric Company has produced vacuum converters in limited quantities. A cross section of this production converter is shown in Fig. 5-20. The purpose of the platinum-rhodium alloy around the tungsten base of the emitter was to allow operation in air. The emitter consisted of a thin coating of strontium-calcium oxide on tungsten and the collector of a thin coating of strontium-barium oxide on tungsten. The typical converter produced between 0.3 and 0.35 watt/cm² at an emitter temperature of 1423°K, a collector temperature of 900°K, and a spacing of about 8 μ. This spacing was maintained by metal spacers seated on ceramic blocks inserted in holes in the collector. Figure 5-21 shows an almost exponential increase of maximum output power density with emitter temperature for these converters. The cur-

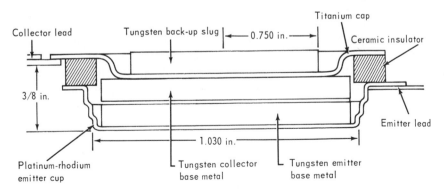

Fig. 5-20. *Cross section of vacuum thermionic converter.* (*Courtesy of E. Baum, General Electric Tube Dept.*)

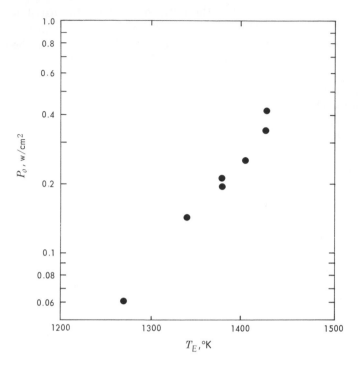

Fig. 5-21. *Variation of output power density with emitter temperature for production-model vacuum converters.   Each point represents the average of several converters.   (Courtesy of E. Baum, General Electric Tube Dept.)*

rent- and power-voltage characteristics for the best of the production converters are shown in Fig. 5-22.   The experimental points were obtained by varying the resistance of a load connected in series with the converter. The efficiency at maximum output was calculated to be about 4.5 percent, based on the Langmuir electron-cooling term and an effective relative emissivity of 0.22.   The best lifetime obtained with this converter was on the order of 50 hours.   Failure was generally due to electrode poisoning by impurities present in the component parts.   Higher output power densities were unattainable because of the difficulty encountered in maintaining uniform electrode spacings less than 8 μ on a production basis.

As is usual with research and development projects, laboratory prototypes tend to work better than their first production-line counterparts. Figure 5-23 shows current-voltage characteristics obtained from vacuum converters with different spacings built at the General Electric Research Laboratory by J. E. Beggs.   These converters were similar in design to that

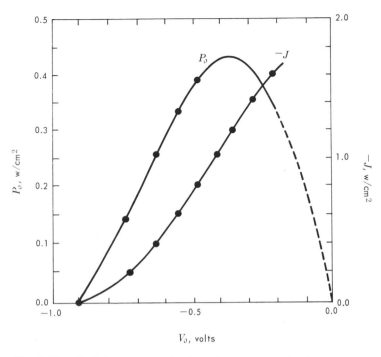

Fig. 5-22. *Variation of output density and output power density with output voltage for the best production converter with $T_E = 1423°K$; $l = 8 \mu$; and $\phi_E = 2.25$ volts. (Courtesy of E. Baum, General Electric Tube Dept.)*

shown in Fig. 5-20, except that smaller spacings were obtained. These curves show the advantage of having a very small electrode spacing, as predicted by theory.

4. Gaseous Converter

4-1. General Remarks

As shown in the previous section, it is necessary to construct the vacuum converter with a spacing on the order of 10 μ to reduce significantly the limiting effects of space-charge. Another way of reducing space-charge effects is to introduce positive ions into the interelectrode space, which was first suggested in this country by V. C. Wilson of the General Electric Research Laboratory. Positive ions can be generated by surface and volume ionization. Copious ionization by either process requires a gas with a low ionization potential. For this reason, cesium, which has at

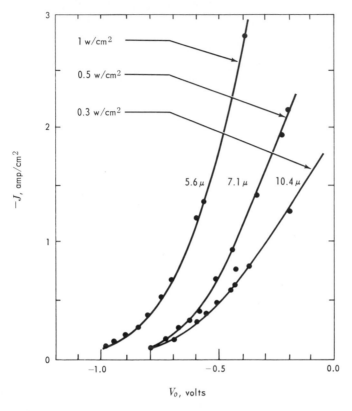

Fig. 5-23. *Current-voltage characteristics of laboratory converters with identical construction except for spacing. Arrows show maximum power points.* $T_E = 1373°K$; $T_C = 873°K$; $\phi_E = 2.04$ *volts*; $\phi_C = 1.60$ *volts*.

3.89 volts the lowest ionization potential in the periodic table, is used in gaseous converters. Another desirable feature of cesium is its relatively low work function of 1.81 volts. This is an advantage because the apparent work function of a cesiated metal surface is usually lowered to a value between that of the base metal and that of cesium, depending on the temperature and pressure (cf. Fig. 5-6). The amount of cesium vapor in the interelectrode space is controlled by regulating the vapor pressure over a pool of liquid cesium. The vapor pressure p_{Cs} in torr is related to the pool temperature T_{Cs} by the equation

$$\ln_{10} p_{Cs} = 11.0531 - 1.35 \ln_{10} T_{Cs} - \frac{4041}{T_{Cs}} \qquad (5\text{-}53)$$

This result was deduced from experimental measurements of positive-ion currents from pure tungsten filaments in saturated cesium vapor by Taylor and Langmuir.[13]   The variation of p_{Cs} with T_{Cs} according to Eq. (5-53) is shown in Fig. 5-24.

The effect on the potential distribution of introducing cesium vapor into a diode can be calculated for thermodynamic equilibrium.   While the results of an equilibrium calculation are not directly applicable to the conversion process, they provide some insight regarding the gross features of the potential distribution in a cesium diode in the absence of strong volume sources of particles.   Consider a physical system composed of neutral cesium atoms, singly charged cesium ions, and electrons, all of which are contained in an isothermal metallic enclosure.   For simplicity, assume that the enclosure consists of two identical parallel plates of infinite extent separated by distance l.   In equilibrium the temperature is independent of position, the average velocities of the individual particles are zero, and the individual particle velocity distribution functions are Maxwellian. Therefore, the system is described by three momentum equations and Poisson's equation.   These equations are

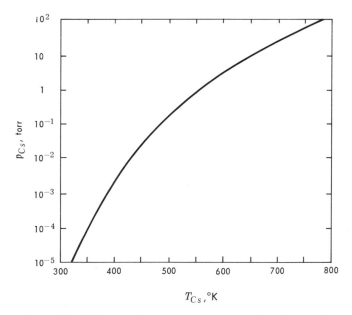

Fig. 5-24.   *Variation of cesium-vapor pressure with cesium-pool temperature.*

$$\frac{dn_a}{dx} = 0 \tag{5-54}$$

$$\frac{\theta \, dn_p}{dx} + \frac{n_p \, dV}{dx} = 0 \tag{5-55}$$

$$\frac{\theta \, dn_e}{dx} - \frac{n_e \, dV}{dx} = 0 \tag{5-56}$$

$$\frac{d^2V}{dx^2} = \frac{e}{\epsilon_0}(n_e - n_p) \tag{5-57}$$

Equations (5-55) and (5-56) are the differential forms of the Boltzmann relations for ions and electrons in equilibrium with an electric field. Equations (5-54) to (5-57), with five boundary conditions, uniquely determine $n_a(x)$, $n_p(x)$, $n_e(x)$, and $V(x)$. The appropriate boundary conditions are:

1. $V(0) = 0$
2. $V'(0) = 0$
3. $n_{eE} = n_e\left(\dfrac{-l}{2}\right) = 2\left(\dfrac{2\pi m_e kT}{h^2}\right)^{3/2} \exp\left(\dfrac{-\phi}{\theta}\right)$
4. $\dfrac{n_e n_p}{n_a} = K$
5. $n_a + n_p + n_e - \dfrac{\epsilon_0}{2kT}\left(\dfrac{dV}{dx}\right)^2 = \dfrac{p}{kT}$

where the origin has been chosen at the center of the enclosure, ϕ is the work function of the walls, K is the so-called "Saha equilibrium constant" for cesium vapor,[14] given by

$$K = \left(\frac{2\pi m_e kT}{h^2}\right)^{3/2} \exp\left(\frac{-I}{\theta}\right)$$

in which I is the first ionization potential of the cesium atom and p is the total pressure in the system, not to be confused with p_{Cs}, the vapor pressure of cesium. While conditions 4 and 5 are used as boundary conditions, they are valid throughout the enclosure. With these boundary conditions, Eqs. (5-54) to (5-57) were solved simultaneously to give a potential distribution of the form

$$V(x) = 2\theta \ln \frac{dn\,(sx,\,\nu)}{cn\,(sx,\,\nu)} \tag{5-58}$$

where cn and dn are Jacobian elliptic functions defined by Milne-Thomson,[15] the parameter ν is the ratio of ion density to electron density at the origin, and the parameter s must satisfy the equation

$$2^{\frac{1}{2}}sL_D = \text{cn}^2\left(\frac{sl}{2}, \nu\right)\text{dn}^2\left(\frac{sl}{2}, \nu\right)$$

where the Debye length $L_D = \left(\dfrac{\epsilon_0\theta}{en_{eE}}\right)^{\frac{1}{2}}$.

It is well known that the potential distribution given by Eq. (5-58) is characterized by a weak-field region, called plasma, in the central part of the metallic enclosure, and high-field regions, called sheaths, next to the walls. In general, the thickness of the sheaths is on the order of the Debye length L_D and the potential drops in the sheaths vary markedly with temperature and pressure. Moreover, the potential (relative to the Fermi level) in the weak-field region does not depend on the composition of the walls. Figure 5-25 shows how the potential distribution varies with p_{Cs} for two tungsten plates at a temperature of 2320°K which are separated by a distance of 2 mm. The work function of bare tungsten was taken to be 4.5 volts, and the work function of the cesiated tungsten walls was taken from Fig. 5-6. According to Fig. 5-25, when the cesium-vapor pressure is greater than 10^{-6} torr, the neutral plasma extends over most of the interelectrode space. This behavior is consistent with the viewpoint that the Debye length is a measure of the distance over which n_e can differ appreciably from n_p without resulting in a potential energy per particle that is much greater than the mean thermal energy.[6] For this reason, the nonequilibrium potential distribution in a cesium converter probably behaves qualitatively like that shown in Fig. 5-25.

In discussing the nonequilibrium characteristics of the gaseous converter, it is customary to distinguish between *low-pressure* operation and *high-pressure* operation. By definition, low-pressure operation occurs when the pressure is so low that the average electron makes no collisions in transit from emitter to collector. In contrast, high-pressure operation occurs when the pressure is high enough that the average electron makes many collisions in transit from emitter to collector. For this reason the following discussion of the gaseous converter has been divided into a section on the low-pressure converter and one on the high-pressure converter.

4-2. *Low-pressure Cesium Converter*

Low-pressure converter operation has been treated by several authors recently by adapting Langmuir's space-charge theory to include ions as

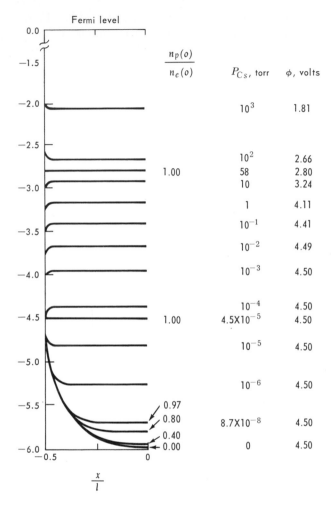

Fig. 5-25. *Equilibrium electric-potential distribution as a function of temperature and cesium-vapor pressure for tungsten walls separated by l meters.*

well as electrons.[16,17] A discussion of the main points of these analyses will be given here. For brevity, the discussion will be limited to electron-rich potential distributions with a minimum at $x = x_m$. It is assumed that the one-dimensional velocity distribution functions for electrons (f_e) and ions (f_p) satisfy the Vlasov equation

$$u \frac{\partial f_i}{\partial x} - \frac{q_i}{m_i} \frac{dV}{dx} \frac{\partial f_i}{\partial u} = 0$$

where i stands for either e or p and q_i is equal to $-e$ for electrons, $+e$ for ions. The system of equations is completed by Poisson's equation

$$\frac{d^2V}{dx^2} = \frac{e}{\epsilon_0}(n_e - n_p)$$

where

$$n_i(x) = \int_{-\infty}^{\infty} f_i(x, u)\, du$$

It is assumed that both electrons and ions leave the emitter with Maxwellian velocity distributions, so that

$$f_e(x, u) = \begin{cases} 2n_{em} \exp\dfrac{V - V_m}{\theta_E} \left(\dfrac{m_e}{2\pi k T_E}\right)^{1/2} \exp\dfrac{-m_e u^2}{2kT_E} & \\ & u \geq \pm u_{el},\ x \gtrless x_m \quad (5\text{-}59) \\ & u < \pm u_{el} \end{cases}$$

and for $V_C < 0$

$$f_p(x, u) = \begin{cases} 2n_{pE} \exp\left(\dfrac{-V}{\theta_E}\right)\left(\dfrac{m_p}{2\pi k T_E}\right)^{1/2} \exp\dfrac{-m_p u^2}{2kT_E}, & u \geq u_{pl} \\ 0 & u < u_{pl} \quad (5\text{-}60) \end{cases}$$

and for $V_C > 0$

$$f_e(x, u) = \begin{cases} 2n_{pE}\left[1 + \mathrm{erf}\left(\dfrac{V_C}{\theta_E}\right)^{1/2}\right]^{-1} \exp\left(\dfrac{-V}{\theta_E}\right)\left(\dfrac{m_p}{2\pi k T_E}\right)^{1/2} & \\ \qquad\qquad \times \exp\dfrac{-m_p u^2}{2kT_E}, & u \geq -u_{pC} \\ 0 & u < -u_{pC} \end{cases}$$

where

$$u_{el} = \left[\frac{2e(V - V_m)}{m_e}\right]^{1/2}$$

$$u_{pl} = \left(\frac{-2eV}{m_p}\right)^{1/2}$$

and

$$u_{pC} = \left(\frac{2eV_C}{m_p}\right)^{1/2}$$

In these equations, n_{em} is the electron density at the potential minimum, V_m is the depth of the minimum, n_{pE} is the ion density at the emitter, and V_C is the surface potential of the collector (cf. Fig. 5-10). As in the Langmuir analysis of the vacuum converter, the constant n_{em} is found by equating the outgoing electron current density at the emitter to J_{eES}:

$$J_{eES} = -e \int_0^\infty u f_e(0, u) \, du = -e n_{em} \left(\frac{2kT_E}{\pi m_e}\right)^{1/2} \exp\left(\frac{-V_m}{\theta_E}\right) \quad (5\text{-}61)$$

The net electron current density is given by

$$J_e = -e \int_{-\infty}^\infty u f_e(x, u) \, du = -e n_{em} \left(\frac{2kT_E}{\pi m_e}\right)^{1/2} = J_{eES} \exp\frac{V_m}{\theta_E} \quad (5\text{-}62)$$

The constant n_{pE} is found in terms of J_{pES}, the ion saturation current, by equating the outgoing ion current density at the emitter to J_{pES}:

$$J_{pES} = \begin{cases} e n_p \left(\dfrac{2kT_E}{\pi m_p}\right)^{1/2} & V_C \leq 0 \\[3mm] e n_{pE} \left(\dfrac{2kT_E}{\pi m_p}\right)^{1/2} \left[1 + \mathrm{erf}\left(\dfrac{V_C}{\theta_E}\right)^{1/2}\right]^{-1} & V_C > 0 \end{cases}$$

the net ion current density is given by

$$J_p = \begin{cases} e n_{pE} \left(\dfrac{2kT_E}{\pi m_p}\right)^{1/2} = J_{pES} & V_C \leq 0 \\[3mm] J_{pES} \exp\dfrac{-V_C}{\theta_E} & V_C > 0 \end{cases} \quad (5\text{-}63)$$

The electron density is found by integrating over all velocities of the distribution given by Eq. (5-59):

$$n_e(x) = n_{em} e^\eta (1 \pm \mathrm{erf}\, \psi^{1/2}) \qquad x \lessgtr x_m$$

where

$$\psi = \frac{V - V_m}{\theta_E}$$

Similarly, from Eq. (5-60):

$$n_p(x) = \begin{cases} n_{pE} e^{\psi_E - \psi} [1 - \mathrm{erf}\,(\psi_E - \psi)^{1/2}] & \psi_C - \psi_E \leq 0 \\[2mm] n_{pE} e^{\psi_E - \psi} [1 - 2\,\mathrm{erf}\,(\psi_E - \psi)^{1/2} \\ \quad + \mathrm{erf}\,(\psi_C - \psi)^{1/2}] \\ \quad \times [1 + \mathrm{erf}\,(\psi_C - \psi_E)^{1/2}]^{-1} & \psi_C - \psi_E > 0,\ \psi - \psi_E \leq 0 \\[2mm] n_{pE} [1 + \mathrm{erf}\,(\psi_C - \psi)^{1/2}] \\ \quad \times [1 + \mathrm{erf}\,(\psi_C - \psi_E)^{1/2}]^{-1} & \psi_C - \psi_E > 0,\ \psi - \psi_E > 0 \end{cases}$$

where $\psi_E = -V_m/\theta_E$ is the value of ψ at the emitter and $\psi_C = (V_C - V_m)/\theta_E$ is the value of ψ at the collector.

The potential distribution is found from Poisson's equation, which in dimensionless variables becomes

$$2\frac{d^2\psi}{d\xi^2} = e^\psi[1 \pm \text{erf } \psi^{1/2}] - \alpha e^{2\psi_E-\psi}[1 - \text{erf } (\psi_E - \psi)^{1/2}] \qquad x \lessgtr x_m,$$
$$\psi_C - \psi_E \leq 0 \qquad (5\text{-}64)$$

with similar expressions for $\psi_C - \psi_E > 0$. In this equation

$$\xi = \left(\frac{2en_{em}}{\epsilon_0\theta_E}\right)^{1/2}(x - x_m)$$

as in the Langmuir analysis, and

$$\alpha = \left(\frac{-J_{pES}}{J_{eES}}\right)\left(\frac{m_p}{m_e}\right)^{1/2} \qquad (5\text{-}65)$$

where Eqs. (5-61) to (5-63) have been used to evaluate the ratio n_{pE}/n_{em} in terms of J_{pES} and J_{eES}.

The parameter α is related to the cesium-vapor pressure through its dependence on J_{pES} [cf. Eq. (5-65)]. By Eq. (5-4), J_{pES} is given by

$$J_{pES} = e\beta(\Gamma_{aE-} + \Gamma_{pE-})$$

where β is the probability that an incoming particle (atom or ion) will leave the emitter as an ion, Γ_{aE-} is the incoming flux of atoms, and Γ_{pE-} is the incoming flux of ions. It is assumed that the sum $\Gamma_{aE-} + \Gamma_{pE-}$ does not change with ion current and is equal to random flux of atoms over the cesium reservoir. Therefore,

$$J_{pES} = \frac{e\beta p_{Cs}}{(2\pi m_a k T_{Cs})^{1/2}} \qquad (5\text{-}66)$$

so that by using Eq. (5-65), the parameter α is related to the cesium-vapor pressure by

$$\alpha = \frac{-e\beta p_{Cs}}{J_{eES}(2\pi m_e k T_{Cs})^{1/2}} \qquad (5\text{-}67)$$

where m_p has been taken equal to m_a.

In all cases, Poisson's equation can be integrated once. The resultant equations (in a slightly different form) were integrated numerically[18] to give current-voltage characteristics for *monotonic* potential distributions. Figure 5-26 shows representative characteristics found by Goldstein[19] for $T_E = 2000°\text{K}$, $\phi_E = 3.35$ volts, $\phi_C = 1.8$ volts, and $l = 25.4 \mu$ (0.001 in.). The variable parameter here is α, which ranges from 0 (vacuum) to 0.4. The corresponding cesium-vapor pressures computed according to Eq. (5-67) are listed in Table 5-1, with the cesium-pool temperatures taken from

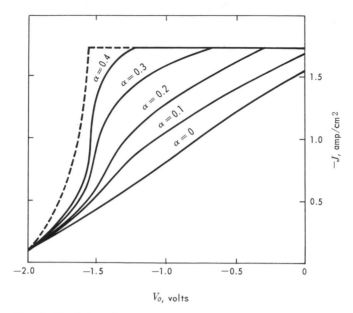

Fig. 5-26. *Effect of positive ions on collisionless current-voltage characteristic. The parameter α is the equilibrium ratio of positive ions to electrons at the emitter.*

Fig. 5-24 and the electron mean free path taken from Fig. 5-8. The dashed curve in Fig. 5-26 represents the upper limit obtainable for zero space-charge. The change in the slope of the characteristics near $V_o = \phi_C - \phi_E$ ($V_C = 0$) is caused by the reflection of positive ions by the electric field near the collector, which becomes retarding for ions when $V_C > 0$ (cf. Fig. 5-10). These current-voltage characteristics illustrate the effectiveness of positive ions in reducing space-charge effects. Current-voltage characteristics for $\alpha > 0.4$ are not given because monotonic potential distributions for $\alpha > 0.4$ do not exist according to this model for the specified electrode spacing. The corresponding power-voltage characteristics are shown in Fig. 5-27.

Table 5-1. *Correlation of α with Cesium-vapor Pressure*

α	p_{Cs}, torr	T_{Cs}, °K	λ, mm	l/λ	V_o, volts
0.1	6×10^{-4}	375	2.5	0.010	3.01
0.2	1.4×10^{-3}	388	1.7	0.015	2.89
0.3	2×10^{-3}	394	1.4	0.018	2.83
0.4	2.7×10^{-3}	400	1.2	0.021	2.77

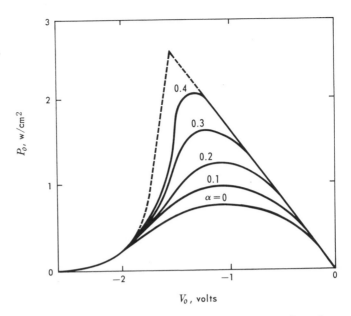

Fig. 5-27. *Effect of positive ions on collisionless power-voltage characteristic. The parameter α is the equilibrium ratio of positive ions to electrons at the emitter.*

Open-circuit voltages for the characteristics shown in Fig. 5-26 can be computed by assuming that at open circuit where the net current $J = J_e + J_p = 0$, the potential minimum is at the collector. Then, the electron current is

$$J_e = J_{eES} \exp \frac{V_C}{\theta_E}$$

and the ion current is

$$J_p = J_{pES}$$

For $J_e + J_p = 0$, it is required that

$$V_C = -\theta_E \ln \frac{-J_{eES}}{J_{pES}}$$

hence

$$V_o = \phi_C - \phi_E + V_C = \phi_C - \phi_E - \theta_E \ln \frac{-J_{eES}}{J_{pES}}$$

The values of V_o for the current-voltage characteristics shown in Fig. 5-26 are given in Table 5-1.

The efficiency of the low-pressure converter is given by an expression similar to Eq. (5-30), except that there are additional heat losses from the emitter associated with the evaporation of ions and atoms from the emitter. These losses are similar in form to the electron-cooling loss given by Eq. (5-28). It is assumed that both ions and atoms leave the emitter with Maxwellian velocity distributions. It is assumed further that the atoms striking the emitter (collector) have a distribution corresponding to the collector (emitter) temperature. Then the atom-cooling loss P_4 is given by

$$P_4 = \Gamma_{a+}(h_a + 2kT_E) - \Gamma_{a-}(h_a + 2kT_C)$$

This can be written

$$P_4 = \Gamma_a(h_a + 2kT_E) + 2\Gamma_{a-}(kT_E - kT_C) \tag{5-68}$$

by using the identity $\Gamma_a = \Gamma_{a+} - \Gamma_{a-}$.

Similarly, the ion-cooling loss P_5 is composed of the ionic heat of evaporation h_p and the average kinetic energy of the escaping ions. The average ionic kinetic energy associated with the y and z directions is $kT_E/2$ for each, and the average ionic kinetic energy associated with the x direction is given by the integral

$$\int_{-\infty}^{\infty} \left(\frac{m_p u^3}{2}\right) f_p(0, u)\, du = \begin{cases} J_p \theta_E & V_C \leq 0 \\ J_p(V_C + \theta_E) & V_C > 0 \end{cases}$$

Therefore, the ion-cooling loss is given by

$$P_5 = \begin{cases} J_p\left(\dfrac{h_p}{e} + 2\theta_E\right) & V_C \leq 0 \\[2ex] J_p\left(\dfrac{h_p}{e} + V_C + 2\theta_E\right) & V_C > 0 \end{cases} \tag{5-69}$$

To compute P_4 and P_5 individually requires separate knowledge about h_a and h_p. However, as far as efficiency calculations are concerned, it is the sum $P_4 + P_5$ which must be computed.

Addition of Eqs. (5-68) and (5-69) gives

$$P_4 + P_5 = \begin{cases} \dfrac{-J_p(h_a - h_p)}{e} + 2J_{a-}(\theta_E - \theta_C) & V_C \leq 0 \\[2ex] \dfrac{-J_p(h_a - h_p)}{e} + 2J_{a-}(\theta_E - \theta_C) & \\[1ex] \qquad\qquad\qquad + J_p V_C & V_C > 0 \end{cases} \tag{5-70}$$

because $J_a + J_p = 0$ in the steady state; i.e., there can be no net flow of nuclei at the surface of the emitter. The arrival rate of atoms is given in terms of J_p and J_{pES} by

$$J_{a-} = J_{a+} - J_a$$
$$= \frac{J_{p+}(1 - \beta)}{\beta} + J_p$$
$$= \frac{J_{pES}(1 - \beta)}{\beta} + J_p$$

and the difference in the atomic and ionic heats of vaporization by[20]

$$h_a - h_p = e(\phi_E - I)$$

Therefore, Eq. (5-70) becomes

$$P_4 + P_5 = \begin{cases} J_p[I - \phi_E + 2(\theta_E - \theta_C)] \\ \qquad + 2J_{pES}(\theta_E - \theta_C)\dfrac{1 - \beta}{\beta} \qquad V_C \le 0 \\ J_p[I - \phi_E + V_C + 2(\theta_E - \theta_C)] \\ \qquad + 2J_{pES}(\theta_E - \theta_C)\dfrac{1 - \beta}{\beta} \qquad V_C > 0 \end{cases} \qquad (5\text{-}71)$$

which is the required relation for the additional heat loss from the emitter caused by the evaporation of atoms and ions. When there is no surface ionization ($\beta = 0$), P_5 is zero and Eq. (5-71) is equivalent to

$$P_4 = 2\Gamma_{a+}(kT_E - kT_C)$$

which is the familiar Knudsen equation for the amount of heat transferred between two plates at temperatures T_E and T_C when there are no particle collisions.

The energy expended in the creation of ions at the emitter by surface ionization is given by the term involving J_p in Eq. (5-71). Note that this energy is negative; i.e., energy is received by the emitter as a result of surface ionization when ϕ_E is larger than $[I + V_C + 2(\theta_E - \theta_C)]$. In general, the energy loss (gain) caused by surface ionization is small compared with the electron-cooling loss, because ion currents are usually much smaller than electron currents.

According to Fig. 5-26, the current-voltage characteristics approach the ideal (space-charge–free) characteristics as the cesium-vapor pressure increases. Even though the analysis presented here breaks down as α approaches unity, this trend has been used as the basis for a simplified treatment of the low-pressure converter. The simplification consists merely in assuming that there are enough positive ions to neutralize the electron space-charge completely, so that the potential distribution in the interelectrode space has no curvature; i.e., the electric field is constant. According to Eq. (5-64), this situation occurs when $\alpha = 1$ and $\psi = \psi_E = \psi_C = 0$; the corresponding potential diagram is shown in Fig. 5-28a. By

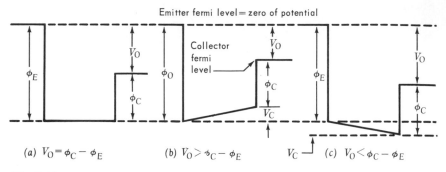

Fig. 5-28. *Possible electric-potential distributions for collisionless model with zero space-charge.*

assuming that the electric field stays more or less constant as V_C is varied (cf. Fig. 5-28*b* and *c*), a simple theory for the low-pressure converter can be developed. In this simple theory, some of the important physical processes, such as the effects of space-charge and of scattering of charge carriers, which occur in a practical device, are not considered. Nevertheless, the results of this simple theory provide insight into the operation of practical thermionic converters by giving the optimum values for important parameters such as work functions and output voltage. In addition, the results give upper limits of power output and efficiency to be expected because the effects which tend to decrease them are ignored.

Based on this collisionless space-charge-free model with zero back emission, the current in the converter is the sum of the electron current and ion current; i.e.,

$$J = \begin{cases} J_e + J_p \\ J_{eES} \exp\left(\dfrac{V_o - (\phi_C - \phi_E)}{\theta_E}\right) + J_{pES} & V_o \leq \phi_C - \phi_E \quad (5\text{-}72) \\ J_{eES} + J_{pES} \exp\dfrac{-V_o + (\phi_C - \phi_E)}{\theta_E} & V_o > \phi_C - \phi_E \end{cases}$$

The requirement for space-charge neutralization is $\alpha = 1$, which by Eq. (5-65) gives $J_{pES} = -\left(\dfrac{m_e}{m_p}\right)^{1/2} J_{eES}$, so that Eq. (5-72) can be written

$$J = \begin{cases} J_{eES}\left[\exp\left(\dfrac{V_o - (\phi_C - \phi_E)}{\theta_E}\right) - \left(\dfrac{m_e}{m_p}\right)^{1/2}\right] \\ \hspace{6cm} V_o \leq \phi_C - \phi_E \quad (5\text{-}73) \\ J_{eES}\left[1 - \left(\dfrac{m_e}{m_p}\right)^{1/2}\exp\dfrac{-V_o + (\phi_C - \phi_E)}{\theta_E}\right] \\ \hspace{6cm} V_o > \phi_C - \phi_E \end{cases}$$

Since $(m_e/m_p)^{1/2} = 1/492$ for cesium, the terms proportional to $(m_e/m_p)^{1/2}$ are usually ignored in these analyses. Then the corresponding power output for zero electrical lead loss is

$$P_o = JV_o = \begin{cases} V_o J_{eES} \exp \dfrac{V_o - (\phi_C - \phi_E)}{\theta_E} & V_o \leq \phi_C - \phi_E \\ V_o J_{eES} & V_o > \phi_C - \phi_E \end{cases}$$

which is the equation of the dashed curve in Fig. 5-27. This expression represents the upper limit of power output that can be obtained from the collisionless converter. It shows that the power output increases as the collector work function decreases, which is correct provided that the saturation emission current of the collector is small compared with that of the emitter. Finally it shows that maximum power occurs for

$$V_o = \phi_C - \phi_E$$

The efficiency-voltage characteristic is

$$\eta = \frac{J(V_o - V_w)}{\displaystyle\sum_{i=1}^{5} P_i}$$

where J is given by Eq. (5-73) and the P_i's are as follows:

$$P_1 = \begin{cases} J[V_o - (\phi_C + 2\theta_E)] & V_o \leq \phi_C - \phi_E \\ -J_{eES}(\phi_E + 2\theta_E) & V_o > \phi_C - \phi_E \end{cases}$$

$$P_2 = (\epsilon_E^{-1} + \epsilon_C^{-1} - 1)^{-1}\sigma(T_E{}^4 - T_C{}^4)$$

$$P_3 = J\left[\frac{\pi^2(\theta_E{}^2 - \theta_C{}^2)}{6V_w} - \frac{V_w}{2} \right]$$

$$P_4 + P_5 = J_{pES}\left[I - \phi_E + \frac{2(\theta_E - \theta_C)}{\beta} \right]$$

$$= -(m_e/m_p)^{1/2}J_{eES}\left[I - \phi_E + \frac{2(\theta_E - \theta_C)}{\beta} \right]$$

To compute the maximum efficiency by optimizing independent variables, it is convenient to consider the potential distribution shown in Fig. 5-28a, for which the efficiency is

$$\eta = \frac{J_{eES}(\phi_C - \phi_E - V_w)}{-J_{eES}\{\phi_E + 2\theta_E - \pi^2(\theta_E{}^2 - \theta_C{}^2)/6V_w + V_w/2}$$
$$+ (m_e/m_p)^{1/2}[I - \phi_E + 2(\theta_E - \theta_C)/\beta]\} + \epsilon\sigma\left(\dfrac{e}{k}\right)^4 (\theta_E{}^4 - \theta_C{}^4)$$

$$(5\text{-}74)$$

This expression can be maximized with respect to V_w, the voltage drop in the electrical lead, and ϕ_E, the emitter work function. The optimum value of V_w is the same as for the vacuum converter [cf. Eq. (5-31)]. The optimum emitter work function $\tilde{\phi}_E$ is given implicitly by

$$\frac{\phi_E}{\theta_E} = \ln M_1 + \sinh^{-1}\left[\frac{(1-\eta)/\eta + (m_e/m_p)^{1/2}}{M_2}\right] \tag{5-75}$$

where

$$M_1 = \frac{2}{\pi^2}\left(\frac{30 m_e C^2}{\epsilon e \theta_E}\right)^{1/2}\left[\left(1 + \frac{\theta_C}{\theta_E}\right)\left(1 + \frac{\theta_C^2}{\theta_E^2}\right)\right]^{-1/2}\left(\frac{m_e}{m_p}\right)^{1/4}\exp I/2\theta_E$$

$$M_2 = 2\pi^2\left[\frac{2\epsilon e \theta_E}{15 m_e C^2}\left(1 - \frac{\theta_C}{\theta_E}\right)\left(1 - \frac{\theta_C^4}{\theta_E^4}\right)\right]^{1/2}\left(\frac{m_e}{m_p}\right)^{1/4}\exp I/2\theta_E$$

with C being the velocity of light. If the heat loss associated with the evaporation of ions and atoms from the emitter $(P_4 + P_5)$ is ignored and if θ_C is small compared to θ_E, the optimum value of ϕ_E is

$$\tilde{\phi}_E = \theta_E \ln\left(\frac{30 \, m_e C^2}{\pi^4 \epsilon e \theta_E}\frac{1-\eta}{\eta}\right) \tag{5-76}$$

When V_w and ϕ_E are eliminated from Eq. (5-74) by means of Eqs. (5-31) and (5-76), the maximum efficiency is found in terms of the emitter temperature, the collector work function, and the effective emissivity of the converter.

Figure 5-29 shows how the maximum efficiency, found by ignoring $P_4 + P_5$ and θ_C, varies with emitter temperature and collector work function for an effective emissivity equal to that of bare tungsten radiating to a blackbody. The equicurrent lines indicate the saturation currents required to give maximum efficiency. This figure shows that low collector work functions are required for high efficiency and that relatively low emitter work functions are required for maximum efficiency at ordinary emitter temperatures. For example, a thermionic converter operating at an emitter temperature of 2000°K with a collector work function of 1.5 volts should have an emitter work function of 2.75 volts (or less), which would give a maximum efficiency of about 27 percent, whereas one with a collector work function of 1 volt should have an emitter work function of 2.6 volts (or less), which would give a maximum efficiency of about 40 percent.

If the only source of positive ions is surface ionization of atoms at the emitter, the efficiencies shown in Fig. 5-29 are optimistic for emitter temperatures below 2000°K. The reason is that below 2000°K the value of the surface ionization probability β is very small for emitter work functions

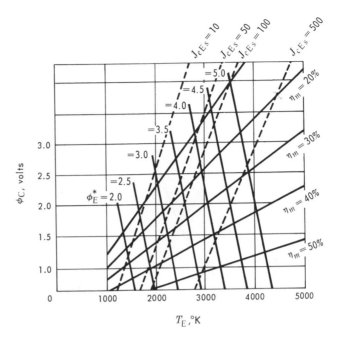

Fig. 5-29.   *Maximum efficiency versus emitter temperatures.* [*After J. H. Ingold, J. Appl. Phys.,* **32**: *769 (1961)*.]

less than the ionization potential of the cesium atom (cf. Fig. 5-7). In this case the heat loss associated with the evaporation of atoms from the emitter, which is the term proportional to β^{-1} in the denominator of Eq. (5-74), cannot be ignored, and Eq. (5-75) must be used for the optimum emitter work function. Figure 5-30 shows the resultant variation of the maximum efficiency with emitter temperature for a collector work function of 1.7 volts and for an effective emissivity equal to that of bare tungsten radiating to a blackbody. The dashed part of the curve indicates the result obtained when the evaporation of ions and atoms is ignored. The equicurrent lines indicate the saturation currents required to give maximum efficiency.

The foregoing collisionless, space-charge-free analysis is based on the assumption that the saturation emission current of the collector is small compared with that of the emitter. However, there are potential applications of thermionic converters for which this assumption breaks down. For example, when the collector is operated at a temperature high enough to radiate waste heat, the collector saturation emission current may not be small enough to be ignored.[21] In this case, there are optimum output voltages which give maximum power output and maximum efficiency.

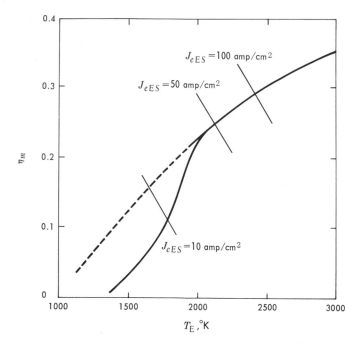

Fig. 5-30. *Maximum efficiency versus emitter temperature for ions produced by surface ionization (solid curve) and by other means (dashed curve).*

These optimum values are determined as follows. It is assumed that space-charge is negligible and that the net electric current is

$$J = J_{eE} - J_{eC}$$

where

$$J_{eE} = \begin{cases} J_{eES} \exp \dfrac{V_o - (\phi_C - \phi_E)}{\theta_E} & V_o \leq \phi_C - \phi_E \\ J_{eES} & V_o > \phi_C - \phi_E \end{cases}$$

is the electron current reaching the collector from the emitter and

$$J_{eC} = \begin{cases} J_{eCS} & V_o \leq \phi_C - \phi_E \\ J_{eCS} \exp \dfrac{-V_o + (\phi_C - \phi_E)}{\theta_C} & V_o > \phi_C - \phi_E \end{cases}$$

is the electron current reaching the emitter from the collector. The corresponding current-voltage characteristic is shown in Fig. 5-31. The companion power-voltage characteristic given by

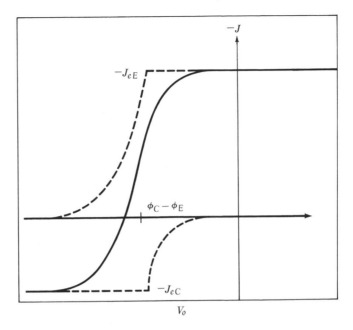

Fig. 5-31.   *Collisionless model with zero space-charge.*

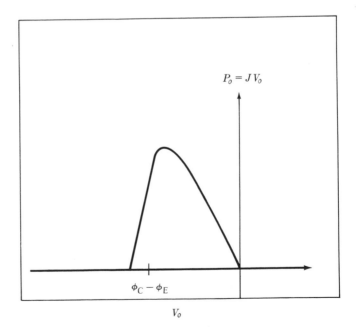

Fig. 5-32.   *Collisionless model with zero space-charge.*

$$P_o = JV_o = \begin{cases} \left[J_{eES} \exp\left(\dfrac{V_o - (\phi_C - \phi_E)}{\theta_E}\right) - J_{eCS} \right] V_o \\ \qquad\qquad\qquad\qquad\qquad\qquad V_o \le \phi_C - \phi_E \quad (5\text{-}77) \\ \left[J_{eES} - J_{eCS} \exp\dfrac{-V_o + (\phi_C - \phi_E)}{\theta_C} \right] V_o \\ \qquad\qquad\qquad\qquad\qquad\qquad V_o > \phi_C - \phi_E \end{cases}$$

is shown in Fig. 5-32. According to this curve, maximum power occurs when $V_o > \phi_C - \phi_E$, which means that the collector saturation emission current J_{eCS} is so large that it is advantageous to sacrifice output voltage to retard J_{eCS}. The optimum output voltage V_o which gives maximum power is found by maximizing Eq. (5-77) (for $V_o > \phi_C - \phi_E$) with respect to V_o and is given implicitly by

$$\left(1 - \frac{\tilde{V}_o}{\theta_C}\right) \exp\frac{-\tilde{V}_o}{\theta_C} = \left(\frac{\theta_E}{\theta_C}\right)^2 \exp\left[\frac{\phi_E}{\theta_E}\left(\frac{\theta_E}{\theta_C} - 1\right)\right]$$

This equation is satisfied to a good approximation when the exponents are equal, i.e., when

$$\tilde{V}_o = -\phi_E\left(1 - \frac{\theta_C}{\theta_E}\right) \tag{5-78}$$

Since $V_o = \phi_C + V_C - \phi_E$, Eq. (5-78) implies an optimum collector work function given by

$$\tilde{\phi}_C = \frac{\theta_C}{\theta_E}\phi_E \tag{5-79}$$

In other words, when the collector work function is less than or equal to the value given by Eq. (5-79), maximum power can be obtained by adjusting the output voltage to the value given by Eq. (5-78).

Just as there is an additional term J_{eC} in the expression for the net current when back emission is considered, there is an additional term in the expression for the electron cooling of the emitter. This additional term represents the energy delivered to the emitter by the electrons which reach the emitter from the collector. By an argument similar to that which gives

$$P_1 = \begin{cases} -J_{eE}(\phi_E - V_C + 2\theta_E) & V_o \le \phi_C - \phi_E \\ -J_{eE}(\phi_E + 2\theta_E) & V_o > \phi_C - \phi_E \end{cases}$$

for the electron cooling of the emitter, it can be shown that the electron heating of the emitter is

$$P_6 = \begin{cases} -J_{eC}(\phi_E - V_C + 2\theta_C) & V_o \le \phi_C - \phi_E \\ -J_{eC}(\phi_E + 2\theta_C) & V_o > \phi_C - \phi_E \end{cases}$$

Therefore, the *net* electron cooling of the emitter is

$$P_1 - P_6 = \begin{cases} -J_{eE}(\phi_E - V_C + 2\theta_E) + J_{eC}(\phi_E - V_C + 2\theta_C) & \\ & V_o \leq \phi_C - \phi_E \\ -J_{eE}(\phi_E + 2\theta_E) + J_{eC}(\phi_E + 2\theta_C) & V_o > \phi_C - \phi_E \end{cases}$$

Inclusion of these terms in Eq. (5-74) does not alter the value of $\tilde{V}_w$. However, for emitter temperatures above 2000°K where the heat loss $P_4 + P_5$ can be ignored, the optimum output voltage is given to a good approximation by Eq. (5-78) and the optimum collector work function by Eq. (5-79).

The effect of back emission on the efficiency is illustrated in Fig. 5-33, which shows maximum efficiency versus collector temperature for $T_E = 2200°K$, $\phi_E = 3.0$ volts, $\phi_C = 1.7$ volts, and $\epsilon = 0.2$. This figure shows that at low collector temperature where $\phi_C < \tilde{\phi}_C = (T_C/T_E)\phi_E$, the efficiency is independent of collector temperature, but at high collector temperature where $\phi_C > \tilde{\phi}_C$, the efficiency decreases approximately linearly with increasing collector temperature. The dividing line between the two regimes occurs approximately at $\phi_C = \tilde{\phi}_C$. In actual devices, the efficiency at low collector temperature is not independent of collector temperature

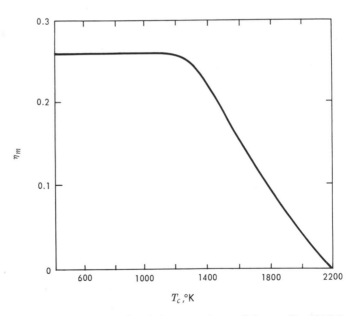

Fig. 5-33. *Effect of back emission on maximum efficiency.* T_E, 2200°K; ϕ_E, 3.0 volts; ϕ_C, 1.7 volts; ϵ, 0.2.

because the work function of the cesiated collector varies with collector temperature. However, the gross behavior is similar to the curve shown in Fig. 5-33.

The requirement $\alpha = 1$ for space-charge neutralization imposes a somewhat severe restriction on the emitter work functions which can be used in low-pressure converters. The reason is that a low emitter work function is required for high emission current, hence high power output, whereas a higher work function is required for copious surface ionization at the emitter. The ideal emitter work function for given cesium-vapor pressure and emitter temperature can be found by solving the equation

$$\alpha = -\frac{J_{pES}}{J_{eES}}\left(\frac{m_p}{m_e}\right)^{1/2} = 1$$

for ϕ_E when J_{pES} and J_{eES} are set equal to $\beta e p_{Cs}/(2\pi m_p k T_{Cs})^{1/2}$ and $-A_R T_E^2 \exp(-\phi_E/\theta_E)$, respectively. Figure 5-34 shows the ideal work function found this way for a variety of cesium-vapor pressures and emitter temperatures. The dashed curves in Fig. 5-34 indicate emitter saturation current levels. As an example, suppose an emission current of 10 A/cm² at 2000°K were desired. Figure 5-34 shows that the required emitter work function would be 3.05 volts, and the cesium-vapor pressure required to neutralize this emission current would be 0.22 torr. (Figure 5-8 shows that the electrode spacing would have to be less than 100 μ for collisions to be unimportant.)

Aside from cesiated refractory metals which require cesium-vapor pressures on the order of 10 torr to give work functions in the neighborhood of 3 volts at 2000°K, there are few refractory materials which meet this requirement. The vacuum emission measurements of Lafferty[22] indicate that there are several boride compounds, particularly lanthanum hexaboride, which might be satisfactory.

If the desired emission current is dropped to 1 A/cm², there are several possible emitter materials. At 2000°K, the required emitter work function is 3.45 volts and the required cesium-vapor pressure has dropped 2 orders of magnitude to about 2×10^{-3} torr. Some of the most commonly used emitter materials which fit into this category are the so-called "dispenser cathodes" made with thorium or uranium as the volatile agent.

For the reason outlined above, namely, that the low-pressure converter requires a relatively low emitter work function at low cesium-vapor pressure, the experimental characteristics of the low-pressure converter have not been investigated as thoroughly as those of the high-pressure converter. However, a survey of the published experimental work on the low-pressure converter shows that, in general, the shapes of the observed current-voltage characteristics are similar to the dashed curve in Fig. 5-26; i.e., the current

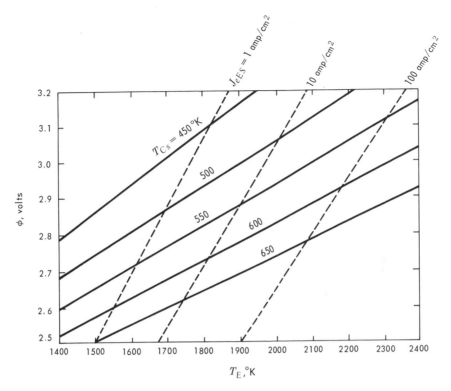

Fig. 5-34. *Work function required for* $\alpha = 1$.

rises exponentially as the output voltage is decreased from open circuit, and then it saturates within a few tenths of a volt of $V_o = \phi_C - \phi_E$.

In one of the earliest experiments on the low-pressure converter, the emitter was tungsten ribbon which was spaced 1.2 mm from a concentric nickel collector.[23] The results obtained agree quantitatively with the simple theory outlined for the collisionless converter with zero space charge. For example, except for a slight rounding near $V_o = \phi_C - \phi_E$, the observed current-voltage characteristics were similar to the dashed curve in Fig. 5-26 when the cesium-vapor pressure was high enough to give a value of α [Eq. (5-67)] equal to or greater than unity. Furthermore, the observed output voltage at maximum power was -2.5 volts, which agrees closely to the theoretical value obtained by taking the difference between the work function of cesium (1.8 volts) and that of polycrystalline tungsten (4.5 volts). Finally, the measured efficiencies agreed with theoretical values computed according to Eq. (5-74) when the smaller losses such as the lead loss were ignored. However, because of the high emitter

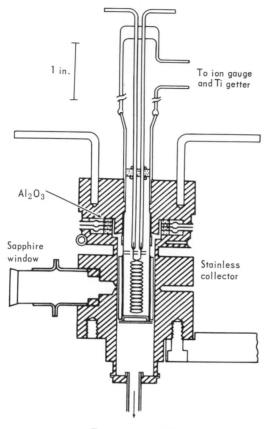

1 in.

To ion gauge
and Ti getter

Al_2O_3

Sapphire
window

Stainless
collector

To cesium reservoir

Fig. 5-35.   *Cross section of experimental thermionic converter.*   (*Courtesy of J. M. Houston, General Electric Research Laboratory.*)

work function, a significant power output was obtained only at very high emitter temperatures where continuous operation would be impractical because of the high evaporation rate of the emitter.   For example, at 2910°K, where a power output of 19 watts/cm² at an efficiency of 10 percent was observed, the emitter evaporated at the rate of 0.7 mm per 1,000 hours.

A more practical example of the low-pressure converter had a cylindrical thoriated tungsten emitter spaced 1 mm from a concentric stainless-steel collector.[24]   The emitter surface area was 13.4 cm².   A cross section of this converter is shown in Fig. 5-35.   The emitter surface could be viewed through a sapphire window and an 0.081-in.-diameter hole in the collector. A magnetically operated nickel shutter was located adjacent to the window to keep materials evaporated by the emitter from darkening the sapphire window. A heater tape was wrapped around the sapphire window to maintain its temperature above that of the cesium reservoir and prevent cesium condensation. The cesium-pool temperature and the collector temperature were monitored with chromel-alumel thermocouples, and the emitter temperature was measured with an optical pyrometer, the brightness temperature being converted to true temperature by assuming the spectral emissivity of tungsten plus a small correction caused by light absorption in the sapphire window. Current-voltage characteristics were obtained by applying a 60 cps voltage of variable amplitude to the collector with respect to the emitter and displaying the characteristic on an oscilloscope screen. The schematic for this experiment is shown in Fig. 5-36. Low-pressure current-voltage characteristics obtained for cesium-pool temperatures of 348, 374, and 424°K are shown in Fig. 5-37. These experimental characteristics differ from the theoretical ones (Fig. 5-26) in two major respects: (1) There are radio-frequency oscillations in the constant-current part of the characteristic which never appear in the retarding part of the characteristic; (2) the current apparently saturates at a value much lower than the saturation emission current at high emitter temperatures for the two lowest cesium-pool temperatures.

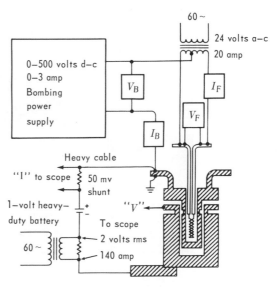

Fig. 5-36. *Circuit used for 60 cps data. (Courtesy of J. M. Houston, General Electric Research Laboratory.)*

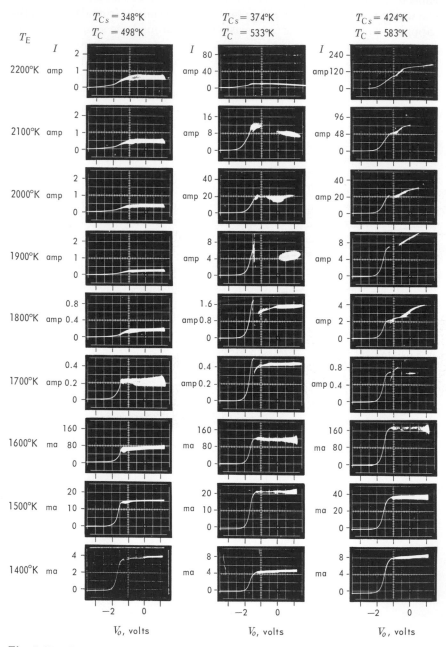

Fig. 5-37.   *Low-pressure current-voltage characteristics.*   (*Courtesy of J. M. Houston, General Electric Research Laboratory.*)

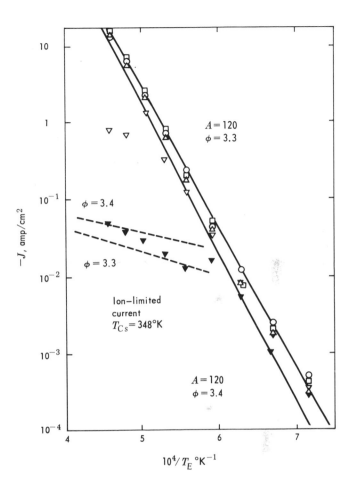

Fig. 5-38. *Short-circuit current density from Fig. 5-37 plotted versus reciprocal emitter temperature. (Courtesy of J. M. Houston, General Electric Research Laboratory.)*

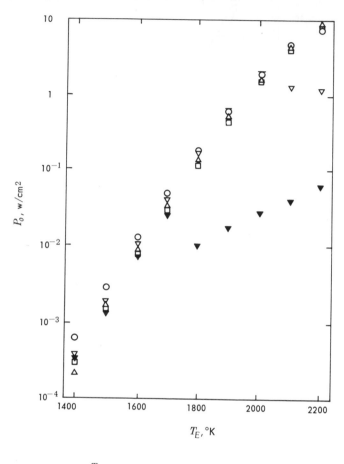

	T_{Cs}	T_C
▼	348°K	498°K
▽	374	533
○	424	583
△	474	683
□	523	743

Fig. 5-39. *Maximum power output from 60 cps J-V data plotted versus emitter temperature for low-pressure converter with thoriated tungsten emitter. (Courtesy of J. M. Houston, General Electric Research Laboratory.)*

The most recent explanation[25] of the oscillations attributes them to ion acoustic waves caused by the interaction of the plasma with an electron beam formed by the acceleration of electrons through an ion-rich sheath at the emitter. This view does not admit oscillations when there is an electron-rich sheath at the emitter. Therefore, it does not fully explain the oscillations, because the characteristics in Fig. 5-37 which show "saturation" at a value less than the saturation emission current correspond to potential distributions with electron-rich sheaths at the emitter. Furthermore, a complete explanation must show why the oscillations are observed only in that part of the current-voltage characteristic for which the potential distribution is retarding for ions coming from the emitter.

The reason that the current apparently saturates at a value below the saturation emission current in some instances can be described qualitatively as an "ion limiting" effect; i.e., the maximum electron current which can reach the collector is $(m_p/m_e)^{1/2}$ times the ion current coming from the emitter. This simple explanation is illustrated in Fig. 5-38, which shows the logarithm of the observed short-circuit current as a function of the reciprocal emitter temperature for different cesium-pool temperatures. The dashed lines in Fig. 5-38 are plots of $492J_p$, where J_p is calculated from Eq. (5-66) and 492 is the square root of the ratio of the mass of a cesium atom to that of an electron. The observed electron currents agree with the ion-limited currents calculated for emitter work functions of 3.3 and 3.4 volts, which values probably bracket the work function of the thoriated tungsten emitter.

The variation of the maximum power output obtained from the characteristics in Fig. 5-37 is shown in Fig. 5-39. Note that the power output is severely limited at the lower cesium-pool temperatures for which the electron current becomes ion-limited. These results agree with the curves in Fig. 5-34, which show that for an emitter work function of 3.3 volts and an emitter temperature of 2000°K, the cesium-vapor pressure required for neutralization is 10^{-2} torr. According to Fig. 5-24, this vapor pressure corresponds to a cesium-pool temperature of 427°K, and Fig. 5-39 shows no ion-limiting effects for a cesium-pool temperature of 424°K. Therefore, it appears that the operation of the low-pressure converter is understood qualitatively. However, it also appears that a detailed theory of the operation of the low-pressure converter is lacking.

4-3. *High-pressure Cesium Converter*

As mentioned earlier, emitter work functions in the neighborhood of 3 volts can be obtained at high temperature with cesiated refractory metals. However, the cesium-vapor pressures required are usually between 1 and

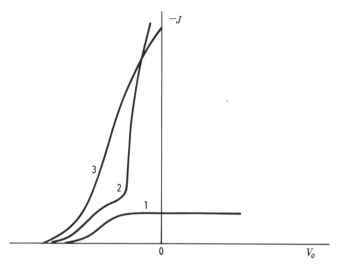

Fig. 5-40. *The three general types of high-pressure current-voltage characteristics.*

10 torr, so that for typical electrode spacings the operation falls into the high-pressure regime as defined at the beginning of this section on gaseous converters.   Therefore, the effect of collisions on charge transport in the converter must be taken into account.   Collisions can be classified according to two types: elastic and inelastic.   By definition, elastic collisions involve no changes in the internal energies of the colliding particles, whereas inelastic collisions involve changes in the internal energy of one of the colliding particles with excitation or ionization of the particle being the result.

On the other hand, experimental high-pressure current-voltage characteristics can be classified according to the three general types shown in Fig. 5-40.   These curves have been labeled in order of increasing emitter temperature (the cesium-vapor pressure and spacing are presumed to be constant).   Curves of Type 1, which are characterized by an apparent saturation far below the saturation emission current of the emitter, are called unignited mode curves.   Curves of Type 2, which are characterized by an abrupt change in shape, are called ignited mode curves.   Curves of Type 3 fall into an intermediate category because the surface and volume sources of ions may be comparable.

Unignited mode.   The qualitative features of the potential distributions which correspond to the unignited mode curves of Type 1 are as follows.   At low emitter temperature and high cesium-vapor pressure, the cesiated emitter has a low work function which results in an electron-rich emitter sheath. The electron current which diffuses to the collector is therefore limited by the retarding sheath at the emitter and by scattering in the electrode gap. The potential distributions near open circuit and near short circuit are shown in Fig. 5-41. The main feature of these distributions is that most of the applied voltage appears in the collector sheath. This behavior does not change even if the emitter sheath is ion-rich at open circuit. A theoretical analysis of the unignited mode is presented below.

For the unignited mode, the source-free steady-state continuity equations for one-dimensional flow are

$$\frac{d\Gamma_e}{dx} = 0 \qquad \frac{d\Gamma_p}{dx} = 0 \qquad \frac{d\Gamma_a}{dx} = 0$$

so that each individual particle current is independent of position. If it is assumed that all the particles have approximately the same temperature and that the terms involving the center-of-mass velocity can be neglected, the steady-state diffusion equations for electrons and ions are [cf. Eq. (5-17)]

$$\frac{1}{\theta}\left(\frac{dn_e\theta}{dx} - n_e\frac{dV}{dx}\right) = \frac{n_e n_a}{nD_{ea}}\left(\langle u_a\rangle - \langle u_e\rangle\right) + \frac{n_e n_p}{nD_{ep}}\left(\langle u_p\rangle - \langle u_e\rangle\right) \qquad (5\text{-}80)$$

$$\frac{1}{\theta}\left(\frac{dn_p\theta}{dx} + n_p\frac{dV}{dx}\right) = \frac{n_p n_e}{nD_{ep}}\left(\langle u_e\rangle - \langle u_p\rangle\right) + \frac{n_p n_a}{nD_{pa}}\left(\langle u_a\rangle - \langle u_p\rangle\right) \qquad (5\text{-}81)$$

When the nondiagonal terms of the pressure tensor are neglected, the momentum equation becomes

$$\frac{dp}{dx} - (n_e - n_p)\frac{dV}{dx} = 0 \qquad (5\text{-}82)$$

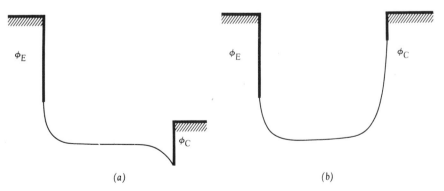

Fig. 5-41. *Type 1 potential distributions: (a) near open circuit; (b) near short circuit.*

where $p = (n_e + n_p + n_a)kT$. Likewise, the energy equation becomes

$$\frac{dQ}{dx} + J\,\frac{dV}{dx} = 0 \tag{5-83}$$

Finally, there is Poisson's equation:

$$\frac{d^2V}{dx^2} = \frac{e}{\epsilon_0}\,(n_e - n_p) \tag{5-84}$$

Equations (5-80) to (5-84) form a complete set of equations which, in principle, can be solved for five unknowns: $n_e(x)$, $n_p(x)$, $n_a(x)$, $T(x)$, and $V(x)$. In practice, however, solving this set of equations requires some simplifying assumptions. For the unignited mode, the following assumptions are made: (1) The fractional ionization is low; i.e., n_e and n_p are much less than n_a; (2) the drift velocities $\langle u_e \rangle$ and $\langle u_p \rangle$ of the charged particles are much greater than the drift velocity $\langle u_a \rangle$ of the atoms by virtue of the body forces associated with the electric field; (3) the atom density n_a is constant in space; (4) the temperature T is constant in space.

The validity of the last assumption is open to question; however, constant-temperature solutions are of interest because they shed light on the gross behavior of the system. Because the number of unknown variables has been arbitrarily reduced from 5 to 3 by assumptions (3) and (4), it is necessary to reduce the number of equations accordingly. The appropriate equations to be set aside are Eqs. (5-82) and (5-83) because momentum and energy cannot be conserved *exactly* in view of assumptions (3) and (4). However, Eqs. (5-82) and (5-83) can be used for consistency checks after a solution to the remaining Eqs. (5-80), (5-81), and (5-84) has been found.

Based on the assumptions listed above, the right-hand sides of Eqs. (5-80) and (5-81) reduce to $-\Gamma_e/D_{ea}$ and $-\Gamma_p/D_{pa}$, respectively, where $D_{ia} = \lambda_{ia}v_i/3 = $ constant. Then the two diffusion equations and Poisson's equation can be combined to give a second-order equation in the electric field E:

$$\frac{d^2E}{dx^2} - \frac{1}{2\theta^2}\,E^3 + \frac{e}{\theta\epsilon_0}\,(Ax - C_1)E - \frac{e}{\epsilon_0}\,B = 0$$

where A and B are constants given by the equations

$$A = \frac{\Gamma_e}{D_{ea}} + \frac{\Gamma_p}{D_{pa}}$$

$$B = \frac{\Gamma_{ea}}{D_{ea}} - \frac{\Gamma_p}{D_{pa}}$$

and C_1 is a constant of integration. This equation can be expressed in the dimensionless form

$$\frac{d^2y}{dz^2} = 2y^3 + zy + \mu \qquad (5\text{-}85)$$

by the substitutions

$$y = -\left(\frac{\epsilon_0}{8e\theta^2 A}\right)^{1/3} E$$

$$z = -\left(\frac{e}{\epsilon_0 \theta A^2}\right)^{1/3} (Ax - C_1)$$

$$\mu = -\frac{B}{2A}$$

Equation (5-85) is one of a set of nonlinear equations studied by P. Painlevé, and its solution is known as the second Painlevé transcendent.[26] Some numerical solutions to this equation have been obtained by Davis et al.[27] for a few initial values of z, y, and dy/dz. However, these initial conditions were not relevant to the high-pressure cesium thermionic converter, so that a numerical program was developed at the General Electric Vallecitos Atomic Laboratory to obtain additional solutions.[23]

The solution to Eq. (5-85) has six constants which must be determined by six boundary conditions. The boundary conditions to be specified are the zero of potential, the electron and ion densities at each electrode, and the net electron current. The densities are related to the electrode temperatures and work functions by taking into account the emission of electrons and ions from the electrodes. The number of particles of type i crossing unit area per unit time in the positive (negative) direction is given by the equation

$$\Gamma_{i\pm} = \int_{-\infty}^{+\infty} dw \int_{-\infty}^{\infty} dv \int_{0}^{\pm\infty} uf_i \, du$$

According to Chapman and Cowling the distribution function f_i is represented by a series

$$f_i = \sum_{j=0}^{\infty} f_i^{(j)}$$

where

$$f_i^{(0)} = n_i \left(\frac{m_i}{2\pi kT}\right)^{3/2} \exp\left(\frac{-m_i}{2kT} C_i^2\right)$$

Therefore,

$$\Gamma_{i\pm} = \frac{n_i v_i}{4} \exp\left(\frac{-m_i u_0^2}{2kT}\right) \pm \frac{n_i u_0}{2}\left\{1 \pm \mathrm{erf}\left[\left(\frac{m_i u_0^2}{2kT}\right)^{1/2}\right]\right\}$$

$$+ \sum_{j=1}^{\infty} \int_{-\infty}^{\infty} dw \int_{-\infty}^{\infty} dv \int_{0}^{\infty} u f_i^{(j)}\, du$$

For the case at hand $\left(\dfrac{m_i u_0^2}{2kT}\right) \ll 1$; and the forward and backward currents are given approximately by

$$\Gamma_{i\pm} = \frac{n_i v_i}{4} \pm \frac{\Gamma_i}{2} \tag{5-86}$$

At the emitter (collector) the total number of particles crossing unit area per unit time in the positive (negative) x direction must equal the rate at which the particles are emitted. The electron-emission rates at the electrodes are given by the Richardson-Dushman equation as follows:

$$-e\Gamma_{eE+} = -e\Gamma_{eES} = -A_R T_E^2 \exp\frac{-\phi_E}{\theta_E}$$

$$-e\Gamma_{eC-} = e\Gamma_{eCS} = A_R T_C^2 \exp\frac{-\phi_C}{\theta_C}$$

The corresponding boundary conditions for the electron densities at the electrodes are found from Eq. (5-86). The result is

$$n_{eE} = \frac{2}{v_e}\left(2\Gamma_{eES} - \Gamma_e\right)$$

$$n_{eC} = \frac{2}{v_e}\left(\Gamma_e + 2\Gamma_{eCS}\right)$$

The ion-emission rates at the electrodes are related to the incident fluxes of neutrals and ions by the equations

$$\Gamma_{pE+} = \beta_E(\Gamma_{aE-} + \Gamma_{pE-}) \tag{5-87}$$

$$\Gamma_{pC-} = \beta_C(\Gamma_{aC+} + \Gamma_{pC+}) \tag{5-88}$$

where β is the probability that an incident particle will leave the surface as an ion, i.e., the surface ionization coefficient. In writing these equations, it has been assumed that the previous history of the incident particles is unimportant insofar as the ionization process is concerned. If, in addition, it is required that there be no loss of nuclei at an electrode, i.e., if

$$\Gamma_{p+} + \Gamma_{a+} = \Gamma_{p-} + \Gamma_{a-}$$

the boundary conditions for the ion densities at the electrodes are found from Eqs. (5-86) to (5-88). Taking $v_a = v_p$, the result is

$$n_{pE} = (1 - \beta_E)^{-1} \left(\beta_E n_{aE} - \frac{2\Gamma_p}{v_p} \right)$$

$$n_{pC} = (1 - \beta_C)^{-1} \left(\beta_C n_{aC} + \frac{2\Gamma_p}{v_p} \right) .$$

With these boundary conditions solutions to the Painlevé equation have been obtained which exhibit a character similar to the equilibrium state.[28] That is, over most of the plasma charge neutrality is nearly maintained, the electric field is very small, and the current is due to the particle concentration gradients. Near the electrode surface there is a region, less than one collision mean free path in extent, of high electric field, the so called "sheath region," where the electric-field component of the current is important. These results suggest that an approximate model of the collision-dominated converter operating in the unignited mode might be formulated by dividing the interelectrode gap into three regions: an emitter-sheath region, a plasma region, and a collector-sheath region. Such a model has been used recently[29] to obtain theoretical current-voltage characteristics of a planar converter. The electron- and ion-particle currents in the plasma region are given by

$$\Gamma_e = -D_{ea} \left(\frac{dn}{dx} + \frac{1}{\theta} nE \right) \tag{5-89}$$

$$\Gamma_p = -D_{pa} \left(\frac{dn}{dx} - \frac{1}{\theta} nE \right) \tag{5-90}$$

where it has been assumed that charge neutrality holds; that is, $n_e \approx n_p = n$. Combining the above equations yields a relation between n_1, the charged-particle density at the emitter sheath-plasma edge, and n_2, that at the collector sheath-plasma edge; i.e.,

$$n_2 = n_1 - \frac{1}{2} \left(\frac{\Gamma_e}{D_{ea}} + \frac{\Gamma_p}{D_{pa}} \right) l \tag{5-91}$$

where l is the electrode spacing. It is assumed that the sheath thickness is negligible compared with l. It is further assumed that a Boltzmann-like relation holds for the charged-particle current in the sheath; i.e., if there is an electron-rich sheath at the emitter, the forward-directed current of electrons at the sheath-plasma edge is given by

$$\Gamma_{e1+} = \Gamma_{eES} e^{-V_1/\theta}$$

and the backward-directed current of ions at the emitter is

$$\Gamma_{pe-} = \Gamma_{p1-}e^{-V_1/\theta}$$

where V_1 is the magnitude of the emitter-sheath potential drop. The above relations are consistent with a collisionless model of the sheath and the Langmuir velocity distribution function described earlier. Similarly, at the collector, with an ion-rich sheath of magnitude V_2,

$$\Gamma_{e2+}e^{-V_2/\theta} = \Gamma_{eC+}$$

and with an electron-rich sheath,

$$\Gamma_{p2+}e^{-V_2/\theta} = \Gamma_{pC+}$$

If the above relations are used together with the relations for the directed currents given by Eq. (5-86), then, assuming an electron-rich sheath at the emitter,

$$\Gamma_{eES}e^{-V_1/\theta} - \left(\frac{n_1 v_e}{4} - \frac{\Gamma_e}{2}\right) = \Gamma_e \qquad (5\text{-}92)$$

$$\Gamma_{pES} - \left(\frac{n_1 v_p}{4} - \frac{\Gamma_p}{2}\right)e^{-V_1/\theta} = \Gamma_p \qquad (5\text{-}93)$$

At the collector with an electron-rich sheath and *no back current*

$$\frac{n_2 v_e}{4} + \frac{\Gamma_e}{2} = \Gamma_e \qquad (5\text{-}94)$$

$$\left(\frac{n_2 v_p}{4} + \frac{\Gamma_p}{2}\right)e^{-V_2/\theta} = \Gamma_p \qquad (5\text{-}95)$$

and with a positive sheath

$$\left(\frac{n_2 v_\epsilon}{4} + \frac{\Gamma_\epsilon}{2}\right)e^{-V_2/\theta} = \Gamma_e$$

$$\frac{n_2 v_p}{4} + \frac{\Gamma_p}{2} = \Gamma_p$$

Equations (5-91) to (5-95) are five equations in six unknowns n_1, n_2, V_1, V_2, Γ_e, and Γ_p. Thus for a given value of Γ_e the other unknowns are determined, and the electric field may be obtained from Eqs. (5-89) and (5-90) and integrated to give the plasma potential drop

$$\Delta V = -\int_0^l E \, dx$$

In this way the current-voltage characteristic can be obtained.

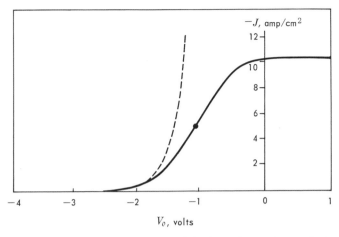

Fig. 5-42. *Current-voltage characteristic from three-region analysis. Dashed curve is Boltzmann curve from ideal model. T_E, 2000°K; ϕ_E, 2.72 volts; ϕ_C, 1.7 volts; T_{Cs}, 648°K (P_{Cs} = 10 torr); l, 18 μ (0.0014 in.); $-J_{eES}$, 68 amp/cm².*

These characteristics always have an apparent saturation current which can be as much as two orders of magnitude lower than the emitted electron current. If the ion current is set equal to zero, the apparent saturation current J'_{eES} is found to be

$$J'_{eES} \propto [J_{eES} \exp - (V_1)_{eq}/\theta_e] \frac{\lambda_{ea}}{l} \tag{5-96}$$

where $(V_1)_{eq}$ is the equilibrium sheath drop. The first factor is interpreted as the electron current able to enter the plasma region, and the second factor represents a transport limitation due to back scattering of electrons. Figure 5-42 shows a current-voltage characteristic obtained from the three-region analysis described above. The dashed curve shows the corresponding collisionless space-charge-free current-voltage characteristic. Note that the current apparently saturates at a value which is 15 percent of the emitter saturation current, in accord with Eq. (5-96). This behavior was observed experimentally by Warner and Hansen.[29] Figure 5-43 shows the density and potential distributions corresponding to the point at $V_0 = 1.09$ volts indicated in Fig. 5-42. These distributions were obtained from a numerical solution of the Painlevé equation for the same conditions of electrode-temperature work functions and spacing. Therefore, it seems reasonable to conclude that the three-region model is a good approximation to the more exact one-region model.

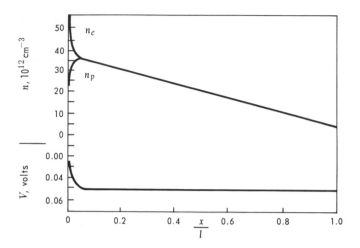

Fig. 5-43. *Density and potential variation from solution of Painlevé equation.* T_E, 2000°K; ϕ_E, 2.72 volts; ϕ_C, 1.70 volts; T, 648°K (P_{Cs} = 10 torr); l, 18 μ (0.0014 in.); $-J_{eES}$, 68 amp/cm².

When the three-region model is applied to the case in which there is an ion-rich sheath at the emitter, the result for the apparent saturation current J'_{eES} becomes

$$\frac{J'_{eES}}{J_{eES}} = \frac{2[\sqrt{\alpha^2 + (\alpha\, 3l/4\lambda_{ea})(3l/4\lambda_{ea} + 1)} - \alpha]}{(3l/4\lambda_{ea})(3l/4\lambda_{ea} + 1)} \tag{5-97}$$

When $\alpha \ll \dfrac{3l}{4\lambda_{ea}}\left(\dfrac{3l}{4\lambda_{ea}} + 1\right)$, Eq. (5-97) reduces to

$$\frac{J'_{eES}}{J_{eES}} = 2\sqrt{\frac{\alpha}{(3l/4\lambda_{ea})[(3l/4\lambda_{ea}) + 1]}}$$

which is similar to the corresponding expression for the electron-rich emitter sheath.   However, when the electron (ion) source at the emitter is small (large) enough that $\alpha \gg \dfrac{3l}{4\lambda_{ea}}\left(\dfrac{3l}{4\lambda_{ea}} + 1\right)$, Eq. (5-97) reduces to

$$\frac{J'_{eES}}{J_{eES}} = 1 - \frac{(3l/4\lambda_{ea})[(3l/4\lambda_{ea}) + 1]}{4\alpha}$$

This equation predicts that the true saturation current J_{eES} can be obtained by making α sufficiently large compared with $(l/\lambda_{ea})^2$.

The qualitative variation of the apparent saturation current with the parameter lp_{Cs} (which is proportional to l/λ_{ea}) embodied in Eq. (5-97) has been observed experimentally by Hatsopoulos.[30]   Using a converter with a rhenium emitter, he measured the apparent saturation current as a function of lp_{Cs} for different values of α.   His results are shown in Fig. 5-44, with theoretical curves computed according to Eq. (5-97).   The agreement is good enough to warrant the conclusion that the three-region model predicts the gross features of the high-pressure cesium converter operating in the unignited mode.

The three-region model with a constant temperature as presented here can be refined somewhat by allowing the electron energy to change with position in the plasma.   This change would be due to:

1. The acceleration of the electrons by the electric field
2. The fact that the mass of the electron is much less than that of the atom, so that the electrons lose only a small fraction of their energy in collisions with atoms

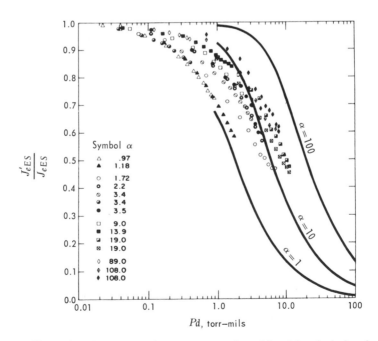

Fig. 5-44. *Dependence of apparent saturations of ion-rich unignited mode on pressure and spacing.   (Experimental data courtesy of G. N. Hatsopoulos, TEECO.)*

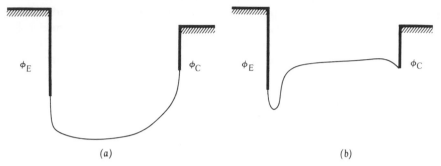

Fig. 5-45. *Type 2 potential distributions showing the sudden change due to onset of volume ionization: (a) just before ignition; (b) just after ignition.*

Such an analysis has been carried out,[31] and the resulting values of J'_{eES}/J_{eES} are somewhat less than the corresponding values obtained from the constant-temperature analysis.

Ignited mode. The qualitative features of the potential distributions which correspond to the ignited-mode curves of Type 2 (cf. Fig. 5-40) are similar to those of the unignited-mode curves of Type 1 near open circuit (cf. Fig. 5-41a). However, a sudden change in the potential distribution must be postulated to account for the sudden change in the slope of the current-voltage characteristic as short circuit is approached. This sudden change is thought to occur as follows. The potential drop in the collector sheath becomes larger and larger as short circuit is approached. As a result, the electrons near the collector become more and more energetic. As the potential drop increases, the sheath thickness increases roughly as $V^{3/4}$ by the Child-Langmuir law. Therefore, the sheath may extend quite far into the interelectrode space, so that the more energetic electrons can ionize atoms in the sheath. Once this impact ionization begins, the potential distribution at the emitter probably changes from very electron-rich to slightly electron-rich, or perhaps even to ion-rich, depending on the amount of volume ionization taking place. A pair of potential distributions showing the behavior described above is given in Fig. 5-45.

The potential distributions which correspond to curves of Type 3 (cf. Fig. 5-40) differ from those of Types 1 and 2 in that the emitter sheath is ion-rich for the entire current-voltage characteristic because the emitter temperature is high enough to supply sufficient ions. For this reason, there is probably no sudden change in this potential distribution at the onset of volume ionization and, therefore, no sudden change in the slope of the current-voltage characteristic.

Because the power outputs associated with the ignited-mode curves of Types 2 and 3 are much higher than those of the unignited-mode curves of Type 1, laboratory converters are generally operated in the ignited mode. Figure 5-46 shows a cross section of a laboratory converter designed by V. C. Wilson and J. Lawrence of the General Electric Research Laboratory. This converter had a tungsten emitter, a nickel collector, and a spacing of 0.127 μ (0.005 in.). The spacing was maintained by tungsten pins which were mounted in alumina cups inserted in the guard ring. The emitter was heated by electron bombardment from a spiral tungsten filament. The current-voltage characteristics shown in Fig. 5-47 were obtained with a circuit similar to that shown in Fig. 5-36.

The curves in Fig. 5-47a are mostly of Type 2, except that the curves for $T_E = 2130°K$ and $T_E = 2235°K$ are of Type 3. At $T_{Cs} = 653°K$, however, even the curves for these high emitter temperatures are of Type 2, as shown in Fig. 5-47b. Figure 5-48 shows the variation of maximum power output with emitter temperature, and Fig. 5-49 shows the corresponding efficiency (without lead losses) as a function of current density for different emitter temperatures.

Another type of laboratory converter is shown in Fig. 5-50. This converter is being used by the authors[37] to study the effect of back emission on high-pressure current-voltage characteristics of Types 2 and 3. For this reason, both emitter and collector can be heated by electron bombardment from spiral tungsten filaments. The tube envelope is 4 in. in diameter, and the planar electrodes, which are replaceable, are 1 in. in diameter.

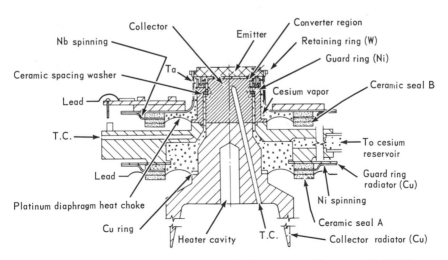

Fig. 5-46. *Cross section of high-pressure thermionic converter.* (*Courtesy of V. C. Wilson and J. Lawrence, General Electric Research Laboratory.*)

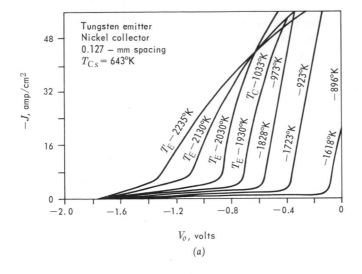

(a)

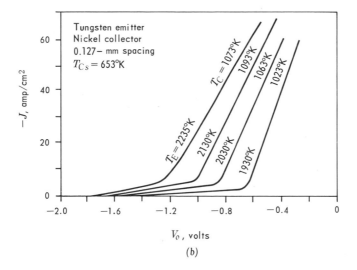

(b)

Fig. 5-47. *High-pressure ignited-mode current-voltage characteristics.* (*Courtesy of V. C. Wilson and J. Lawrence, General Electric Research Laboratory.*)

The electrode gap, which can be seen through the window in Fig. 5-50, can be varied from zero to 6.5 mm by a bellows arrangement. There are three windows spaced 90° apart through which the interelectrode space can be viewed. There are radiation shields concentric with each cylindrical electrode support which have notches through which the electrode tem-

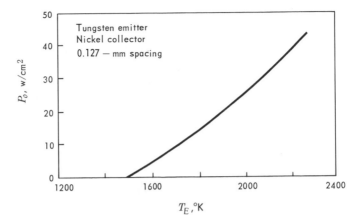

Fig. 5-48. *Measured maximum power output of high-pressure converter operating in ignited mode. (Courtesy of V. C. Wilson and J. Lawrence, General Electric Research Laboratory.)*

peratures can be measured pyrometrically. These radiation shields are electrically isolated so that they can be used as guard rings.

Figure 5-51 shows how the current-voltage characteristic obtained from this converter changes with increasing collector temperature. Note that when the collector temperature is equal to that of the emitter, there is no power output which is in agreement with the second law of thermodynamics. Figure 5-52 shows how the current-voltage characteristic

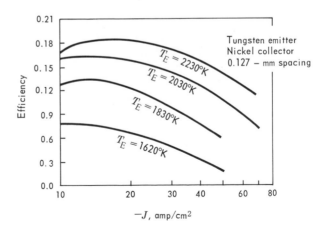

Fig. 5-49. *Measured efficiency (without lead losses) as a function of current density for various emitter temperatures. (Courtesy of V. C. Wilson and J. Lawrence, General Electric Research Laboratory.)*

Fig. 5-50. *Laboratory converter designed to investigate effects of back emission.*

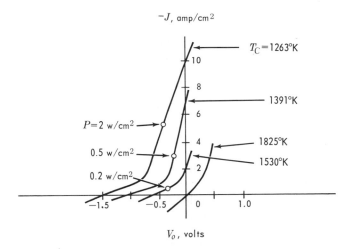

Fig. 5-51. *Effect of collector temperature on current-voltage charac-teristic. T_E, 1825°K; T_{Cs}, 613°K; l, 0.51 mm.*

obtained from this converter changes with spacing. Note that the main effect of decreasing the spacing is to shift the ignited part of the charac-teristic uniformly in the direction of higher output voltage, even though the open-circuit voltage does not change. As a result, the characteristic appears to change from Type 2 at large spacing to Type 3 at small spacing.

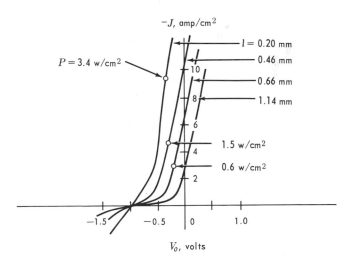

Fig. 5-52. *Effect of spacing on current-voltage characteristic. T_E, 1880°K; T_C. 1355°K; T_{Cs}, 635°K.*

However, this is only an apparent change, because there is no reason to expect the emitter-sheath structure to change with spacing unless the spacing becomes of the order of a sheath thickness.

At the present time, there is no quantitative theory by which the ignited-mode curves of Types 2 and 3 can be calculated. However, the following qualitative theory of the ignited mode seems to be widely accepted. The potential distributions corresponding to the ignited-mode curves of Type 2 are thought to be like that shown in Fig. 5-45*b*; i.e., there is a double sheath near the emitter which is electron-rich on the emitter side and ion-rich on the plasma side. This is sometimes called the Langmuir mode because Langmuir analyzed a *collisionless* diode composed of an electron emitter facing an ion emitter and found double-sheath solutions for the potential distribution.[32] The electron current entering the plasma from the emitter is assumed to be limited by the retarding emitter sheath as found for the collisionless model; i.e.,

$$J_e = J_{eES} e^{V_m/\theta_E}$$

The contribution to the back current due to scattering is ignored so that the current density measured at the collector is J_e.

The energy-balance equation for electrons is based on the third moment of the Boltzmann equation for electrons. For planar geometry, this becomes [cf. Eq. (5-16)]

$$\frac{d}{dx}\left(\tfrac{1}{2} n_e m_e \langle u_e^3 \rangle\right) - e\Gamma_e \frac{dV}{dx} = n_c \Delta \tfrac{1}{2} m_e \langle u_e^2 \rangle \tag{5-98}$$

where the quantity on the right represents the change in the average energy of the electrons caused by collisions of all kinds—inelastic as well as elastic. The upper limit to the plasma electron temperature can be estimated from this equation by ignoring the energy loss due to collisions. If T_e is constant, Eq. (5-98) can be integrated to give

$$\tfrac{1}{2} n_e m_e \langle u_e^3 \rangle = (\tfrac{1}{2} n_e m_e \langle u_e^3 \rangle)_E + e\Gamma_e V(x) \tag{5-99}$$

where $V(\text{o}) = 0$. If the Langmuir distribution function derived in the section on the vacuum converter is used to compute the energy flow at the emitter,

$$(\tfrac{1}{2} n_e m_e \langle u_e^3 \rangle)_E = e\Gamma_e(-V_m + 2\theta_E) \qquad V_m < 0 \tag{5-100}$$

at the emitter. In the plasma, the directed motion of the electrons gained in the accelerating part of the double sheath can be assumed to be randomized by collisions. Then it can be assumed that the distribution

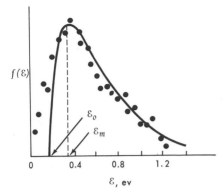

Fig. 5-53. *Electron energy distribution measured in plasma. Solid curve is plot of $f(\mathcal{E}) \propto (\mathcal{E} - \mathcal{E}_o)^{\frac{1}{2}} exp\ [-(\mathcal{E} - \mathcal{E}_o)/kT_e]$: emitter, Ta; collector, Cu; T_E, 1483°K (0.13 ev); T_{Cs}, 522°K; T_e, 3482°K (0.3 ev).*

becomes Maxwellian in the center of mass [cf. Eq. (5-38)], giving approximately

$$\tfrac{1}{2}n_e m_e \langle u_e^{3} \rangle = \tfrac{5}{2}e\Gamma_e\theta_e(x) \tag{5-101}$$

in the plasma.   Equations (5-99) to (5-101) can be combined to give

$$\theta_e(x) = \tfrac{4}{5}\theta_{eE} + \tfrac{2}{5}[V(x) - V_m] \tag{5-102}$$

This expression gives an estimate of the upper limit of the plasma electron temperature θ_e.

Recent measurements reported by Bullis and Wiegand[33] tend to corroborate the qualitative picture outlined above.   Using a Langmuir probe,† they measured the electrical-potential electron temperature and electron energy distribution as a function of position in a cesium discharge in a planar diode composed of a tantalum emitter spaced about 5 mm from a copper collector.   The measured potential distributions were qualitatively similar to the assumed shape in Fig. 5-45b.   The ion-rich sheath extends several mean free paths into the electrode gap, which is contrary to the belief that sheath thicknesses are comparable to the Debye length.   The measured electron temperature in the plasma was about twice the emitter temperature; this indicates that inelastic collisions are important because if there were no inelastic collisions, the plasma electron temperature computed according to Eq. (5-102) should be about twice the measured value.

Measured electron-energy distributions in the ignited mode appeared to be Maxwellian in the center of mass except at very low energies.   An energy distribution $f(\mathcal{E})$ measured at short circuit is shown in Fig. 5-53.

† Describing the Langmuir probe and its use in plasma diagnostics is beyond the scope of this work.   For more information, the reader should consult a standard reference such as J. D. Cobine's *Gaseous Conductors*.

The dots are the experimental points, and the solid line is a theoretical curve which has the form of a shifted Maxwellian, i.e.,

$$f(\mathcal{E})\alpha(\mathcal{E} - \mathcal{E}_0)^{1/2} \exp\left(- \frac{\mathcal{E} - \mathcal{E}_0}{kT_e}\right) \tag{5-103}$$

where $\mathcal{E}$ is the electron energy, $\mathcal{E}_0$ is the energy associated with the velocity of the center of mass, and T_e is the electron temperature. The electron temperature can be obtained from this experimental data by maximizing Eq. (5-103) with respect to $\mathcal{E}$. The result is $kT_e = 2(\mathcal{E}_m - \mathcal{E}_0)$ where $\mathcal{E}_m$ is the value of $\mathcal{E}$ at which $f(\mathcal{E})$ is maximum. In Fig. 5-53, $\mathcal{E}_m$ is about 0.35 ev and $\mathcal{E}_0$ is 0.20 ev; this gives kT_e equal to 0.3 ev, which is about twice the emitter temperature. Based on this experimental data, the assumption that the energy distribution of the electrons in the plasma is Maxwellian in the center of mass seems reasonable.

4-4. Other Gaseous Converters

Several methods have been used recently to improve converter performance at lower emitter temperatures and larger electrode spacings for which the practical problems associated with long lifetime are alleviated. These methods involve the use of additives, i.e., the addition of a second gas to the converter. One purpose of an additive is to increase the emission capabilities of the emitter without hindering the flow of electrons from emitter to collector. Two additives which have been used for this purpose are cesium fluoride and barium.

In the case of cesium fluoride, it is believed that the fluorine increases the cesium-free work function of the emitter, so that the corresponding cesiated work function is lowered. This action results in higher emission capability for a given cesium pressure or, conversely, lower optimum cesium pressure, hence less scattering, for a given emission capability.

For example, it has been shown that the addition of cesium fluoride to a cesium converter with a molybdenum emitter doubled the power output in the emitter temperature range 1800–2000°K.[34] However, the same investigators found only a small increase with a rhenium emitter, indicating that the higher-base work functions are not affected beneficially by cesium fluoride.

Barium, on the other hand, modifies the work function of a refractory metal much like cesium, except that greater coverage is obtained for the same vapor pressure. In addition, the electron-scattering cross section of barium is lower than that of cesium. However, because of the high ionization potential of barium, cesium is still required to eliminate space-charge, but much lower cesium pressure suffices to neutralize emission currents than is required to give a low emitter work function.   Therefore, by using barium to adjust the emitter work function and cesium to neutralize space-charge, ideal converter operation may be approached at practical spacings.   This has been shown in a recent experiment in which a tungsten emitter at 2000°K gave power output of over 8 watts/cm², which remained nearly independent of spacing between 0.01 mm and 0.10 mm.[35]   The vapor pressure of barium in this experiment was about 1 torr and that of cesium about $\frac{1}{10}$ torr.

Another additive which has been used in thermionic-converter investigations is xenon.   It was found that the addition of 60 torr of xenon to the converter increased the power output by approximately 15 percent at a power output of about 8 watts/cm².[36]   A tentative explanation for the increased power is that it is due to a decrease in the internal-voltage loss required for production of ions by volume ionization.[36]   This explanation implies that the ion-diffusion rate is reduced by the additive, although the electron-diffusion rate is unaffected.   That the electron-diffusion rate is not impeded by the xenon is attributed to the fact that the electron-xenon scattering cross section is peaked in the forward direction.

The characteristics for cesium plus xenon typically have a lower short-circuit current and a higher voltage at low current.   This behavior might be due to a change in the work function caused by impurities introduced with the xenon.   The pure cesium measurements were reproduced after the xenon was removed.   However, while the xenon was being pumped out, the electrodes were maintained at 1300°K, and any surface contamination that was present might have been removed at that time.

4-5. *Application*

The main application of thermionic energy conversion is the production of electricity for use in regions long considered inaccessible, such as remote polar regions, deep undersea regions, and outer space.   At the present time, the development of a space-power supply composed of a heat source, thermionic converters, heat sink, and power-conditioning equipment is being vigorously pursued in this country.   Two heat sources have been seriously considered: the sun and a nuclear reactor.   The latter seems more capable of reliably providing energy at the high temperatures and high heat fluxes associated with the high-pressure cesium converter because the solar-heated device requires large concentrators and thermal storage capability.   The waste heat is dissipated by radiation, with heat being transferred from the converter collectors to the radiator directly by conduction or indirectly either by a liquid-metal coolant or by an evaporation-condensation cycle (heat pipe).

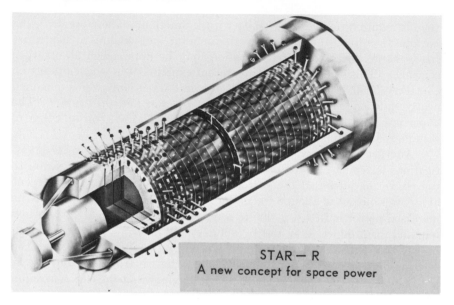

STAR — R
A new concept for space power

Fig. 5-54. *Ten-kwe nuclear-thermionic space power plant with thermionic converters on the reactor surface.*

In the former design, the converters are placed on the surface of the reactor, and the radiator is ultimately connected to the converter collectors. Consequently, the radiating area cannot be much larger than the reactor surface area.   Therefore, the electrical power output per unit volume of the system is limited by the amount of heat which can be radiated from the surface of the system.   Figure 5-54 shows a concept for a 10-kwe nuclear-thermionic space-power plant under study by the General Electric Special Purpose Nuclear Systems Operation.   The reactor is a hollow pipe about 1 ft in diameter by 3 ft long, with converters between the core and the neutron reflector, which is also the radiator.   Each converter has its own cesium reservoir at the end of a short tube which extends from the collector.

For an electrical power output on the order of megawatts, the direct radiation scheme is not feasible.   Instead, the converters are envisioned to be part of the fuel elements, and the waste heat is transferred to an external radiator by a liquid-metal coolant.   Figure 5-55 shows a concept for a multi-megawatt nuclear-thermionic space-power plant under study by the General Electric Special Purpose Nuclear Systems Operation. The thermionic reactor shown in Fig. 5-55 is a compact, fast spectrum reactor.   This system takes full advantage of the high thermal energy produced by nuclear fission by locating the thermionic-converter cells in

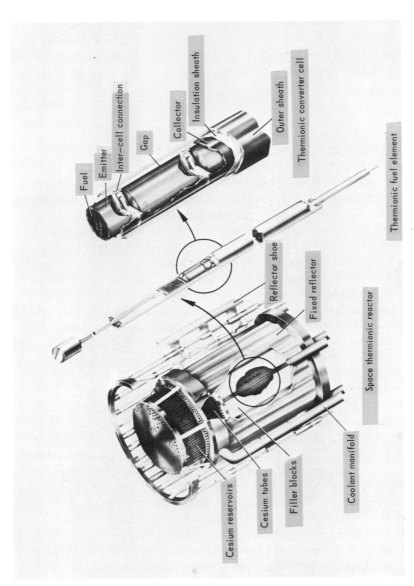

Labels on figure:

Fuel

Emitter

Inter—cell connection

Gap

Collector

Insulation sheath

Outer sheath

Thermionic converter cell

Thermionic fuel element

Reflector shoe

Fixed reflector

Space thermionic reactor

Cesium reservoirs

Cesium tubes

Filler blocks

Coolant manifold

Fig. **5-55.** *One-Mw nuclear-thermionic space power plant with thermionic converters inside reactor as part of fuel elements.*

the reactor core. The thermionic cells each contain nuclear fuel and are connected in series to form a thermionic fuel element. The thermionic fuel elements are then assembled to form a core similar to those commonly used in conventional reactors.

Summary

Vacuum converters are operated with relatively low emitter temperatures (1200 to 1400°K) and require very small electrode spacings (less than 10 μ). Prototype vacuum converters with the following characteristics have been built and tested: power output, 1 watt/cm²; efficiency, 5 percent; lifetime, tens of hours. Theoretically, the vacuum converter is well understood. In this chapter the operating characteristics of the vacuum converter were examined theoretically from two viewpoints: (1) by assuming that electron-electron collisions are unimportant (Langmuir's collisionless space-charge theory); and (2) by assuming that electron-electron interactions result in a distribution which is Maxwellian in the center of mass. The results of the two approaches are in close agreement which, is remarkable since the velocity distributions for the two cases are quite different for large currents. A quantitative comparison between experiment and either theory is difficult to make because of the paucity of published experimental data. However, both theories are in qualitative agreement with experiment in that each predicts that the power output should increase rapidly with decreasing spacing because of the accompanying decrease in space-charge.

    Prototype low-pressure converters have yielded 10 watts/cm² at 10 percent efficiency with emitter temperatures up to 2300°K and electrode spacings up to 1 mm. They differ from vacuum converters mainly in that space-charge is decreased by the addition of positive ions instead of by constructing very small electrode spacings. From an engineering standpoint, this is a significant difference because very close spacings are difficult to maintain for useful lifetimes. The most widely used method of adding positive ions to a converter is that of introducing cesium vapor. The vapor then becomes ionized on the hot emitter, which is usually a dispenser type. A second function of the cesium vapor is to coat the collector, providing the low collector work function required for high power output and efficiency. The operation of a low-pressure converter can be adequately understood by considering the ideal model which ignores space-charge. When there are sufficient ions, this assumption leads to good agreement between theory and experiment. Consequently, the ideal model can be used to predict upper limits of performance to be expected.

    Prototype high-pressure converters have yielded more than 40 watts/cm^2 for emitter temperatures of 2200°K and electrode spacings of 100 μ. Corresponding efficiencies of 20 percent have been measured. As a result of these high performance levels the high-pressure converter is the most promising of the different types of converters. The high-pressure converter differs from the low-pressure converter mainly in that the cesium-vapor pressure is high enough to develop a partial coating of cesium on the emitter, which is usually a refractory metal. For high emitter temperatures, the cesium-vapor pressure required to give the optimum emitter work function is between 1 and 10 torr. At these pressures, collisions with atoms and ions limit the transport of electrons from emitter to collector. If insufficient ions are produced by surface ionization on the emitter, space-charge effects are important also. However, the limiting aspects of space-charge can be reduced, perhaps even eliminated, by operating in the ignited mode, which is accompanied by copious volume ionization, or by operating at high emitter temperature where sufficient ions are produced by surface ionization at the emitter.

Although it can be argued that the unignited mode is understood qualitatively, it is clear that the ignited mode is not well understood from a theoretical point of view. Needless to say, the problem is a difficult one, the main difficulty being the nonlinearity of the differential equations which describe the particle flows. In spite of this difficulty, the problem should be pursued because its solution will undoubtedly suggest new approaches for improving converter performance. A quantitive understanding of the vacuum converter and its limitations led to the development of the cesium converter, whereby an order of magnitude improvement in converter performance was realized. There is every reason to expect that a similar improvement in the cesium converter can be made upon the attainment of a quantitative understanding of its operating characteristics.

References

1. Born, M.: *Atomic Physics*, Hafner Publishing Company, Inc., New York, 1957.
2. Ingold, J. H.: *J. Appl. Phys.*, **34**: 2033 (1963).
3. Taylor, J. B., and I. Langmuir: *Phys. Rev.*, **44**: 423 (1933).
4. Houston, J. M., and H. F. Webster: a comprehensive review in *Advances in Electronics*, pp. 125–206, Academic Press Inc., New York, 1962.
5. Rasor, N. S., and C. Warner: *J. Appl. Phys.*, **35**: 2589 (1964).
6. Spitzer, L., Jr.: *Physics of Fully Ionized Gases*, Interscience Publishers (Division of John Wiley & Sons, Inc.), New York, 1956.
7. Hansen, L. K., and C. Warner: *Rept. on Thermionic Conversion Specialist Conf.*, Gatlinburg, Tenn., Oct. 7–9, 1963, pp. 44–50.

8. Chapman, S., and T. G. Cowling: *The Mathematical Theory of Non-uniform Gases*, Cambridge University Press, New York, 1960.
9. Hirschfelder, J. O., C. F. Curtiss, and R. B. Bird: *Molecular Theory of Gases and Liquids*, John Wiley & Sons, Inc., New York, 1954.
10. Webster, H. F.: *J. Appl. Phys.*, **30:** 488 (1959).
11. Kittel, C.: *Introduction to Solid State Physics*, John Wiley & Sons, Inc., New York, 1956.
12. Blue, E., and J. H. Ingold: *Rept. on Thermionic Conversion Specialist Conf.*, Cleveland, Ohio, October, 1964, p. 160.
13. Taylor, J. B., and I. Langmuir: *Phys. Rev.*, **51:** 753 (1937).
14. Fowler, R. H.: *Statistical Mechanics*, 2d ed., Cambridge University Press, New York, 1936.
15. Milne-Thomson, L. M.: *Jacobian Elliptic Functions*, Dover Publications, Inc., New York, 1950.
16. Auer, P. L., *J. Appl. Phys.*, **31:** 2096 (1960).
17. McIntyre, R. G., *J. Appl. Phys.*, **33:** 2485 (1962).
18. Goldstein, C. M.: *J. Appl. Phys.*, **35:** 728 (1964).
19. Goldstein, C. M., private communication.
20. Dobretsov, L. N., "Electron and Ion Emission," *NASA Tech. Trans.*, F-73.
21. Wilson, V. C., and R. C. Hamilton, *Astronautics and Aerospace Eng.*, **1:** 62 (1963).
22. Lafferty, J. M.: *J. Appl. Phys.*, **22:** 299 (1951).
23. Hernquist, K. G., M. Kanefsky, and F. H. Norman: *RCA Rev.*, **19:** 244 (1958).
24. Houston, J. M.: *Rept. on 23rd Annual Conf. on Physical Electronics*, M.I.T., March, 1963, p. 376.
25. Chivian, J. S.: *J. Appl. Phys.*, **35:** 302 (1964).
26. Painlevé, P.: *Acta Math.*, **25:** 1 (1902).
27. Davis, H. T., W. Scott, G. Springer, and D. Resch: *Studies in Differential Equations*, Northwestern University Press, Evanston, Ill., 1956.
28. Blue, E., J. H. Ingold, and W. J. Ozeroff: *J. Advanced Energy Conversion*, **2:** 395 (1962).
29. Warner, C., and L. K. Hansen: *Rept. on 23rd Annual Conf. on Physical Electronics*, M.I.T., March, 1963, p. 400.
30. Hatsopoulos, G. N.: *Rept. on 24th Annual Conf. on Physical Electronics*, M.I.T., March, 1964, p. 307.
31. Warner, C.: *Rept. on Thermionic Conversion Specialist Conf.*, Gatlinburg, Tenn., October, 1963, p. 51.
32. Langmuir, I.: *Phys. Rev.*, **33:** 976 (1929).
33. Bullis, R. H., and W. J. Wiegand: *Rept. on 24th Annual Conf. on Physical Electronics*, M.I.T., March, 1964, p. 224.
34. Jester, A. A.: *Report on Thermionic Conversion Specialist Conference*, Cleveland, Ohio, October, 1964, p. 93.
35. Psarouthakis, J.: *Report on Thermionic Conversion Specialist Conference*, Cleveland, Ohio, October, 1964, p. 100.
36. Kaplan, C.: *Report on Thermionic Conversion Specialist Conference*, Cleveland, Ohio, October, 1964, p. 333.

37. Blue, E., and J. H. Ingold: *Report on International Conference on Thermionic Electrical Power Generation*, London, Section 3, September, 1965.

Symbols

A cross-section area

A_R Richardson's constant

b impact parameter

$\mathbf{c}$ particle velocity

$\mathbf{C}$ $\mathbf{c} - \mathbf{c}_0$

$\mathbf{c}_0$ $\langle \mathbf{c} \rangle = \int \mathbf{c} f(\mathbf{c}) \, d\mathbf{c}$

D_{ij} binary diffusion coefficient

ε Fermi energy

e electronic charge

$\mathbf{E}$ electric field

$\mathbf{F}$ force per unit mass

f particle distribution function

h_a, h_p heats of vaporization of atoms, ions

h Planck's constant

I ionization potential

$\mathbf{I}$ identity tensor

$\mathbf{J}$ electric current density

k Boltzmann's constant

K Saha's equilibrium constant

L_D Debye length $(kT_e\epsilon_0/e^2 m_e)^{1/2}$

l electrode spacing

m mass

n particle density

p_{Cs} cesium-vapor pressure

p total pressure

$\mathbf{P}$ pressure tensor

P_o output power density

P_1 electron cooling

P_2 radiation cooling

P_3 thermal conduction loss in lead wire

P_4 atom-cooling loss

P_5 ion-cooling loss

$\mathbf{Q}$ heat-flux vector

T temperature (°K)

t_c collision time

T_{Cs} cesium-pool temperature

u, v, w components of $\mathbf{c}$
V electric potential
V_o output voltage

Greek

α equilibrium value of the ratio n_{iE}/n_{eE}
β ionization probability
ϵ_0 specific inductive capacity (permittivity of free space)
η efficiency
η^* efficiency ignoring losses associated with lead wire
θ kT/e
κ thermal conductivity
λ mean free path
Λ $L_D/(e^2/12\pi\epsilon_0 kT_e)$ ratio of Debye length to average radius of interaction
μ rate of arrival of atoms
ξ reduced space variable
ρ electrical resistivity
σ elastic scattering cross section, Stefan-Boltzmann constant
υ mean thermal speed $(8kT/\pi m)^{1/2}$
ϕ work function
χ scattering angle
ψ reduced potential

Subscripts

a atom
I case I
II case II
C collector
e electron
E emitter
p ion
w lead wire
$-$ negative x direction
$+$ positive x direction
m potential minimum
S saturation value

INDEX

INDEX

337